Experiencing
ONENESS

A Couple's Study for Growth in Intimacy

Harold and Bette
Gillogly

Joy Publishing
P.O. Box 9901
Fountain Valley, CA 92708

ACKNOWLEDGEMENTS

There has been a strong and beautiful chain of events and people which has secured the completion of this book. God started the chain by giving us the courage to make life-changing choices which were prerequisite to writing *Experiencing Oneness*. We are thankful for the hundreds of Promise Keepers' men who expressed to us their eagerness for a guidebook on marriage they could study with their wives. God used their passion to know and obey His Word to compel us to meet their need.

Rick and Peggy Story are two of the first links of the chain with their encouragement and counsel since the moment we excitedly shared with them our sense of urgency in writing this study. Peggy also added her skilled editing of the basic text which, along with Alice Large's proof-reading, smoothed out the finished product. We appreciate their generous assistance. The chain continued to inter-link with Stephen Bolt's contribution of the chapter on finances. Since our financial expertise would fit into a thimble with room to spare, we appreciate Stephen's knowledgable and experienced communication of practical financial principles and the sacrifices he made to meet our publishing deadline.

We also thank the five gracious and skillful artists whose talents brighten these pages. They were essential links to be sure. Linda Cable designed the eye-catching cover. Karin Boer drew exquisite illustrations to visually describe what words could not. Kurt Hartel created and sketched all the cartoons (Kurtoones) throughout the book. And Milt and Gladys Hughes took the cover photographs. We also thank the two couples who so willingly gave their time and permission to have their pictures displayed on the front cover. And we are grateful for the more than a dozen couples who helped "test" this study. Their suggestions were invaluable.

To complete the chain, we would like to express our appreciation to our publisher, Woody Young. His encouragement and belief in us has seemed unwavering. This project certainly would not exist without his support.

Unless otherwise indicated, Scripture quotations used are from The Holy Bible, New International Version of the Bible, copyright © 1978 by the New York International Bible Society. Passages followed by "KJV" are taken from The Holy Bible, King James Version.

Printed in the United States of America.
10 9 8 7 6 5 4 3 2 1

Gillogly, Harold and Bette
Experiencing Oneness

ISBN 0-939513-90-0

Joy Publishing
P.O. Box 9901
Fountain Valley, CA 92708

TABLE OF CONTENTS

NOTES

READ THIS FIRST!

ATTENTION! This is not a book you read — it is a book you **DO**!

Experiencing Oneness is an interactive marriage study for you as a couple. It is broken into "bite-sized" studies for each day which can be completed in about 15 to 30 minutes. It is designed for you and your mate to study God's principles about marriage together, and then to interact with the teaching and with one another.

It is our deepest desire that the two of you learn to apply God's Word to your marriage relationship, for we know by experience that is where true happiness lies. The divorce rate drops dramatically for couples who regularly read the Bible together, pray together and attend church together. <u>For such couples, according to a recent Harvard study, the rate of divorce is only **1 in 1,287 (less than .08%)**!</u> This is why we have written *Experiencing Oneness* — to provide you a convenient, systematic way to develop the discipline of studying the Bible and praying together, thereby strengthening your marriage bond.

The day's studies are separated by the ——◆◆●◆◆—— symbol. There is usually ample Scripture in each day's study, and there is also an applicable Scripture passage at the end of the day's study in the **REFLECT TOGETHER** section. This is followed by a **PRAY TOGETHER** section in which we suggest a short prayer for you to pray together concerning that day's study. The **REFLECT** and **PRAY** sections are identified with the cross and anchor symbol (like the one to the left), signifying the lasting relationship bond that reading God's Word and praying together can fortify.

Since each day is a topical study for you to complete together, we offer an opportunity at the end of the day's study for both of you to write your personal application from the study for that day. These **daily application sections** are bound by an intertwined rope symbolizing couples jointly "tying together" the significance of the study. A daily application might simply be the learning or reminder of a truth, or it can be a definite behavioral change one or both of you commit yourselves to.

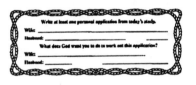

There are also opportunities throughout each day's study for you to **interact** with what you have read. Every time you see four little feet walking across the page (like the example to the left), <u>you know they will be followed by something for you to do</u>. We realize the space we allowed after a lot of the questions won't be enough for you to write your complete answer, that's why there is so much empty space in the side margins for you to write. Take advantage of it.

Each marriage subject is divided into 7 days of study, but they don't have to be consecutive days. You can do the seven studies in three weeks or three days -- it's completely up to you. We would recommend **consistency**, however, for the simple fact that <u>consistency helps us 'stick to' our commitments</u>. The topical chapters are arranged in a logical growth order, but because each subject more or less stands alone, you can choose the order in which you wish to study each topic. If you feel you have the most challenges in a particular area, you don't have to wait two months to get to your area of felt need. You can begin with that chapter if you wish.

Although *Experiencing Oneness* is designed as a couple's study, it can also be used in a couples' group with each couple doing the days' studies as homework. Group discussion questions are provided at the end of each chapter for this purpose. It can also be used in premarital and marital counseling, with the couple again doing the days' studies as homework. It is our prayer that, however you choose to use this book, it will prove an **instrument of growth** in your life and in the lives of those you love.

NOTES

*The purposes of a man's heart
are deep waters, but a man [or
woman] of understanding draws
them out. (Prov. 20:5)*

COMMUNICATION:
AN ESSENTIAL INGREDIENT IN MARRIAGE
Chapter 1

Day 1

Understanding Communication—the essential ingredients:

Definition: Communication is a process (either verbal or non-verbal) of sharing information and/or feelings between two people in such a way that both UNDER-STAND what is being conveyed.

Many define communication as the transference of information from one person to another. But it is much more than that, isn't it? Feelings, as well as information, must be communicated between spouses. Understanding of both the information and feelings is the goal. But lots of times we simply don't get that far. We think we've communicated — but we haven't.

A middle-aged woman walked into an attorney's office and declared that she wanted to divorce her husband. The attorney asked, "Do you have any **grounds**?" "Sure," the wife replied, "we have about 3 acres."

The attorney shook his head, "No, no, what I mean is do you have a **grudge**?" "No," she sadly replied, "we only have a carport."

By this time the attorney was getting pretty irritated. "I don't think I'm getting across here. You know, like does he **beat you up**?" "Why no," she replied innocently, "I almost always get up before he does."

"Madam," the exasperated attorney de-manded, "why on earth do you want a divorce?" "Because," she retorted, "I just can't **communicate** with that man!"

Now, that story is just fiction (at least we hope it is). But it points out a sad condition among marriages — real marriages. Most couples do not communicate well. In fact, according to a recent survey, couples talk together about 2 1/2 minutes a day, and that includes "Pass the salt." Not much real communication is going to happen in 2 1/2 minutes a day, is it?

Communication has these three ingredients:

1. Words = About **7%** of what someone says gets through to us by the words they use. That is, you understand only 7% of what your mate says to you by listening to his/her words.

2. Tone = Tone of Voice comprises **38%** of what we understand. That is, when your mate talks, to a considerable degree, you perceive what he/she is saying by the tone of voice they are using.

Words = 7%

Tone = 38%

Non-Verbals = 55%

3. Non-verbals = This is the most influencing part of communication with a whopping **55%** contributing to our understanding. So, the way you look and act when you are saying something to me, directly influences how I understand what you are saying.

Here's an illustration: A wife, with her arms crossed over her chest, looking extremely beligerent, barks in a sarcastic tone, "O.K. If you really want to go, I'll go with you!" What did the **words** say? Yeah, but what did she really say? How do you know? That's right. It was her tone of voice and her non-verbals.

And yet, when you think of communicating something to your mate, what do you think most about? The words you will use, right? But now that you know **how** you say something is more important than **what** you say, you need to start paying more attention to **how**.

Listening and Feedback

Know why we put "feedback" with "listening"? Because **when we get feedback, we know we are being listened to.** We aren't talking about grunting at the appropriate times. What we are talking about is called the **COMMUNICATION CYCLE**.

It goes like this. When a pilot is ready to take off, the tower gives him specific instructions. "You may now begin to taxi down runway 2 and take off after the United jet in front of you."

The pilot replies, "I can now begin to taxi down runway 2 and take off after the United jet in front of me?" The tower then answers the pilot with either, "Yes, that is right," or "No, you are to do such and such."

What they did was complete a Communication Cycle. One mate might say something. The other feeds back what the first said. Then the first mate can say, "Yes, that's what I mean," or "No, what I meant was...." We don't suggest you use this all the time; it wouldn't be appropriate in every situation. But how many mis-understandings would you avoid if you used it even once a day?

In listening, we filter what the other person is saying through our own opinions and needs. If you stuffed tissues in your ears, then tried to listen to someone talking, what they said could get really distorted, couldn't it? Those tissues are like the filters of your own opinions and experiences and needs. That's why we can misunderstand others so easily.

But objective, careful, unbiased **listening** to your spouse is essential to developing good understanding. So, what do you do with your filters? You are going to have to make a choice to see them for what they are, remove them and really try to listen to your mate **objectively**, **carefully**, and in an **unbiased** way.

Objective, careful, unbiased listening to your spouse is essential to developing good understanding.

Communication Cycle Exercise:

Husband, you go first. Tell your wife your plans for tomorrow...what your day will look like.

Wife, repeat back to your husband what you think he said.

Husband, convey to your wife how well she understands what you communicated and clarify anything that needs it.

Notes

OK, wife, your turn. Tell your husband your plans for tomorrow...what your day will look like.

Husband, repeat back to your wife what you think she said.

Wife, convey to your husband how well he understands what you communicated and clarify anything that needs it.

Write at least one personal application from today's study.

Wife: _____

Husband: _____

What does God want you to do to work out this application?

Wife: _____

Husband: _____

REFLECT TOGETHER: Read Proverbs 16. Notice how many times the subject of communication is mentioned in this Proverb. Notice also the instructions concerning communication which are given.

PRAY TOGETHER: Dear Father, help us communicate our thoughts and feelings to one another. And help us listen objectively, carefully and in an unbiased way.

Day 2

Understanding the Ingredients of Better Communication

Levels of Communication

Level 5 - Cliche'

Level 5 — CLICHE' — No risk, nothing of yourself, elevator talk.

Here are some examples: "How are you?" "Beautiful weather." "I like your suit."

There's a place for this. It's not intended to be engaging conversation. When someone says to you as you pass on the street, "Hi, how are you?" they expect the typical response of "Fine, and you?" They want to get their response of "Fine" before they get out of earshot. They do not want to hear how you **really** are—they don't even slow down enough to "engage" in any higher level of conversation.

This is OK — we need this level of communication. If we really engaged everyone we met, we would be totally overwhelmed and weighed down with everyone's problems.

Level 4 — FACT — Telling what you know, information giving. Reporting of facts, but with no personal commentary. Here are some examples: "The baby had diarrhea all morning." "The bigwigs from headquarters visited the office today."

This is the level we deal with a lot on the job. The flow of information up and down the lines of authority is very critical to making good business decisions. Often that is all that is desired of you—they don't want to know your opinion on the matter or how you **feel** about it. Just give them the facts! When we get home at night, we are so often locked into this kind of communication, we say to each other, "How was your day? Just the facts, Ma'am."

Level 3 — OPINION — Telling what you think.

Now, you're getting a little deeper. You are sharing ideas and decisions. There is a nominal personal risk, not much, but some. This is where real communication begins.

An example might be: "I think if next summer is as hot as this one, we need to put air conditioning in our car." (I'm stating my opinion.) Or: "I think Johnny should play less with his friends and spend more time on his school work."

Level 2 — EMOTION — Telling what you feel.

This is sharing what you feel about facts, ideas, and judgments. Not the opinions themselves, but how you feel about them.

If you are to really share yourself with your mate, you must get to the level of sharing your feelings. But emotional communication must be non-judgmental. That is, if you judge your mate for what he or she is feeling, you can be sure they'll think twice before they share their feelings with you again.

Here are a couple of examples: "When we're under continual financial stress, I feel discouraged, hopeless, and fearful." "When you say complimentary things about me in public, I feel very valuable and worthwhile."

Level 1 — TRANSPARENCY — Complete emotional openness and truthfulness in relationship.

This is the sharing of hopes, fears, dreams, fulfillments, disappointments and other deep emotions. It is total personal involvement, not just a single fleeting emotion shared.

This Role-play is an example:

Mate 1:　I don't know if I ought to take this promotion right now. I'm not sure I'm ready to be a manager.

Mate 2:　It is something you've looked forward to, isn't it?

Mate 1:　Well, yes. But not quite so soon.

Mate 2:　Are you a little fearful of not doing the kind of job you know you could if you had just a little more time to prepare?

Mate 1:　Yeah, I think I needed another six months to really get ready for this position.

Mate 2:　Then it is something you really want. Would there be any hesitation at all if you knew you would succeed and do the job well?

Mate 1:　Of course not—but I don't know that and that's why I'm a little scared.

How about asking your mate sometime, "What is your greatest need today?" Do you ever ask her or him that question? It could be the start of some great transparent sharing.

Notes

Did you use cliche communication with anyone this week?_____

With whom?_____

Think of your communication with your mate this week. What was the highest level you reached?_____

What were you talking about?_____

Why we should seek Transparency

We don't seek transparency with EVERYONE.

All day long, we interact with people on a very superficial basis. We don't reveal our real selves. Instead we touch our lives with others like this ❭❬. The problem is that when we get home, we need to shift to this kind of interaction ✖. But usually we are in such a habit, we stay like this ❭❬ even with our spouses. When you turn that doorknob on your front door, you need to remind yourself, "Now I'm home. Now I can be real."

Transparency yields PERSONAL BENEFITS.

Gen 2:20 — So the man gave names to all the livestock, the birds of the air and all the beasts of the field. But for Adam no suitable helper was found.

This is one of the saddest verses in Scripture. Every animal and bird had someone 'like them,' but Adam had no one like him at all. He was truly alone. Over all the rest of creation, God declared, "It is good." But when God saw the man He had made was lonely, He said, "It is **not good** for the man to be alone" (Gen. 2:18).
You know the rest of the story. God anesthetized Adam and made Eve from one of his ribs. Then He brought her to Adam and in verse 24, performed the first marriage ceremony. But verse 25 is the clincher.

Gen 2:25 — The man and his wife were both naked, and they felt no shame. They were naked **outside** and **inside**. They had **no inhibitions**, nothing that hindered their oneness. They had no shame in their bodies, in their minds, nor in their emotions.

You say, "That's OK for them. But we're different." Yes, you are different. You and your mate have baggage and hang ups that Adam and Eve did not have. But there is good news — if you are a child of God, He has redeemed you. He has bought you back — you, your mate, your problems, and your baggage. 1 Peter 1:18-19 — *For you know that it was not with perishable things such as silver or gold that you were **redeemed from the empty way of life handed down to you from your forefathers**, but with the precious blood of Christ, a lamb without blemish or defect.*

And it is His desire that you know the oneness that Adam and Eve shared. He made you to know complete transparency in your marriage, for He intends to take away your loneliness through it. And He has paid for you to have the right to experience that same transparency that Adam and Eve knew. God alone can give you the power to claim that right.

Gen 2:20 — So the man gave names to all the livestock, the birds of the air and all the beasts of the field. But for Adam no suitable helper was found.

Gen 2:25 — The man and his wife were both naked, and they felt no shame.

1 Peter 1:18-19 — For you know that it was not with perishable things such as silver or gold that you were redeemed from the empty way of life handed down to you from your forefathers, but with the precious blood of Christ, a lamb without blemish or defect.

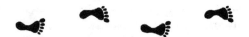

Rate your level of communication with your spouse, with #10 being "consistently transparent":

Wife: 1   2   3   4   5   6   7   8   9   10 (circle one)

Husband: 1   2   3   4   5   6   7   8   9   10 (circle one)

Is there currently a matter you need to transparently communicate with your spouse? Do so now or set an appointed time to talk about it.

Write at least one personal application from today's study.

Wife: _____

Husband: _____

What does God want you to do to work out this application?

Wife: _____

Husband: _____

REFLECT TOGETHER: Read Genesis 2:15-25 for more about why and how God made Adam and Eve for each other.

PRAY TOGETHER: Thank You, Lord, for giving me my life partner. You have paid a great price to give us back the transparency Adam and Eve knew. Help us learn to live in transparency with each other.

Essential Commitments For Transparent Communication

Day 3

Make a commitment to express FORGIVENESS.

Read Colossians 3:12 and 13 in the margin.

When you forgive — as you are commanded — **express your forgiveness to your spouse.** Say it out loud. And say it with more than words.

You might say you forgive and NOT forgive — on the other hand, you might forgive and **NOT** express it. Both leave guilt and barriers.

In my (Bette's) family of 6 kids, we would do our share of wrongs to one another but would hardly ever apologize and express forgiveness. I knew a spat was over when everyone started talking and being nice to one another again. I seldom knew where I stood.

Col. 3:12, 13 — *Therefore, as God's chosen people, holy and dearly loved, clothe yourselves with compassion, kindness, humility, gentleness and patience. Bear with each other and forgive whatever grievances you may have against one another. Forgive as the Lord forgave you. Clothe yourself with compassion...Forgive as the Lord forgave you.*

Notes

With our kids we taught, actually demanded, a complete cycle of forgiveness when a wrong was done to another: 1 - The offender had to apologize to the offended, 2 - The offender had to seek the forgiveness of the offended and 3 - The offended had to express forgiveness to the offender.

Now, they weren't always ready to do this immediately — sometimes it took awhile before all three steps were accomplished. But it wasn't over until all three occurred. Getting all three steps to happen before the offense can be put to rest is like saying, "It ain't over 'til it's over. Really over. Dead and buried, not buried alive."

How do you let your mate know you have forgiven him/her for an offense?

Wife _____

Husband _____

I need to express sincere forgiveness to my mate by:

Wife _____

Husband _____

Make a commitment to express how you FEEL.

Read the Scriptures in the margin.

You are not being honest with God or yourself or one another if you do not share how you feel.

The problem is we don't always **know** how we feel. And our mates do not always know how they feel. We need to take the trouble and time to find out. We are commanded to carry each other's burdens. It's not just a suggestion; it is the **law of Christ.** (There will be more about this in the next section.)

God is not afraid of our feelings.

In the passage above, David unloads some pretty heavy feelings on the Lord. Did God say, "Oh, Davey, don't say that!" No, He wasn't even shocked. You can not shock Him with your feelings. And you know what else? We don't have to be afraid of our own feelings either. And we do not have to be afraid of our spouse's feelings.

Psa. 42:4,9,11 — These things I remember as I pour out my soul: how I used to go with the multitude, leading the procession to the house of God, with shouts of joy and thanksgiving among the festive throng. I say to God my Rock, "Why have you forgotten me? Why must I go about mourning, oppressed by the enemy?" Why are you down-cast, O my soul? Why so disturbed within me? Put your hope in God, for I will yet praise him, my Savior and my God.

Gal. 6:2 — Carry each other's burdens, and in this way you will fulfill the law of Christ.

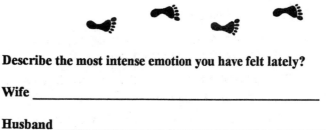

Describe the most intense emotion you have felt lately?

Wife _____

Husband _____

Ephesians 4:15 — *Instead, speaking the truth in love, we will in all things grow up into him who is the Head, that is, Christ.*

Make a commitment to speak the TRUTH in LOVE

Ephesians 4:15 — *Instead, speaking the truth in love, we will in all things grow up into him who is the Head, that is, Christ.*   When we are mature, we will speak the truth in love.

The motive for speaking the truth MUST be love!! Don't speak the truth for truth's sake — but for love's sake. This means that sometimes you will just "bite your tongue" and not say what may be the truth because, at the time, it would not be the loving thing to do.

Illustration — You just had some friends over for dinner and fellowship. Everything was great — the main dish, the salad, the dessert and the fellowship. The only negative was that the vegetables were overdone.

Afterward, your spouse who prepared the meal, asks you how you think the evening went. You want to mention the veggies, but instead say "I think it went very well — the meal was great and so was the fellowship." Some people use part of the verse (the "speak the truth" part) to excuse their negativity. That's what this spouse could have done. But instead he spoke the truth "in love."

What do you think your motives are sometimes when you tell your spouse the truth?

Wife _____

Husband _____

Write at least one personal application from today's study.

Wife: _____

Husband: _____

What does God want you to do to work out this application?

Wife: _____

Husband: _____

REFLECT TOGETHER: Read Colossians 3:8-17. Notice that peace is the result of forgiveness, honesty and love.

PRAY TOGETHER: Lord God, help us fulfill these commitments to forgive each other, to be honest about our feelings, and to speak truth in love. Help us always see talking and listening with one another as top priority.

Make a commitment to express total ACCEPTANCE.

Read the Scriptures provided in the margin.

You did not and can not do anything to earn God's love — He accepts you just as you are. You, in turn, need to accept your spouse **as they are.** That means you accept them **with their feelings** — you accept them when they're feeling good, and you accept them when they're feeling low or angry.

Many times we fail to express acceptance when we unknowingly "shut down" the free expression of feelings our spouse is trying to communicate to us.

Ways we reject our mate's feelings:

DEFEND/EXPLAIN — When our mate starts expressing his/her feelings about something we said or did, we react with, "The reason I said that...", "What I meant was..."

Scriptural Example: Exodus 32:21-24 — *He said to Aaron, "What did these people do to you, that you led them into such great sin?" "Do not be angry, my lord," Aaron answered. "You know how prone these people are to evil. They said to me, 'Make us gods who will go before us. As for this fellow Moses who brought us up out of Egypt, we don't know what has happened to him.'*

So I told them, 'Whoever has any gold jewelry, take it off.' Then they gave me the gold, and I threw it into the fire, and out came this calf!"

Do you think Aaron did a little defending and explaining to Moses and to God? When we do this to our spouses we are not open to their feelings — our concern is strictly **self protection.**

QUICKLY APOLOGIZE — Our spouse might start to say that he/she was hurt by something, and we react, "I'm really sorry that....," "I shouldn't have said that...."

Scriptural Example: 1 Samuel 15:24-26 — *Then Saul said to Samuel, "I have sinned. I violated the LORD'S command and your instructions. I was afraid of the people and so I gave in to them. Now I beg you, forgive my sin and come back with me, so that I may worship the LORD." But Samuel said to him, "I will not go back with you. You have rejected the word of the LORD, and the LORD has rejected you as king over Israel!"* These verses are preceded by a lot of defending and explaining by Saul. His apology is not accepted as sincere by Samuel

When we quickly apologize for an offense, it is not taken as sincere by our spouse — neither does it allow them to express their feelings adequately.

Role-play Illustration:

Scenario: It's Thursday. You're getting ready to leave for the weekend. One mate has done his/her list of jobs, but the other mate has forgotten to do one thing. He/She was supposed to call some good friends who had invited you to a game night they were having and cancel because you were too busy getting ready to go. You two were even supposed to bring a dessert.

Mate 1:   I'm done with my jobs, how are you doing? What did George and Tilly say when you told them we weren't coming tonight?

1 John 4:10-11 — *This is love: not that we loved God, but that he loved us and sent his Son as an atoning sacrifice for our sins. Dear friends, since God so loved us, we also ought to love one another.*

Psa. 103:13-14 — *As a father has compassion on his children, so the LORD has compassion on those who fear him; for he knows how we are formed, he remembers that we are dust.*

Exodus 32:24b — *...Then they gave me the gold, and I threw it into the fire, and out came this calf!"*

1 Samuel 15:24c — *I was afraid of the people and so I gave in to them.*

Notes

Mate 2: OOPS. I forgot. I was so busy!

Mate 1: (Starting to get upset) But they're counting on us to bring the dessert! We can't operate like this with people.

Mate 2: I couldn't help it, I just had too much to do today to remember to do it. I'm sorry.

Do you use the Defend and Explain or Quick Apology technique to shut down your mate's feelings?

Wife _____

Husband _____

If so, what is your mate's usual response?

Wife _____

Husband _____

ATTACK — Our mate may start to ask why we did something, and our reaction is, "I admit what I did was wrong, but you...", "Well, maybe you're right, but what I can't understand is why you..."

Scriptural Example: Mark 14:66-71 — *While Peter was below in the courtyard, one of the servant girls of the high priest came by. When she saw Peter warming himself, she looked closely at him.*
"You also were with that Nazarene, Jesus," she said.
But he denied it. "I don't know or understand what you're talking about," he said, and went out into the entryway.
When the servant girl saw him there, she said again to those standing around, "This fellow is one of them." Again he denied it.
After a little while, those standing near said to Peter, "Surely you are one of them, for you are a Galilean."
Can't you hear Peter as he screams his last denial. His yelling worked. They didn't even suggest again that he had been with Jesus.
He began to call down curses on himself, and he swore to them, "I don't know this man you're talking about."

You've heard the expression that "A good offense is the best defense." But this does not work in human relations! Oh, it works in getting the focus off you, and it works in inciting anger and self defense rather than your having to deal with an emotion you don't want to accept. But it pushes our mates away from us, carrying away with them their feelings that we wouldn't let them express.

Mark 14:71 — He began to call down curses on himself, and he swore to them, "I don't know this man you're talking about.

Roleplay Illustration:

Scenario: You both have just gotten back from a fellowship group pot-luck. One mate is sulking, and, in fact, sulked through the entire evening. The other mate is angry because of this.

Mate 1: I can't believe how you acted at that pot-luck. I was so embarrassed. You didn't talk with anyone. You sat in the corner reading that stupid computer magazine for a whole hour.

Mate 2: What did you expect? You took me for granted and arranged the whole thing. You're always taking me for granted.

Do you use the Attack technique to shut down your mate's feelings?

Wife _____

Husband _____

If so, what is your mate's usual response?

Wife _____

Husband _____

Write at least one personal application from today's study.

Wife: _____

Husband: _____

What does God want you to do to work out this application?

Wife: _____

Husband: _____

REFLECT TOGETHER: Read Romans 15:1-13. Who gets praise when you accept each other (v.7)?

PRAY TOGETHER: Father, thank you for loving and accepting us just as we are. Help us love and accept each other as You do. Help us not be defensive when we try to express our feelings to one another.

More Shutdown Techniques

Day 5

ADVISE — Our mate may express a feeling of frustration, and we react, "Maybe you should...", "It seems to me that if you..."

Scriptural Example: Job, Chapters 4-11

Call if you will but who will answer you?...But if it were I, I would appeal to God: I would lay my cause before him....So hear it and apply it to yourself. (Eliphaz—Chapters 4 &5)

But if you will look to God and plead with the Almighty, if you are pure and upright, even now he will rouse himself on your behalf and restore you to your rightful place.

Job 5:8 — *But if it were I...*

Job 8:6 — *...if you are pure and upright...*

Notes

Ask the former generations and find out what their fathers learned... (Bildad—Chapter 8)

Yet if you devote your heart to him and stretch out your hands to him, if you put away the sin that is in your hand and allow no evil to dwell in your tent, then you will lift up your face without shame.... (Zophar—Chapter 11)

Poor Job! All he got from his three "friends" (Eliphaz, Bildad and Zophar) was advice. It was good advice...it was just unnecessary advice. Our mates simply need to express their feelings, they are not asking for, or needing our advice. But so often we think that our advice is exactly what they need. Afterall, if they would just listen to us, they wouldn't have these problems or negative feelings. Right?

Roleplay Illustration:

Scenario: One mate is feeling very frustrated because he/she can't get control of his time.

Mate 1: Boy, I'm really under it — I had a list a mile long to get done today, then Mr. Stone called and asked me to help him haul that stuff away. The work on my list went down the drain.

Mate 2: Well, you know if you'd turn the TV off when you're working on the computer, you'd end up having more time to do your jobs on your list. You can't watch a football game and concentrate on the computer at the same time. You could get up earlier, too — staying in bed till 9 o'clock on Saturday mornings doesn't help you get your list done.

Mate 1 Come on now — watching a football game is about the only relaxation I get around here. If I get any work done during a game I consider it a plus.

Do you use the Advise technique to shut down your mate's feelings?

Wife _____

Husband _____

If so, what is your mate's usual response?

Wife _____

Husband _____

DISDAIN — Our mate starts to express a feeling we don't think is right, or that makes us uncomfortable, so we say, "I don't really see why you feel...," "Oh, honey, there's no need to feel...," "You shouldn't feel like that...." Or we might simply shut them down with silence.

Scriptural Example: John 12:1-7 — *Six days before the Passover, Jesus arrived at Bethany, where Lazarus lived, whom Jesus had raised from the dead. Here a dinner was given in Jesus' honor. Martha served, while Lazarus was among those reclining at the table with him. Then Mary took about a pint of pure nard, an expensive perfume; she poured it on Jesus' feet and wiped his feet with her hair. And the house was filled with the fragrance of the perfume.*

But one of his deciples, Judas Iscariot, who was later to betray him, objected, "Why wasn't this perfume sold and the money given to the poor? It was worth a year's wages." He did not say this because he cared about the poor but because he was a thief; as keeper of the money bag, he used to help himself to what was put into it.

"Leave her alone," Jesus replied. "It was intended that she should save this perfume for the day of my burial. You will always have the poor among you, but you will not always have me."

Judas thought Mary's feelings were stupid, and that it was a lot more logical to feel another way (like him). But he was wrong, and Jesus told him so. We often feel our mates do not have the right to feel the way they do. So, instead of giving them permission to feel, we try to **stop** them from feeling anything that makes us uncomfortable.

CORRECT — Our mates may try to explain a feeling they are having, and we tell them, "What I think you really mean is...," "I don't think you feel..."

Scriptural Example: Matthew 16:21-23 — *From that time on Jesus began to explain to his disciples that he must go to Jerusalem and suffer many things at the hands of the elders, chief priests and teachers of the law, and that he must be killed and on the third day be raised to life.*

Peter took him aside and began to rebuke him. "Never, Lord!" he said. "This shall never happen to you!"

Jesus turned and said to Peter, "Get behind me, Satan! You are a stumbling block to me; you do not have in mind the things of God, but the things of men."

Matthew 16:22 — Peter took him aside and began to rebuke him.

Now, we shouldn't ever say to our mates, "Get behind me, Satan!" Even though we might feel like it sometimes. But we have to watch ourselves that we don't try to correct them and tell them how they really feel. Notice, we are saying not to **tell** them. **Asking** is O.K.

Roleplay Illustration:

Scenario: One mate just got back from helping her/his friend who is sick. He/she feels worthwhile for doing this. But the other mate feels neglected.

Mate 1:   I really feel good knowing I helped Mary. I think we are making real headway in her feelings of depression.

Mate 2:   Yesterday it was Becky, the day before it was Sandy. You're so busy helping others that you're neglecting your own responsibilities. Do you realize what time it is? It's 7:00 — the kids and I had to fare for ourselves for dinner tonight. Hot-dogs two or three times a week doesn't set well with me.

I don't see why you need to do that to feel good anyhow. Your family has enough needs to keep you busy. Besides, you probably don't feel good because you're helping someone. You feel good because you've got someone thinking how great you are.

Do you use the Disdain or Correct techniques to shut down your mate's feelings?

Wife _____

Husband _____

Notes

If so, what is your mate's usual response?

Wife _____

Husband _____

Where is the focus in each of these six techniques for shutting down your mate's feelings?

On yourself ___   On your mate ___

Write at least one personal application from today's study.

Wife: _____

Husband: _____

What does God want you to do to work out this application?

Wife: _____

Husband: _____

REFLECT TOGETHER: Read Matthew 26:6-13. Notice how much value Jesus places in the woman's outpouring of love.

PRAY TOGETHER: Lord, we know we shut down each other's feelings with these techniques. Help us never think each other's feelings are stupid, but are always worth our attention.

Day 6

Proverbs 20:5 — *The purposes of a man's heart are deep waters, but a man of understanding draws them out.*

Reflect — We act as a mirror of their feelings.

Ways we can accept our mate's feelings:

Proverbs 20:5 — *The purposes of a man's heart are deep waters, but a man of understanding draws them out.* Read that again. This time apply it to your marriage. *The purposes of your mate's heart are deep waters, but the husband or wife of understanding draws them out.*

REFLECT — When our mates try to express how they are feeling, we can say something like, "It sounds as if you feel...," "Guess you really felt...when..."

When we simply "feedback" to our spouse what we hear and observe, we act as a mirror to them for their feelings. They often do not realize what they are feeling at the time—reflecting helps them see their feelings. When done without judgment or rejection, it allows our mate to recognize and understand their feelings.

Roleplay Illustration:

Remember the roleplay illustration for Defend and Explain and Quick Apology? It was the night before you were going away together for the weekend. You both were busy preparing to leave. One mate had forgotten to call some good friends to cancel the game night you had been invited to. You were even supposed to bring dessert. The first time we included this roleplay, we showed you how your partner's feelings could be shut down by using the Defend and Explain and Quick Apology techniques. This time, we want you to see the dramatic difference using **Reflect** can make.

Mate 1:   I'm done with my jobs, how are you doing? What did George and Tilly say when you told them we weren't coming tonight?

Mate 2:   OOPS. I forgot. I was so busy!

Mate 1:   (Starting to get upset) But they're counting on us to bring the dessert! We can't operate like this with people.

Mate 2   It sounds like you feel I did it on purpose. Are you angry at me or at the situation?

Mate 1   I feel like we have to go to the game night now, even though we don't have time!

Mate 2:   Is it that you feel frustrated at the obligation then?

Mate 1:   Yeah, we're letting them down. They were counting on our dessert.

Mate 2:   Would it help if we bought a cake and dropped it by with our apologies? Would that fulfill your sense of obligation and make you feel better?

Mate 1:   That would make me feel a lot better. I'm sorry I yelled. I know you had more than enough to think of today.

What would you like your partner to say to you when he/she is trying to reflect your feelings?

Wife _____

Husband _____

CLARIFY — We might also say something like, "Are you saying that...?" "I wonder if you feel..."

Clarify — ...it adds the element of identifying something that isn't obvious.

Clarifying goes one step further than simply reflecting — it adds the element of identifying something that isn't crystal clear or obvious. It asks our mate to stop for a moment, to think and evaluate, and then to confirm or deny the observation or idea posed. Notice, we are not telling them how they feel, we are asking.

Roleplay Illustration:

Remember the Roleplay Illustration for Attack? The scenario was that you both had just arrived home from a fellowship group pot-luck. One mate had sulked through the entire evening. The other mate was angry. The first time this roleplay was used, we wanted you to see how Attacking your mate will shut down their feelings. This time, we hope you see how different the outcome can be when you simply **Clarify** your

Notes

mate's feelings.

Mate 1: I can't believe how you acted at that pot-luck. I was so embarrassed. You didn't talk with anyone. You sat in the corner reading that stupid computer magazine for a whole hour.

Mate 2: Are you saying you're angry because I didn't talk all evening?

Mate 1: I think you've got the picture.

Mate 2: I wonder if you feel angry because you think now everyone will know that you're married to a bump-on-a-log?

Mate 1: You're not a bump-on-a-log! But everyone at that party is sure going to think you are. I don't want my friends to feel sorry for me!

Mate 2: Well, I'm not a real social person. But tonight I guess maybe I was trying to punish you for making me go. Did you really think I wanted to go?

Mate 1: (Surprised) Didn't you want to go? You love potlucks. I told Edith we'd be there...I just assumed you'd want to.

Mate 2: I had a lot of work I needed to do tonight. Usually I do like potluck parties...all that food. But not tonight.

What would you like your mate to say when he/she is trying to clarify your feelings?

Wife _____

Husband _____

Explore — ...like you would a cave.

EXPLORE — As we talk about their feelings for a while, we might say, "I'm not sure what you mean...," "When else do you feel like that? I don't quite understand how you feel about..." "Are you saying you're afraid if you do that...?"

Explore is exactly that — exploring like you would a cave. You've seen what is obvious. Now, what is down this tunnel? Our feelings can run really deep. It feels so good to get them out in the light of day where we can see them.

Roleplay Illustration:

Remember the Roleplay Illustration for using Advise as a shut-down technique on our mate? One mate was feeling really frustrated because he/she couldn't get control of his time? Let's look at the same scenario again, but this time, use the **Explore** technique.

Mate 1: Boy, I'm really under it — I had a list a mile long to get done today, then Mr. Stone called and asked me to help him haul that stuff away. The work on my list went down the drain.

Mate 2: I'm not sure what you mean. Do you have too much to do or do you feel like you're just not organized?

Mate 1: Both, I guess. No, I take that back. I could get it all done if I just didn't have any interruptions. When something comes up that I haven't planned on, I feel like I've lost control.

Mate 2: Is there another way to organize your schedule so that you wouldn't feel so frustrated? I don't think you can stop the interruptions unless you wanted me to tell people you're not available. I'd be willing to do that.

Mate 1: Well, I guess I could set my schedule allowing for interruptions. If I expected them, maybe they wouldn't bother me so much.

What would you like your partner to say to you when he/she is trying to Explore your feelings?

Wife _____

Husband _____

EXTEND — And finally, we might say, "You really felt...Did you also feel...?" "I can see that you feel...If I were in your shoes, I might also feel..." "Do you feel like that?"

In allowing your mate to extend his/her feelings, you are giving them permission to have all the feelings they want. If you got a promotion, you might feel *glad*, but you may also feel *validated*, and you may feel like that so-and-so in your office who is always putting you down *got his come-uppance*. You might also feel *relieved* that your finances are in better shape with your raise. See? There are all kinds of feelings you can have at the same time.

Roleplay Illustration:

Remember the roleplay that showed the Disdain and Correct methods of shutting down our mate's feelings? This was the scenario: One mate had just gotten back from helping a friend who was sick. He/she felt worthwhile for doing this. But the other mate felt neglected. This time through, notice how the whole evening changed because **Extend** was used instead of the shut downs.

Mate 1: I really feel good knowing I helped Mary. I think we are making real headway in her feelings of depression.

Mate 2: You feel good? Would you say you are feeling fulfilled?

Mate 1: Yeah, it really makes me feel like I'm doing something worthwhile.

Mate 2: Well, I know you're really helping a lot of people. Maybe you're finding some of your spiritual gifts of ministry, huh?

Mate 1: You know...you're right. I really do feel like I've finally found my niche. Thanks for being so supportive of me in this. You're one in a million. You know I don't mean to neglect you like I've been doing lately. This ministry is new to me and I'm kind of having a hard time getting a handle on it. I don't know what I'd do without your understanding.

Mate 2: Well, now that you mention it, I have had to fix the kids and myself hot-dogs a couple of times this week. I would really like you to schedule your helping others earlier in the day so it didn't infringe upon our family time.

Mate 1: You're right. I've kind of gotten caught up in it, haven't I? You know, you're being so sweet about this, I think I'm going to bake you some brownies tonight. How does that sound?

Notes

What would you like your partner to say to you when he/she is trying to Extend your feelings?

Wife _____

Husband _____

Where is the focus in these four ways of accepting your mate's feelings?

On yourself _____   On your mate _____

Write at least one personal application from today's study.

Wife: _____

Husband: _____

What does God want you to do to work out this application?

Wife: _____

Husband: _____

REFLECT TOGETHER: Read 1 John 4:7-21. One definition of love is "acceptance." Substitute the word "acceptance" in this passage for the word "love."

PRAY TOGETHER: Father, help us remember that our mate's feelings are "deep waters." Give us each the determination and the grace to "draw them out."

Day 7

Communication is a three-way proposition.

Keep all communication lines open

Communication is a three-way proposition, not just a two-way. God is in your marriage too, remember? And you will find that when you are communicating with Him, you are sharing yourselves with one another. It works the other way around too. When you are **not** opening up and sharing yourselves with each other, the communication lines to God will also be strained.

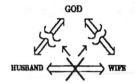

BARRIERS BETWEEN
HUSBAND AND WIFE
BREAK EACH'S
COMMUNION WITH GOD

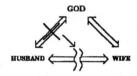

BARRIERS BETWEEN
HUSBAND AND GOD
BREAK COMMUNION
WITH WIFE

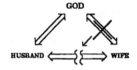

BARRIERS BETWEEN
WIFE AND GOD BREAK
COMMUNION WITH
HUSBAND

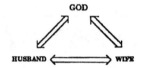

NO BARRIERS PRODUCE
OPEN LINES AMONG ALL
THREE

WRAP-UP: Complete the following exercises.

1. The following is a survey of your relationship's communication pattern. Fill it out separately — before going over it together. This is only for you and your partner's information, so that your communication can grow. So agree not to "blame" or to "defend" while you go over this together.

	Never	Seldom	Sometimes	Often	Always
(1) I really listen to you when you talk...					
(2) I feel you listen to me...					
(3) I understand your NONVERBALS...					
(4) We communicate on the "FACT" level...					
(5) We communicate on the "OPINION" level...					
(6) We communicate on the "EMOTION" level...					
(7) We communicate on the "TRANSPARENCY" level...					
(8) I accept your feelings...					

Notes

	Never	Seldom	Sometimes	Often	Always
(9) I feel you accept my feelings...					
(10) When I am wrong, I admit it...					
(11) When you are wrong, you admit it...					
(12) You help me understand my feelings...					

2. Sitting together, have the wife talk about anything she would like for five minutes. Be sure to time this. During the time she is talking, the husband is to listen and not think about what he will say, nor is he to ask any questions. At the end of the five minutes, he is to repeat back what was said as closely as possible to show he was listening to what his wife was saying. He should also share what he thought she was feeling or what feelings she was expressing.

    After the husband repeats what he can and tells what he heard, the wife responds by telling him whether or not he really heard what she was saying.

    Then husband and wife are to shift roles. The husband is to talk five minutes, the wife to listen and the entire process is to be repeated. Do two more turns if you have time now or do them later.

3. Sit facing each other. Take turns making statements that start with the word "I." Do not make long statements and do not clarify or ask questions. Simply make the state-ment and then let your spouse make one. Alternate in this manner for at least ten turns.
    As you go along share more and more of how you FEEL. Examples of how this process might occur is given below:
    "I feel funny sitting down and doing this."
    "I feel that this is going to be different and I am looking forward to it."
    "I wish we could do this more often."
    "I guess I will feel funny letting others know we did something like this."

Write at least one personal application from today's study.

Wife: _____

Husband: _____

What does God want you to do to work out this application?

Wife: _____

Husband: _____

REFLECT TOGETHER: Read 1 John 1:5-7. How do these verses apply to keeping all communication lines open?

PRAY TOGETHER: Dear Lord, help us keep the communication lines open with You and with each other. Open our eyes to any barriers we might be building between us.

GROUP DISCUSSION: If you are using this study in a group of couples, the following questions should be used as group discussion:

1. What are some of the barriers to emotional and transparency levels of communication that couples experience?

2. What are some definite actions we can take to move toward level one and level two communication?

3. Which of the six ways of rejecting your mate's feelings do you tend to practice? Which of the four ways of accepting your mate's feelings do you feel would help you the most if practiced?

Have a frank discussion

THOT-TALK
Chapter 2

Day 1

THOT-TALK AND HOW IT AFFECTS COMMUNICATION

Is THOT-TALK a subject we should investigate? Well, would you say a topic is important if the Bible speaks about it over 300 times? If you do, then this subject is extremely important — to God and to us. It is so important, in fact, that Proverbs 23:7 states, *As a man thinks within himself, so is he.* If what we think makes us who we are, we need to examine very carefully what we think.

What exactly is it? **THOT-TALK** is inner **CONVERSATION**: messages you tell yourself about yourself, your spouse, your experiences, the past, future, God, etc. They are the thoughts that evaluate facts and events in your life. Sometimes they are clear statements in your mind; sometimes they are merely images or impressions. Whichever kind you have, you're not alone. Everyone talks to themselves.

Proverbs 23:7 — *As a man thinks within himself, so is he.*

TP 2-5a

It is important that we take a close look at our THOT-TALK, because it shapes our attitudes, our feelings, and our beliefs. How do we get to feel certain ways? We get there by the process of THOT-TALK.

Most people believe that outside events, other people, or circumstances cause and shape our emotions, behavior, and verbal responses. But that isn't true! Our THOUGHTS are the source! When we first discovered this, we didn't like it one bit. "Wait a minute," our self-defenses wailed, "if this is true, we can't blame anyone else for how we feel, what we say or even what we do! *We* are responsible!" You might not like this any better than we did, but hang with us. It gets worse... and then a whole lot better.

Thot-Talk shapes our attitudes, our feelings, and our beliefs.

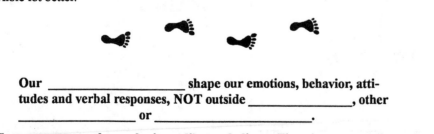

Our _____ shape our emotions, behavior, attitudes and verbal responses, NOT outside _____, other _____ or _____.

Here are some truths we don't act like we believe. There is a very good reason we don't want to believe these truths. They force us to face our personal responsibility. These truths are:

TP 2-5b

Notes

- Most of our **EMOTIONS** (OUR FEELINGS) — anger, depression, guilt, worry, happiness, sense of well-being, contentment, etc. — are initiated and escalated by our THOT-TALK.
  Whether the emotions we are feeling are good or bad, they **start in our minds**, and they **grow in our minds.**

- The way we **BEHAVE** (OUR BEHAVIOR) toward our spouse is determined by our THOT-TALK — **not by our mates' behavior.**
  We make judgments and then act on them. We can not blame our spouse for the way we act toward them. Oh, dear, this one is really painful, isn't it?

- **WHAT** we say and **HOW** we say it (OUR WORDS AND ATTITUDES) are a direct expression of our THOT-TALK.
  Think about this for a moment. Our emotions, our behavior, our attitudes and our communication (that just about sums us up, doesn't it?) all come from our THOT-TALK. WOW! No wonder the Bible talks about it so often and even states specifically, "As [I] think within [myself], so [am I]."

Negative THOT-TALK has at least two things in common:

> It is almost always **UNTRUE.**

Negative Thot-Talk is almost always untrue.

> > Right? We usually wind up with negative feelings and behaviors by concentrating on what we really don't know to be true. There are exceptions, but most of the time, our negative THOT-TALK is simply not true.

Negative Thot-Talk focuses my attention on myself.

> It **FOCUSES** our attention on ourselves, not on our mates or family.

> > Focus...a very important word. Did you know you can hold a nickel so close in front of your eyes that it looks bigger than a new Cadillac? Which would you rather focus on? That's right, the one that's worth more. When we let our negative THOT-TALK control us, we become so focused on ourselves that we overlook all the great things about our mates and families.

Which of these truths about Thot-Talk do you sometimes act like you don't believe?

Wife: _____

Husband: _____

Why?

Wife: _____

Husband: _____

Philippians 4:8 — *Finally, brothers, whatever is true, whatever is noble, whatever is right, whatever is pure, whatever is lovely, whatever is admirable — if anything is excellent or praiseworthy — think about such things.*

We are commanded to think on the POSITIVE — Philippians 4:8 — *Finally, brothers, whatever is true, whatever is noble, whatever is right, whatever is pure, whatever is lovely, whatever is admirable — if anything is excellent or praiseworthy — think about such things.*

We can't get any plainer than that. There is no room in this command for negative THOT-TALK, is there?

Let's look at each of these eight characteristics, making sure we understand what they mean:

1. True — truthful; conforming to reality. No fantasies here.

2. Noble — honest; honorable. No deceit here.

3. Right— just; righteous; living up to God's standard. No unethical practices here.

4. Pure — free from defilement; uncontaminated. No immorality here.

5. Lovely — pleasing; agreeable. No ugly words or behavior here.

6. Admirable — known to be worthy of admiration. No bad reputation here.

7. Excellent — virtuous; having moral excellence. No sinful lifestyle here.

8. Praiseworthy — worthy of affirmation and praise. No hypocrisy here.

...think about such things.

Pick three qualities from Paul's list and give the corresponding characteristic of your mate.

Wife: 1. _____

         2. _____

         3. _____

Husband: 1. _____

         2. _____

         3. _____

Write at least one personal application from today's study.

Wife: _____

Husband: _____

What does God want you to do to work out this application?

Wife: _____

Husband: _____

REFLECT TOGETHER: Re-read Philippians 4:8-9. What do you want to think about?

PRAY TOGETHER: Dear Father, we see how important our thoughts are. Help us learn to apply Philippians 4:8 in our lives.

Notes

Day 2

1 Samuel 18:8-9 — *Saul was very angry; this refrain galled him. "They have credited David with tens of thousands," he thought, "but me with only thousands. What more can he get but the kingdom?" And from that time on Saul kept a jealous eye on David.*

No, I do not want to think that. It is not true.

Patterns of negative THOT-TALK and what we can do about them.

Let's explore four common negative **THOT-TALK** patterns. There are others, but these are probably the most common. Do you see yourself in any of the following?

Personalizing:

This is a **THOT-TALK** pattern in which we think that situations revolve around us. Remember when you were a teenager with a zit? There was nothing worse in the whole world than having a pimple and a date on the same day. Remember walking into a room, knowing all eyes turned to glare at the **huge** bump on your face? Well, that's *personalizing*. Not *all* eyes turned, did they? And not everyone noticed your zit. But it sure felt like it, didn't it?

BIBLICAL ILLUSTRATION: 1 Samuel 18:5-9 — Saul and David
Whatever Saul sent him to do, David did it so successfully that Saul gave him a high rank in the army. This pleased all the people, and Saul's officers as well.
When the men were returning home after David had killed the Philistine, the women came out from all the towns of Israel to meet King Saul with singing and dancing, with joyful songs and with tambourines and lutes. As they danced, they sang: "Saul has slain his thousands, and David his tens of thousands."
Saul was very angry; this refrain galled him. "They have credited David with tens of thousands," he thought, "but me with only thousands. What more can he get but the kingdom?" And from that time on Saul kept a jealous eye on David.

Was David after Saul's kingdom? Did Saul have any **real** reason to be so jealous of David? No, but he let his jealousy (which grew out of his negative THOT-TALK) control him until it burgeoned into an obsession that finally destroyed him.

EVERYDAY ILLUSTRATION: Your husband comes home from work. He's frustrated and grumpy because of something that happened at the office. You immediately assume, "It must have been something **I** did. He's mad at me again. **I** always get blamed for everything."

RESULTS: You devalue yourself and **PULL AWAY** from your mate or you **ATTACK** him. "What did I do this time? You're always coming home angry, and I pay for it. You just don't love me anymore!" A very tense and angry evening is almost sure to follow.

SOLUTION: CHALLENGE the Negative Thought —Substitute Positive THOT-TALK — **"No, I do not want to think that. It is not true."**

"Is he angry at me or is he just angry? He can feel frustrated if he had a bad day. It doesn't mean he loves me less. I won't take his frustration personally. I will allow him the freedom to express his frustration without blaming him. Maybe he really needs to talk about it." Such positive thoughts would allow you to say, "Sounds like you had a difficult day, do you want to talk about what happened?"

Is Personalizing a Thot-Talk pattern you use?

Wife: _____   Husband: _____

How about your spouse?

Wife: _____   Husband: _____

If your answer was "no" to both questions, who *do* you know who personalizes?

Wife: _____

Husband: _____

Do you (or they) tend to pull away or attack when personalizing?

Wife: _____

Husband: _____

Magnifying and Minimizing:

This is a THOT-TALK pattern in which we blow negative events out of proportion and overlook the positive ones. The whole day could have been great except for one little thing — but we let that one incident steal all the good thoughts. When we magnify, we often catastrophize. We look at every inconvenient event as a catastrophe.

BIBLICAL ILLUSTRATION: 1 Kings 19:3-18 — Elijah after Mt Carmel
Elijah was afraid and ran for his life...He came to a broom tree, sat down under it and prayed that he might die. "I have had enough, Lord," he said. "Take my life; I am no better than my ancestors."....
And the word of the Lord came to him: "What are you doing here, Elijah?"
*He replied, "I have been very zealous for the Lord God Almighty. The Israelites have rejected your covenant, broken down your altars, and put your prophets to death with the sword. **I am the only one left**, and now they are trying to kill me too."....*
(After the wind, earthquake and fire the still small voice came) When Elijah heard it, he pulled his cloak over his face and went out and stood at the mouth of the cave. Then a voice said to him, "What are you doing here, Elijah?"
*He replied, "I have been very zealous for the Lord God Almighty. The Israelites have rejected your covenant, broken down your altars, and put your prophets to death with the sword. **I am the only one left**, and now they are trying to kill me too."*
*(But God answered)...Yet I reserve **seven thousand** in Israel — **all** whose knees have not bowed down to Baal and all whose mouths have not kissed him."*

1 Kings 19:14 — *He replied, "I have been very zealous for the Lord God Almighty. The Israelites have rejected your covenant, broken down your altars, and put your prophets to death with the sword. **I am the only one left**, and now they are trying to kill me too."*

Poor Elijah. He had just performed mighty miracles on Mt. Carmel, but now, all he could see was Israel's sin and his isolation. He magnified the bad and minimized the good. As a result, he felt miserable.

EVERYDAY ILLUSTRATION: "This is the worst thing that could happen to me! I can't live like this. Everything is ruined!" Have you ever said anything like that? What about using the word, "horrible"? We catastrophizers love that word, so we say things like: "You locked the keys in the car? This is horrible! Why do these things always happen to me?" Also, do you ever have trouble accepting compliments? Do your replies sound like this? "Oh, this old suit? I've had it for ten years and the seat is shiny." "My hair? Thanks, but it really needs to be cut."

RESULTS — You **BLAME** YOURSELF or someone else for whatever happened. "I'm not going to do anything with you anymore. You spoiled the whole day by

Notes

locking the keys in the car. Now what are we going to do? We're stuck! And it's all your fault."

SOLUTION: CHALLENGE the Negative THOT-TALK — Substitute Positive THOT-TALK — **"No, I do not want to think that. It is not true."**

No, I do not want to think that. It is not true.

"She didn't lock the keys in the car on purpose. It was a mistake I've made myself. It's not the end of the world. So we're locked out. We can hike to a phone and call the auto club. Even that can be an adventure if I let it be."

Are Magnifying and Minimizing Thot-Talk patterns you use?

Wife: _____

Husband: _____

How about your spouse?

Wife: _____

Husband: _____

If your answer was "no" to both questions, who *do* you know who magnifies and minimizes?

Wife: _____

Husband: _____

Do you (or they) tend to blame yourself or someone else when magnifying and minimizing?

Wife: _____

Husband: _____

Write at least one personal application from today's study.

Wife: _____

Husband: _____

What does God want you to do to work out this application?

Wife: _____

Husband: _____

REFLECT TOGETHER: Re-read 1 Kings 19:3-18. Have you ever felt like Elijah?

PRAY TOGETHER: Oh, Lord God, Help us catch ourselves when we're thinking negative thot-talk and challenge it. Help us magnify the good and minimize the bad instead of the other way around.

Either/Or Thinking and Blaming:

This is perhaps the sneakiest negative THOT-TALK pattern. We think that we, our mates or our children are either a **total** success or a **total** failure. This causes us to blame our **total** selves or our **total** marriage or mates or children.

If we use this pattern regularly, we begin to abandon hope and quit trying. We fail to realize that necessary changes don't occur all at once. We **can** change specific behaviors when we work consistently on **one thing** at a time.

BIBLICAL ILLUSTRATION: Genesis 25:29-33; 27:36a — Esau & Jacob
...Once when Jacob was cooking some stew, Esau came in from the open country, famished. He said to Jacob, "Quick, let me have some of that red stew! I'm famished!" ....Jacob replied, "First sell me your birthright." "Look, I am about to die," Esau said. "What good is the birthright to me?" But Jacob said, "Swear to me first." So he swore an oath to him, selling his birthright to Jacob.
(Later, when Esau learned that Jacob had also deceitfully taken the blessing that was rightfully his:)
*Esau said, "Isn't he rightly named Jacob? He has deceived me these two times: He **took** my birthright, and now he's taken my blessing!"*

Obviously, Esau was an either/or type of guy. **Either** he ate a bowl of stew right then and there, **or** he would die. (He threw in a little maximizing too, didn't he?) He saw his situation as either **total** success (If I eat right now, I live.), or **total** failure (If I don't eat right now, I die.). Neither was true, nor was he willing to accept the responsibility of his own choice. He blamed Jacob for **taking** his birthright. Either/or thinking usually leads to blaming. And as long as we put the blame on someone else, or even on ourselves, we will not change.

EVERYDAY ILLUSTRATION: "I blew it again. I impulsively bought that motor bike when I promised not to spend any more money this month. I'm a total loser. I don't know how she puts up with me. What's the use?" Or, if the shoe is on the other foot, we might say, "YOU blew it again. YOU spent over the budget. YOU'RE to blame. What am I going to do with you?"

RESULTS: You **DEVALUE** yourself or your spouse and children. When you fail to see specific behavior as something you **can** change, you do not change. You slip into a downward spiral which ends with giving up. "I'll never get it right anyway. Why try?" Sometimes we practice this either/or-blame pattern with our spouses and children. As a result, we often leave them feeling hopeless and discounted.

SOLUTION: **CHALLENGE** the Negative Thot-talk—Substitute Positive THOT-TALK — **"No, I do not want to think that. It is not true."**

Day 3

Genesis 25:32 — *"Look, I am about to die," Esau said. "What good is the birthright to me?" "*

No, I do not want to think that. It is not true.

Notes

"My compulsive spending is something God says I **can** change. As I obey His Word and learn self-control, I will change and grow as a person. I don't have to stay like I am. I know it won't be easy, but I can take one step at a time. This is what I'm going to do today...."

Is Either/Or Thinking and Blaming Thot-Talk patterns you use?

Wife: _____

Husband: _____

How about your spouse?

Wife: _____

Husband: _____

If your answer was "no" to both questions, who *do* you know who uses Either/Or Thinking and Blaming?

Wife: _____

Husband: _____

Do you (or they) tend to devalue yourself or your spouse when practicing these Thot-Talk patterns?

Wife: _____

Husband: _____

Jumping to Conclusions and Mind Reading:

In this THOT-TALK pattern, we tell ourselves what our mates are thinking or feeling. We think we can read their minds, so we form conclusions based on past experience rather than their present behavior. We think we know what they're going to say and how they're going to act, so we **react** accordingly. We can cause ourselves and our mates a lot of unnecessary grief by doing this.

BIBLICAL ILLUSTRATION: Genesis 12:10-20 — Abraham and Sarah in Egypt
Now there was a famine in the land, and Abram went down to Egypt to live there for a while because the famine was severe. As he was about to enter Egypt, he said to his wife Sarai, "I know what a beautiful woman you are. When the Egyptians see you, they will say, 'This is his wife.' Then they will kill me but will let you live. Say you are my sister, so that I will be treated well for your sake and my life will be spared because of you."
(Pharaoh took Sarai into his palace, but the Lord inflicted diseases on them. So he called Abram in and reprimanded him, giving him back his wife and sending him away.)

Abraham (Abram) thought he knew exactly what the Egyptians would think and do,

Genesis 12:12 — *When the Egyptians see you, they will say, 'This is his wife.' Then they will kill me but will let you live.*

so he reacted according to his "mind reading abilities". He devised a dangerous scheme that could have gotten both Sarah and him killed. He certainly expended a lot of energy jumping to conclusions, didn't he?

EVERYDAY ILLUSTRATION: "What's the point in taking her these flowers? She's just going to say 'What did you do?' She doesn't appreciate all the stuff I do for her anyway. I don't know why I even bother. In fact, if she opens her mouth and says one negative thing, I'm going to tell her off."

RESULTS — You become **ANGRY** or upset with your mate or children for no reason. You can make yourself depressed or anxious because of some fictitious scenario you painted in your mind, shutting down communication before it has a chance to start. This is a fool proof way of making yourself and everyone in your house miserable.

SOLUTION: CHALLENGE the Negative Thot-talk — Substitute Positive THOT-TALK — **"No, I don't want to think that. It is not true."**

No, I do not want to think that. It is not true.

"I have no way of knowing how she's going to react. I can at least take her these flowers and give her a chance to respond. I might be surprised. If she doesn't act overjoyed about them, it's not the end of the world, after all. I'll find another way of showing her I love her."

PERSONAL ILLUSTRATION: I (Harold) had to stay late at work one night, and wanted to let Bette know so she wouldn't worry. (This is a very good practice, men.) When a voice I had often heard disguised as an elderly woman's answered, I knew it was our prankster son playing one of his practical jokes. "Hello," said the feeble voice.

"Adrian, I know that's you. So cut the joke, and let me speak with Mom."

"You must have the wrong number, Young Man."

"This is not the wrong number! Let me speak with Bette. I'm in a hurry to leave here."

"There's no Bette here. You must have the wrong number."

I was rushed and my fuse was short. "This has gone far enough! I want to talk to Bette **NOW** — will you get her for me or not?"

"But there is no Bette who lives here."

I slammed the phone down on the prankster's ear and left work. I fumed all the long way home, growing angrier by the minute. That boy had gone too far this time, and I was going to make him pay for this prank!

I got home, rushed in, slammed the front door, and bounded up the stairs, heading straight for Adrian's room. He pretended to be asleep, but he didn't fool me. "Adrian, you're in big trouble! You went too far with that phone prank!"

"Huh? What? What phone prank?"

"You know good and well what phone prank! Didn't you know I really wanted to talk to your Mom when I called?"

"I haven't answered the phone all night, Dad."

I turned to Bette who had come out into the hallway to see what was happening, and began to spout my tale of woe. "I called this evening to let you know how late I was going to be, and *YOUR* son was playing one of his practical jokes and wouldn't let me talk to you."

Notes

With a quizzical expression on her face, she laid her hand comfortingly on my arm. "Honey, our phone hasn't rung all evening."

I was dumbfounded. Somewhere out there was a very upset, innocent old lady. Whoever and wherever she is, I hope she has forgiven me by now.

Are Jumping to Conclusions and Mind Reading Thot-Talk patterns you use?

Wife: _____

Husband: _____

How about your spouse?

Wife: _____

Husband: _____

If your answer was "no" to both questions, who *do* you know who jumps to conclusions and reads minds?

Wife: _____

Husband: _____

Who do you (or they) make miserable when using these Thot-Talk patterns?

Wife: _____

Husband: _____

Which of these four patterns do you tend to practice the most?

Wife: _____

Husband: _____

Personalizing

Magnifying and Minimizing

Either/or Thinking and Blaming

Jumping to Conclusions and Mind Reading

Think of a recent experience when you used that particular Thot-Talk pattern. Describe to one another how the scenario would have been different had you challenged your negative Thot-Talk and used positive Thot-Talk instead.

> Write at least one personal application from today's study.
>
> Wife: _____
>
> Husband: _____
>
> What does God want you to do to work out this application?
>
> Wife: _____
>
> Husband: _____

REFLECT TOGETHER: Read Genesis 12:10-20 to get the whole story of how Abraham jumped to conclusions.

PRAY TOGETHER: Dear God, thank You that You can change us as we obey You. Help us obey You by not allowing negative thot-talk to control us.

THOT-TALK, Me and My Partner's Feelings

Day 4

Ways I Reject my Partner's Feelings:

These are the same "shutdown" techniques we discussed in the last chapter. Now we are adding the dimension of THOT-TALK so you will see how each of them starts in our minds. Remember — our words, behavior, attitudes and feelings stem from our THOT-TALK.

DEFEND/EXPLAIN: When we personalize or catastrophize, our goal is to avoid handling a negative feeling. So we start explaining why we did such and such. We think things like, *He's going to try to blame this on me. Well, it wasn't my fault.* We just want off the hook, so we say things like..."The reason I said that was...." "What I meant was...."

Defend/Explain

QUICK APOLOGY: Again, we want to be let off the hook. We don't want to admit any mistakes, so our THOT-TALK is, *I don't want to hear this stuff. She always gets upset about everything.* We then say things like, "Oh, I'm sorry...." "I shouldn't have said that. I take it back. Sorry."

Quick Apology

ATTACK: We magnify the bad and attack our mates when they start to express a feeling that might threaten us. We think, *I don't have to put up with this. He's worse than I am.* So we say things like..."O.K. what I did was wrong, but you...." " Well, maybe you're right, but what I can't understand is why you...."

Attack

ADVISE: We think our mates do some things completely wrong. After all, the only way they could do it totally right is to do it **our** way. So when they express some frustration, we say things like..."Maybe you should do it this way...my way...." "It seems to me that if you would just do it this way...."

Advise

Notes

Disdain

DISDAIN: We think in either/or terms, so when our mates try to express feelings of inadequacy, it scares us. We think things like, *You're supposed to meet all my needs. You're the one who should always be strong.* Then we say things like... "You shouldn't feel like that...." "Honey, there's no need to feel...." Or we fall silent, and don't answer them at all.

Correct

CORRECT: We think we can read our mate's mind better than they can — or perhaps our mate thinks or talks slower than we do — so we jump to conclusions and try to tell them what they actually mean. We say things like... "What I think you really mean is...." "I don't think you feel...You probably just feel...."

Philippians 2:4 — *Each of you should look not only to your own interests, but also to the interests of others.*

We use all these shut down techniques to protect ourselves from feelings that make us uncomfortable. Again, notice the focus in all six of these is on ourselves, not our mate's. Philippians 2:4 is very relevant here: *Each of you should look not only to your own interests, but also to the interests of others.* We know it's impossible to never use these shut downs. However, by becoming aware of them, we can allow the Holy Spirit to enable us to root them out of our lives.

Now that you see how Thot-Talk initiates these 6 shut down techniques, which of them do you find yourself practicing most often?

Wife: _____

Husband: _____

Ways I Accept my Partner's Feelings

Proverbs 20:5 — *The purposes of a man's heart are deep waters, but a man of understanding draws them out.*

Proverbs 20:5 — *The purposes of a man's heart are deep waters, but a man of understanding draws them out.*

What a great verse! We need to be wives and husbands "of understanding" who draw out our mate's heart purposes. Here are four ways we can obey this principle. Again, notice how positive Thot-Talk makes a difference in how we respond to our mate.

Reflect

REFLECT: If we think...*I'm not going to take what she's saying personally. I'm going to see if I can help her express her feelings completely.* Then we'll say things like... "It sounds as if you feel...." "Guess you really felt...when...."

Clarify

CLARIFY: If we think...*I'm not going to assume I know what he's trying to say. I'm going to help him say whatever is on his mind.* Then we'll say things like... "Are you saying that...?" "I wonder if you feel...?"

Explore

EXPLORE: If we think...*I'm going to focus on my mate this time. I won't put her down for not being perfect. I'm not perfect either.* Then we'll say things like... "I'm not sure what you mean...." "When else do you feel like that?" "I don't quite understand how you feel about...." "Do you feel _____?"

Extend

EXTEND: If we think...*This time I'm going to put myself in his shoes and try to understand how he's feeling. It isn't horrible that he feels this way. I'm going to accept his feelings.* Then we'll say things like... "You really felt...Did you also feel...?" "I can see that you feel....If I were in your shoes, I might feel the same way." "Do you feel like that?"

Just as all **The Ways We Reject Our Mate's Feelings** have something in common, so do the four **Ways We Accept Our Mate's Feelings**. Do you know what that is? Once again, it has to do with our focus. When we determine to focus on our mates' needs instead of on our own self protection, wonderful things happen to our communication. It becomes deeper, more genuine and open, kinder and more understanding.

Which of these 4 positive Thot-Talk patterns would help you the most to accept your mate's feelings?

Wife: _____

Husband: _____

Write at least one personal application from today's study.

Wife: _____

Husband: _____

What does God want you to do to work out this application?

Wife: _____

Husband: _____

REFLECT TOGETHER: Read Philippians 2:3-4. Notice how humility is the key to obeying these verses.

PRAY TOGETHER: Dear Jesus, help us focus on what each other is trying to communicate and how they are feeling. Help us not to look only at our own interests by always trying to protect ourselves.

Role-plays of Communication with Negative/Positive THOT-TALK. *Day 5*

These role-plays will seem a little familiar. They are similar to those in Chapter One. But just as we added the dimension of THOT-TALK to the acceptance and rejection methods, so we add it here. We hope these role-plays will help you understand how **THOT-TALK is the first step** in either rejecting our mates' feelings or accepting them. First, we'll show negative Thot-Talk leading to shutting down the other's feelings. Then positive Thot-Talk leading to acceptance of the other's feelings.

Defend and Explain, Quick Apology and Personalizing vs. Reflect and Positive THOT-TALK Role-play

Scenario: It's Thursday. You're getting ready to leave for the weekend. One of you has completed your list of jobs, but the other has forgotten to do one thing. He/She was supposed to call good friends who had invited you to a game night, and cancel because you were too busy preparing to leave. You were even supposed to bring a

Notes

dessert.

NEGATIVE: Defend and Explain, Quick Apology and Personalizing

Mate 1:   I'm done with my jobs, how are you doing? What did George and Tilly say when you told them we weren't coming tonight?

Mate 2:   OOPS. I forgot. I was so busy!

Mate 1:   (Starting to get upset) But they're counting on us to bring the dessert! We can't operate like this with people.

Mate 2:   (Thot-Talk) *He always blames me. He must think I'm just stupid. Well, I'm not stupid. I just forgot.* (Says to Mate 1) I couldn't help it. I just had too much to do today to remember it. I'm sorry.

POSITIVE: Reflect and **POSITIVE** THOT-TALK

Mate 1:   I'm done with my jobs, how are you doing? What did George and Tilly say when you told them we weren't coming tonight?

Mate 2:   OOPS. I forgot. I was so busy!

Mate 1:   (Starting to get upset) But they're counting on us to bring the dessert! We can't operate like this with people.

"It sounds like...."

Mate 2:   (Thot-Talk) *I'm not going to take his anger personally. He can be angry about the situation. It's all right. I'm going to try to help him express it.* (Says to Mate 1) It sounds like you feel I did it on purpose. Are you angry with me or about having to go?

Mate 1:   We don't have time to go, but now I feel like we have to!

Mate 2:   Is it that you feel frustrated with the obligation then?

Mate 1:   Yeah, we're letting them down. They were counting on our dessert.

Mate 2:   Would it help if we bought a cake and dropped it by with our apologies? Would that fulfill your sense of obligation and make you feel better?

Mate 1:   That would make me feel better. I'm sorry I yelled. I know you had more than enough to think of today.

Do you identify with this Role-play? How?

Wife: _____

Husband: _____

Attack, Magnify and Minimize vs. Clarify and Positive THOT-TALK Role-play

Scenario: You both have just gotten back from a pot-luck dinner. One mate is sulking, and, in fact, sulked through the entire evening. The other mate is angry about this.

NEGATIVE: Attack, Magnify and Minimize

Mate 1:   I can't believe how you acted at that pot-luck. I was so embarrassed. You didn't talk with anyone. You sat in the corner reading that stupid computer magazine for a whole hour.

Mate 2:   (Thot-Talk) *This was the worst evening of my life! Nothing was good about it. Even the food didn't taste right. She always makes plans for us. I'll teach her.* (Says to Mate 1) What did you expect? You took me for granted and arranged the whole thing. You're *always* taking me for granted!

POSITIVE: Clarify and Positive THOT-TALK

Mate 1:   I can't believe how you acted at that pot-luck. I was so embarrassed. You didn't talk with anyone. You sat in the corner reading that stupid computer magazine for a whole hour.

Mate 2:   (Thot-Talk) *I acted like the whole evening was horrible. But to tell the truth, I was with people I really like and ate pretty good food. She sometimes takes me for granted, but not all the time. If I had talked this over with her when it first came up, this whole incident could have been avoided. I'm going to take my mind off my own feelings and focus on her feelings instead. After all, I did it to hurt her, and succeeded."* (Says to Mate 1) Are you saying you're angry because I didn't talk all evening?

"Are you saying...."

Mate 1:   I think you get the picture.

Mate 2:   I wonder if you feel angry because you're afraid every-one will know that you're married to a bump-on-a-log?

Mate 1:   You're not a bump-on-a-log! But everyone at that party is sure going to think you are. I don't want my friends to feel sorry for me!

Mate 2:   Well, I'm not a very sociable person. But tonight I guess I tried to punish you for making me go. Did you really think I wanted to go?

Mate 1:   (Surprised) Didn't you want to go? You love potlucks. I told Edith we'd be there...I just assumed you'd want to go.

Mate 2:   I had a lot of work I needed to do tonight. Usually I do like pot-luck parties...all that food, but not tonight.

Do you identify with this Role-play? How?

Wife: _____

Husband: _____

Advise and Either/Or Thinking and Blaming vs. Explore and Positive THOT-TALK Role-play

Scenario: One mate is feeling very frustrated because he/she can't get control of his time.

NEGATIVE: Advise and Either/Or Thinking and Blaming

Mate 1:   Boy, I'm really under it — I had a list a mile long to get done today. Then Mr. Stone called and asked me to help him haul that stuff away. The work on my list went down the drain.

Mate 2:   (Thot-Talk) *Well, I knew it. If he would just do things my way, he wouldn't have any problems. He's so totally stubborn.* (Says to Mate 1) You know, if you'd turn the TV off when you're working on the computer, you'd have

Notes

more time to do the jobs on your list. You can't watch a football game and concentrate on the computer at the same time. You could get up earlier, too—staying in bed 'til 9 o'clock on Saturday morning sure doesn't help you get your list done!

Mate 1: Come on now—watching a football game is about the only relaxation I get around here. If I get any work done during a game I consider it a plus.

POSITIVE: Explore and Positive THOT-TALK

Mate 1: Boy, I'm really under it — I had a list a mile long to get done today. Then Mr. Stone called and asked me to help him haul that stuff away. The work on my list went down the drain.

"I'm not sure what you mean...."

Mate 2: (Thot-Talk) *This time I'm going to put myself in his shoes. I know he needs more self-control, but telling him what to do won't help him get it.* (Says to Mate 1) I'm not sure what you mean. Do you have too much to do or do you feel unorganized?

Mate 1: Both, I guess. No, I take that back. I could get it all done if I just didn't have any interruptions. When something comes up that I haven't planned on, I feel like I've lost control.

Mate 2: Is there another way to organize your schedule so you won't be so frustrated? I doubt you can stop the interruptions unless you want me to tell people you're not available. I'd be willing to do that.

Mate 1: Well, I could set my schedule to allow for interruptions. If I expect them, maybe they won't bother me so much.

Do you identify with this Role-play? How?

Wife: _____

Husband: _____

Disdain and Correct and Jumping to Conclusions and Mind Reading vs. Extend and Positive THOT-TALK Role-play

Scenario: One mate just got back from helping a sick friend. He/she feels worthwhile for doing this, but the other mate feels neglected.

NEGATIVE: Disdain and Correct and Jumping to Conclusions and Mind Reading

Mate 1: I really feel good knowing I helped Mary. I think we're making headway in her feelings of depression.

Mate 2: (Thot-Talk) *I bet she just wants to get out of being here at home and taking care of the kids and me. She never puts us first.* (Says to Mate 1) Yesterday it was Becky, the day before it was Sandy. You're so busy helping others that you're neglecting your own responsibilities. Do you realize what time it is? It's 7:00 — the kids and I had to fare for ourselves for dinner tonight. Hot-dogs two or three times a week doesn't set well with me.

I don't see why you need to help others to feel good anyhow. Your family has enough needs to keep you busy. Besides, you probably don't feel good just because you're helping someone. You feel good because you've got someone thinking how great you are.

POSITIVE: Extend and Positive THOT-TALK

Mate 1:   I really feel good knowing I helped Mary. I think we're making headway in her feelings of depression.

Mate 2:   (Thot-Talk) *I have no way of knowing her motives. To tell the truth, she puts us first a lot. I'm not going to major on my selfish feelings, I'm going to focus on her and how she's feeling.* (Says to Mate 1) You feel good? Would you say you are feeling fulfilled?

"Would you say...."

Mate 1:   Yeah, it really makes me feel like I'm doing something worthwhile.

Mate 2:   Well, I know you're helping a lot of people. Maybe you're finding some of your spiritual gifts, huh?

Mate 1:   You know...you're right. I feel like I've finally found my niche. Thanks for being so supportive of me. You're one in a million. You know, I don't mean to neglect you like I've been doing lately. This ministry is new to me and I'm having a hard time getting a handle on it. I don't know what I'd do without your understanding.

Mate 2:   Well, now that you mention it, I have had to fix the kids and me hot-dogs a couple of times this week. I would really appreciate it if you scheduled helping others earlier in the day so that it doesn't infringe upon our family time.

Mate 1:   You're right. I've sure gotten caught up in it, haven't I? You know, you're being so sweet about this, I think I'll bake you some brownies tonight. How does that sound?

Do you identify with this Role-play? How?

Wife: _____

Husband: _____

Write at least one personal application from today's study.

Wife: _____

Husband: _____

What does God want you to do to work out this application?

Wife: _____

Husband: _____

REFLECT TOGETHER: Read 1 Peter 1:13-22. Notice how obeying God purifies us and enables us to love each other sincerely.

PRAY TOGETHER: Father God, thank You that You have given us the grace to "gird up the loins of our minds." Help us focus on each other's needs before we think of our own.

Notes

Day 6

2 Corinthians 10:5b — *...we take captive every thought to make it obedient to Christ.*

1 Peter 1:13 — *Gird up the loins of your mind.*

Romans 12:2a — *Do not conform any longer to the pattern of this world, but be transformed by the renewing of your mind..*

Lamentations 3:18-24 — *So I say, "My splendor is gone and all that I had hoped from the Lord."*

I remember my affliction and my wandering, the bitterness and the gall. I well remember them, and my soul is down-cast within me. Yet this I call to mind and therefore I have hope:

Because of the Lord' are not consumed, for his compassions never fail. They are new every morning; great is your faithfulness. I say to myself, "The Lord is my portion; therefore I will wait for him."

How to Control your THOT-TALK.

Keep TRACK of them:

2 Corinthians 10:5b — *...we take captive every thought to make it obedient to Christ.* Recognize the type of THOT-TALK you are having. Catch yourself at it and take note of what you're telling yourself. If necessary, write down your THOT-TALK each time you become aware of it.

COUNTER them:

1 Peter 1:13 — *Gird up the loins of your mind.*   Romans 12:1, 2 — *Renew your mind.* Challenge them. Bring your thoughts to trial and examine the evidence. The Judge is God and His Word. How does your THOT-TALK measure up to that? If it doesn't conform with what God says, it must be a lie. Throw it out! Say out loud, *No, I don't want to think that. It is not true.* Or make up your own phrase with which to counter your thoughts. Memorize it. Keep it on the tip of your tongue. Be prepared to challenge your THOT-TALK.

What phrase will you use to counter your negative Thot-Talk? Write it here:

Wife: _____

Husband: _____

The Power to CHANGE: Lamentations 3:18-24 —Jeremiah challenges his negative THOT-TALK and substitutes the positive —

So I say, "My splendor is gone and all that I had hoped from the Lord."

*I remember my affliction and my wandering, the bitterness and the gall. I well remember them, and my soul is down-cast within me. **Yet this I call to mind and therefore I have hope:***

*Because of the Lord's great love we are not consumed, for his compassions never fail. They are new every morning; great is your faithfulness. **I say to myself, "The Lord is my portion; therefore I will wait for him."***

What a powerful Scripture! Jeremiah had a choice. Was he going to nurse his gloomy thoughts and drown in self-pity? Or was he going to counter his negative THOT-TALK and tell himself the truth. We have the same kind of choice...every day. We can capture our thoughts and make them obedient to Christ. Or we can let the devil have a field day with our minds.

What was Jeremiah's negative Thot-Talk?

_____

_____

How did he counter his negative Thot-Talk?

_____

_____

What was the result?

_____

_____

It is time to CHOOSE: Do you want closeness with your mate? Then you must choose it. Do you want an intimate marriage? Then you must choose to take control of your thoughts instead of letting them control you.

We know you want to stop telling yourself lies about your mate and children. So each time a choice arises, you must be ready to choose the truth. To do that, you must keep these four simple facts in mind.

1. The choice is mine.
2. I alone am responsible for my choices and behavior.
3. I must be ready to accept the consequences of my choices and behavior.
4. God commands me to capture my thoughts and make them obedient to Him, and He will empower me to obey.

The choice is mine

I alone am responsible

I must be ready to accept the consequences

God commands me to capture my thoughts

PERSONAL ILLUSTRATION: Several years ago, we needed a 4-wheel drive vehicle because the area where we live is mountainous and snowy. We looked for quite awhile before finally finding a used 4 wheel drive station wagon. It was yellow...lemon yellow. We should have taken that as a warning.

I (Bette) didn't feel "good" about buying that car. I couldn't put my finger on why, but my woman's intuition was flashing warning signals. Harold, on the other hand, after considering all our options, felt strongly that we should buy it. I held out for days while he tried to persuade me. Finally, I "gave in."

Immediately, the car began to fall apart — the oil seals, the engine, the battery, the clutch. With each new problem, my THOT-TALK went something like this: *This is all his fault. If he hadn't badgered me about this stupid car, we wouldn't have all this trouble and expense.* Was I telling myself the truth? Absolutely not! **I had a choice.** I could have explained my reticence to Harold even though I didn't understand it. I could have suggested that we pray about it longer. Instead, **I made the choice** to "give in." Now, I was determined to make him pay for it.

As I confronted my problem (my THOT-TALK, not the car), I saw that I again had a choice. I could continue to punish Harold for wanting the stupid car in the first place, or I could correct my THOT-TALK. After some emotional struggle and the Holy Spirit's work in my heart, I changed my THOT-TALK to this: *We are both responsible for buying this car. I must take responsibility for my choice to give in. I am going to stop punishing Harold. We need to hang together and do the best we can with what we've got.*

Immediately, there was a change in my attitude, and that precipitated a change in my behavior. Both choices in that experience really were **mine** to make. Not only that, I alone was responsible for each choice. And I had to take responsibility, even though I

The choices were mine to make.

Notes

didn't want to, for my choices and my behavior. We aren't saying this is easy. Obeying God is seldom easy. But He gives us the power to obey Him, and it is so much better than the alternatives.

Discuss the following questions together: What would happen to our communication and to our emotional oneness if:

We chose to CHALLENGE our negative THOT-TALK when it first starts?

The choices are yours to make.

We chose to FOCUS on each other's need to communicate his/her feelings instead of on our own needs?

We chose to COMMUNICATE how we feel in a loving way instead of sulking and nursing our negative THOT-TALK?

Write at least one personal application from today's study.

Wife: _____

Husband: _____

What does God want you to do to work out this application?

Wife: _____

Husband: _____

REFLECT TOGETHER: Re-read Lamentations 3:18-24.

PRAY TOGETHER: Because of Your great love, Oh Lord, we are not consumed, for Your compassions never fail. They are new every morning; great is Your faithfulness. Help us, Lord, to be faithful and compassionate mates.

Day 7

WRAP UP: Answer these individually first, then talk together about each question.

1. I have decided to change my negative THOT-TALK pattern identified on Day 3. I need your help in this process. The ways you could help me turn this negative pattern into positive THOT-TALK are:

Wife: _____

Husband: _____

2. I know I reject your feelings sometimes by using the six ways talked about on Day 4. Because I want to accept your feelings, I would appreciate your making me more aware of this by:

Wife: _____

Husband: _____

3. I would sense you were accepting my feelings more if you practiced: (circle one) Reflecting, Clarifying, Exploring, Extending. Here's an illustration of how that would help me:

Wife: _____

Husband: _____

REFLECT TOGETHER: Read Romans 12:1-3. Notice what you have to renew before you can obey God's will.

PRAY TOGETHER: Dear Lord, transform us into the image of Your Son Jesus as we renew our minds. Help us be mates of understanding who draws out our partner's heart.

GROUP DISCUSSION: If you are using this study with a group, the following can be used as group discussion questions.

1. How do you think THOT-TALK shapes your attitudes, behavior, feelings and beliefs? Can you give an illustration (positive and negative)?

2. Of the 4 patterns of Thot-talk, which do you tend to practice most?

3. How does THOT-TALK affect the way we reject or accept our partner's feelings?

4. Which steps for controlling and changing your negative THOT-TALK would help you the most?

Have a frank discussion

HOW TO GET A HANDLE ON ANGER
Chapter 3

Day 1

ANGER IS THE MAJOR CAUSE OF MARRIAGE FAILURES today because it alienates husbands and wives. So declares David Mace, who has over fifty years of marriage counseling experience. The problem is not that anger happens in marriage — but that we don't know how to **handle** our own anger nor the anger of our mates. **We mis-use anger.**

We mis-use anger.

Kinds of Anger

There are basically two kinds of anger: righteous and sinful. We usually refer to the righteous kind as "righteous indignation." Not all anger is bad. We **should** be angry about some things. There is an urgent need for righteous anger directed toward the injustices inflicted upon the helpless. Jesus displayed this type of anger when He drove the money changers out of the temple. The other kind of anger is sinful; **not because** it wells up inside us, but because we **don't know how to deal with it** once it's there. Let's take a look at 5 specific differences between **righteous** and **sinful** anger. Which one do you identify with most?

Righteous Anger

vs.

Sinful anger

Righteous Anger	vs.	Sinful Anger
1. Unselfish		1. Selfish
2. Always controlled		2. Often uncontrolled
3. Directed toward the act		3. Directed toward person
4. Has no resentment resentment/retaliation		4. Harbors bitterness and or revenge
5. Maybe **2%** of our anger		5. Probably **98%** of our anger

These percentages aren't clinical. We didn't get them from a survey. They simply reflect our observations of others and ourselves. Be honest, though, aren't they about right? The bulk of our experience is with sinful anger — therein lies our problem. We need to investigate anger so that we can get a handle on it. Then maybe it won't handle us so much.

Is your experience of Righteous Anger higher or lower than the suggested percentage?

Wife: _____

Husband: _____

How about Sinful Anger?

Wife: _____

Husband: _____

How Sinful Anger affects us.

Selfish anger is not a harmless emotion. Make no mistake, when we nurse anger we **suffer its consequences** in our lives: bodies, minds and spirits. Here are just a few results of anger in our lives.

1. It becomes a HABIT: the more we are angry, the more we become angry.

Proverbs 22:24-25 says, *Do not make friends with a hot-tempered man, do not associate with one easily angered, or you may learn his ways and get yourself ensnared.* Anger is a trap because it is a habit, a learned habit.

We must be aware of the people and situations which trigger our anger, not to blame them but to guard ourselves. What happens when you drive? Do you become a different person behind the wheel? Do you get even when other drivers cut you off? You're not alone. Anger is the second greatest cause of traffic accidents in the United States. Anger is a learned behavior — a habit. So we must learn to break the habit every time we are in an anger-triggering situation.

Proverbs 22:24-25 *Do not make friends with a hot-tempered man, do not associate with one easily angered, or you may learn his ways and get yourself ensnared.*

2. It reduces our ability to REASON clearly.

Proverbs 14:17a — *A quick tempered man does foolish things.* Anger robs us of our perspective.

It's like looking at a room through a straw. You can see only a limited part of the furnishings and people. In the same way, anger restricts our view. Our perspective is limited, so we see only partial truths. Think about the last time you felt angry. Be honest. Your ability to see everything clearly was hampered, wasn't it?

Proverbs 14:17a — *A quick tempered man does foolish things.*

3. It upsets the chemical balance of our bodies and can cause PHYSICAL ILLNESS.

Here are some symptoms: migraine headaches, thyroid malfunction, ulcerative colitis, toxic goiters, high blood pressure, ulcers, heart attacks, backaches, rheumatism, arthritis, allergies, indigestion, asthma — to name a few. These symptoms are not always the result of our mis-handling anger, but they can be. Are you getting the idea that anger can be hazardous to your health?

Proverbs 12:18 says, *Reckless words pierce like a sword, but the tongue of the wise brings healing,* healing to the one who speaks and to the one who listens.

Proverbs 12:18 *Reckless words pierce like a sword, but the tongue of the wise brings healing*

4. It pushes the PEOPLE we love away from us.

Proverbs 25:24 — *Better to live on a corner of the roof than share a house with a quarrelsome wife* [or husband]. Do you enjoy being around an angry person? Of course not! Then do you want to be the one other people avoid?

Proverbs 25:24 — *Better to live on a corner of the roof than share a house with a quarrelsome wife.*

5. It makes the people we love angry at us.

Proverbs 15:1 — *A gentle answer turns away wrath, but a harsh word stirs up anger.*

Leviticus 26:39b-40, 42 — *...because of their fathers' sins they will waste away. But if they will confess their sins and the sins of their fathers...I will remember my covenant with Jacob....*

Anger begets anger. Proverbs 15:1 — *A gentle answer turns away wrath, but a harsh word stirs up anger.* When we act angrily, we ignite our mates' defense systems. The scripture is true. When we act and speak harshly, we trigger our mates' and children's anger.

6. It gives my family a poor EXAMPLE that will effect my children, grandchildren and generations to come.

Read Leviticus 26:39b-40, and 42 in the margin.

Why do you handle anger the way you do? You probably respond the same way your parents or others close to you responded. You may need to acknowledge your parents' incorrect way of handling anger and forgive them. Because anger is a learned response, you also need to acknowledge that your children probably handle anger the same way you do. If that frightens you, the time to act is now. Confess your mis-use of anger, receive God's forgiveness, and master the proper responses to anger. The wrong ways of dealing with anger your parents handed down to you (and perhaps their parents to them) can stop with your generation. That's good news!

The bottom line is that selfish anger does not do ONE positive thing for me, my spouse, my children or for anyone else around me!

Besides these six, list any other results you can think of.

Wife: _____

Husband: _____

Which of the results of anger do you experience?

Wife: _____

Husband: _____

Write at least one personal application from today's study.

Wife: _____

Husband: _____

What does God want you to do to work out this application?

Wife: _____

Husband: _____

REFLECT TOGETHER: Read Proverbs 15:1-5. Did you know your "tongue" can bring healing?

PRAY TOGETHER: Dear God, help me not allow anger to control me. And help me get rid of the affects it has had on me and my family.

The truth about anger:

Day 2

Here are four truths about anger. If we really believe these truths and act upon them, we will take a **giant step** toward handling our anger.

1. We get angry because real life is not the way we think it OUGHT to be.

Psalm 37:8 — *Refrain from anger and turn from wrath; **do not fret** — it leads only to evil.*

"She should understand me." "He shouldn't treat me this way." There are a lot of "shoulds" and "shouldn'ts" in this world. We want to be treated a certain way. In fact, we think we **deserve** to be treated a certain way. And when we aren't, we become angry and resentful. If we refuse to let go of our expectations of what "ought to be," we will end up bitter and depressed old codgers.

2. Expressing your anger does not lessen your anger. It usually INCREASES it.

Proverbs 30:33c — *...stirring up anger produces strife.*

It's amazing how many of us still believe the old "pressure cooker theory" which promotes the benefits of "letting off steam." Have you ever seen a pressure cooker at work? There's a little valve on top that releases steam when the pressure builds up too much. Then the pressure cooker is fine until the next time the steam builds. But we are people, not pressure cookers. When we let off a little steam, it usually turns into a lot of steam; our partner's defenses kick in, so we let off more steam. This trend definitely **escalates the anger and conflict.**

3. How you deal with your anger was LEARNED.

Read Ephesians 4:22-24 in the margin.

This is good news. Whatever we learned, we can unlearn. Then we are free to develop **NEW** responses to handle our anger and get it under control. God is in the process of renewing believers (v. 23). As we grow, He expects us to behave responsibly in obedience and holiness (v. 24). So, not only **can** we change, but we are actually **given the power** to do so.

4. Your partner is not RESPONSIBLE for making you angry. You are.

Matthew 5:22a — *But I [Jesus] tell you that anyone who is angry with his brother will be subject to judgment.*

Have you ever said, "**You** make me so angry"? This truth snatches from us our "right" to say that, or even think it. Jesus makes it clear that each of us is **responsible for his own anger.** The Bible never says we are responsible for another's anger, but it says plenty about how we should handle our own. This is a hard truth to hear and to apply in our lives; but since **we are responsible**, we must take this truth to heart.

Psalm 37:8 — *Refrain from anger and turn from wrath; do not fret — it leads only to evil.*

Proverbs 30:33c — *...stirring up anger produces strife.*

Ephesians 4:22-24 — *You were taught, with regard to your former way of life, to put off your old self, which is being corrupted by its deceitful desires; to be made new in the attitude of your minds; and to put on the new self, created to be like God in true righteousness and holiness.*

Matthew 5:22a — *But I [Jesus] tell you that anyone who is angry with his brother will be subject to judgment.*

Notes

Which of these 4 Truths About Anger is the hardest to believe and apply?

Wife: _____

Husband: _____

Why?

Wife: _____

Husband: _____

BLAME fuels the fires of anger.

Proverbs 27:4a — Anger is cruel and fury is overwhelming.

Proverbs 27:4a — *Anger is cruel and fury is overwhelming.*

We blame our mates thinking that we can IMPROVE them.

What a useless and self-defeating pursuit! Does being blamed make **you** straighten up and become a nicer person? Does it make **you** want to change for the better? **Blame does not work...it overwhelms.**

When you blame, you TRIGGER your partner's self-defense system.

Proverbs 17:14 Starting a quarrel is like breaching a dam; so drop the matter before a dispute breaks out.

Proverbs 17:14 says, *Starting a quarrel is like breaching a dam; so drop the matter before a dispute breaks out.*

The dictionary defines "a breach" as "a gap made by battering a wall." Boy, does that describe blame! It's like battering the wall of a dam until it breaks. The results? A destructive flood.

When you blame, it keeps your anger GOING.

It doesn't make it go away. This is another facet of the "pressure cooker theory." It doesn't work, remember?

When you blame, it distracts you from discovering a SOLUTION to your frustration.

Our oldest daughter once had a pet rat. "Roger" would jump into the big wheel in his cage and run, and run and run. Unfortunately, Roger never got anywhere. When he finally tired out and slumped off the wheel, he'd still be in the same old place — his cage. Blame is like that. It never gets us anywhere, and wears us out trying. And what makes it even **more counterproductive**, is that we get so accustomed to the "wheel of blame," we can't see that it **keeps us** from finding the true escape route.

Ephesians 4:32 — Be kind and compassionate to one another, forgiving each other, just as in Christ God forgave you.

The solution? Ephesians 4:32 — *Be kind and compassionate to one another, forgiving each other, just as in Christ God forgave you.* **FORGIVENESS releases you** from the pressure of making your mate PAY for what they have done to you.

You're not the judge, jury and executioner. **God is**, and **He forgives**. God forgives you, not because you **deserve** to be forgiven, but because He **chooses** to forgive you. Your mate may not deserve your forgiveness, but you can choose to show compassion. You don't need to wait until forgiveness is deserved. God gives you the **power to forgive by choice**...like Him. The truth is, **blame will make you sick; forgiveness will make you well.**

Illustration: I (Harold) grew up in a family where blame seemed to be the natural consequence of wrongdoing. When something went wrong, the guilty party was searched out, blamed, shamed and disciplined. Only after displaying satisfactory repentance were they forgiven. You might call them "search and destroy" missions. Carrying this pattern into our marriage got me into trouble more than once. I eventually learned that when something goes wrong, I can't find the person to blame and nail them to the wall. If there is a problem, we need to discuss it, but **without blame**. I still need to remind myself that blame **does not work**.

Blame will make you sick; forgiveness will make you well.

List some negative effects of blame in your relationship with your mate?

Wife: _____

Husband: _____

If you tend to blame, how can you apply the solution of forgiveness?

Wife: _____

Husband: _____

Write at least one personal application from today's study.

Wife: _____

Husband: _____

What does God want you to do to work out this application?

Wife: _____

Husband: _____

REFLECT TOGETHER: Read Ephesians 4:22-27. Who gets a foothold when we allow anger to stay in our lives?

PRAY TOGETHER: Dear Father, help me take responsibility for my anger. And help us open ourselves to You, so that You can teach us a better way to handle it.

Notes

Day 3

Anger is like a toothache....

"Is there something I'm afraid of right now?"

Anger is a SECONDARY emotion.

It is a symptom that indicates something else is happening inside us. Anger is actually a **response to another emotion** we are feeling.

Have you ever had a toothache? Was there something below the surface making your tooth hurt...like a cavity? What if you put "Numbs-it" on your tooth every half-hour? Would that take care of the problem? No. To treat a toothache, you go to the dentist. He drills out the cavity or does whatever is necessary to take care of the problem **inside** the tooth. Our anger is like a toothache. We need to discover what's **inside the anger** before it can be cured. We must drill underneath the anger to the real problem. **The primary emotions that usually cause anger are:**

FEAR — We might be afraid our partners will over-ride us, control us, verbally attack us, ignore us, or disagree with us. To protect ourselves from that **fear**, we attack in anger.

Illustration:

Mate 1: I think we should paint this bathroom blue. Then we can have blue and beige accents.
Mate 2: I don't know. I've never cared much for blue.
Mate 1: You never want to do what I want! Everything has to be your way!

Here's a **personal illustration**. When our daughter Elicia was two years old, she escaped my (Bette's) watchful eye for a split second and ran into the street to rescue her ball. I ran after her, scooped her up in my arms and hugged her close. But **relief** was not my only emotion. After hugging her, I held her at arms length to ensure that my fierce scolding about running into the street made a big impression on her. Within seconds, my **fear** showed itself as **anger**.

Red Flag Question: Fear often erupts into expressions of anger in dramatic ways. When you **burst** into anger, you should ask yourself: "Is there something **I'm afraid of** right now?"

In the first illustration, Mate 1's **fear** needs attention. What is she/he afraid of? And why? These questions must be examined for the anger to be dealt with properly.

Can you relate a time when FEAR was the underlying emotion in your anger or in your mate's anger?

Wife: _____

Husband: _____

HURT — The second primary emotion usually found under anger is hurt. Many things can hurt us: a sharp word, lack of appreciation, or our mate's forgetfulness about something important to us. We usually don't even recognize that it **is** hurt we are feeling because we so quickly cover it with anger.

Illustration: Imagine you just spent your entire day off cleaning the house. It's spotless. When your husband (or wife) gets home, he doesn't even notice. He explodes into the house, scatters his stuff all over, and then flops down in front of the TV. You would probably be angry with him, wouldn't you? However, the underlying problem is that you're hurt because you perceive he doesn't appreciate you and all you do around the house. **That** is what needs to be addressed.

Red Flag Question: The red flag questions this time are; "Am I feeling hurt? **What is hurting me?**" You must recognize and deal with the hurt in order to manage the anger.

"Am I feeling hurt? What is hurting me?"

Can you relate a time when HURT was the underlying emotion in your anger or in your mate's anger?

Wife: _____

Husband: _____

FRUSTRATION — When things don't go the way we want, or the way we think they "ought to," we get frustrated. Or when confronted with a problem we can't solve, we get frustrated. There are, of course, a lot of little annoyances and quirks about your mate that **you can not solve or control**; that's why they trigger such frustration in you.

Illustration: Jean and Charley were painting the trim on their house. Charley painstakingly showed Jean exactly how to cut in around the window frames. That way seemed awkward to Jean, so she did it her way. Even though Jean's job was still up-to-standard, Charley scathingly remarked that she should have done it his way and sulked the rest of the afternoon. What was underneath Charley's anger? He was not **in control** as he felt he **should be**, so he felt frustrated.

Red Flag Question: "Why am I frustrated? What am I doing to **frustrate myself**?" We can see only one good solution to frustration: give your partner (and other people and circumstances) permission to be different from what you expect. Allow your spouse the freedom to be him or herself. It is foolish to fret over things you cannot control. Remember Psalm 37:8? *Don't fret — it leads only to evil...*evil for ourselves, as well as evil for others.

"Why am I frustrated? What am I doing to frustrate myself?"

Have you seen the bumper sticker that says: "If at first you don't succeed, do it the way your wife told you to in the first place"? We laugh at it because somewhere deep inside us, we **want** to cling to that attitude, don't we?

Psalm 37:8 — *Don't fret — it leads only to evil...*

Can you relate a time when FRUSTRATION was the underlying emotion in your anger or in your mate's anger?

Wife: _____

Husband: _____

Which Red Flag question would be the most helpful for you in discovering the underlying emotion(s) of your anger?

Wife: _____

Husband: _____

Notes

> Write at least one personal application from today's study.
>
> Wife: _____
>
> Husband: _____
>
> What does God want you to do to work out this application?
>
> Wife: _____
>
> Husband: _____

REFLECT TOGETHER: Read Psalm 37:1-8. Notice how "fretting" gets us into trouble.

PRAY TOGETHER: Lord God, help me recognize what is under my anger. Give us grace to confront our fears, hurts and frustrations.

Day 4

Responses to Anger

The ways that DON'T WORK — The Deadly R's.

Repression — SWALLOWING our anger leads to resentment (another deadly R).

Ephesians 4:26-27 — *In your anger do not sin. Do not let the sun go down while you are still angry, and do not give the devil a foothold.* Anger here means *resentment,* that slow burning anger we try to keep well hidden.

When we repress our anger, we actually **deny** it exists. We say things like, "No, I'm not angry!" Then we feel our stomachs churning from the effort of swallowing it. "Repressors" usually believe these two lies:

Lie #1 — Anger is **SIN**...so if I'm a good Christian, I shouldn't get angry.

Lie #2 — Being angry always means **LOSING CONTROL**: yelling and stomping your feet, etc., so if I don't do that, I'm controlling my anger. Being a nice person is better than yelling. People who express their anger are not nice. But I'm a nice person.

Results:

We STORE UP the pressure like air in a balloon until it finally bursts. Carrying all that pressure around can make us bitter faultfinders. Hebrews 12:15 — *See to it that no one misses the grace of God and that **no bitter root grows up to cause trouble** and defile many.*

Ephesians 4:26-27 — In your anger do not sin. Do not let the sun go down while you are still angry, and do not give the devil a foothold.

Hebrews 12:15 — See to it that no one misses the grace of God and that no bitter root grows up to cause trouble and defile many.

We'll never forget the day we traveled with a couple who had been married over twenty-five years. We brought up what we thought was the innocent topic of differences that husbands and wives experience. After we had related a few funny anecdotes, the wife began crying. With great difficulty, she choked back her tears and sat like a stone for most of the remaining trip. We couldn't help but think, "Oh, oh, there's a balloon that's about to burst. And when it does...look out!"

Our anger OOZES out in subconscious ways: burning dinner, having a headache at bedtime, avoiding people, pouting, teasing, sarcasm, silence, gossip, or even depression.

Resentment is like guerrilla warfare, because it is sneaky. We can bury it so well — we don't even know it's there. If one or more of the ways anger tends to re-emerge is common in your life, maybe it's a signal for

Repressing anger is just as sinful as uncontrollably expressing it.

you to dig deep and let go of repressed anger. Don't disregard red flags. God gives them to us as warning signals, compelling us to stop and pay attention.

Remember Lie #1? The hardest thing for repressors to do is admit that **repressing anger is just as sinful as uncontrollably expressing it.** We want so much to believe that repressing anger is a **virtue.** But the Bible doesn't back us up on this one. It very specifically declares that **repression is sin.**

Are you a repressor?

Wife: _____ Husband: _____

Is your mate?

Wife: _____ Husband: _____

What do you see in your life as a result of repressing anger?

Wife: _____

Husband: _____

Expression — Rage. UNCONTROLLED anger.

This is the other deadly **R.** Proverbs 29:11 — *A fool gives full vent to his anger, but a wise man keeps himself under control.*

This is very strong language. God calls us **fools** if we do not control our anger. Perhaps God declares this because only a fool would destroy the most important

Proverbs 29:11 — *A fool gives full vent to his anger, but a wise man keeps himself under control.*

Notes

human relationship in the world. That's exactly what uncontrolled anger does: it destroys marriages and families. "Expressors" believe these two lies:

Lie #1 — If I **VENT** my anger, I can get it off my chest and everything will be fine. (Here's that old "pressure cooker" theory again. And it's **still** a lie.)

Lie #2 — I **YELL** when I'm angry. That's just the way I am; I can't change. Besides, I have a right to punish people who don't meet my expectations.

Results — Rage is like open warfare because it blows up the bridges between us. If we blow up too many bridges, how will we connect? We alienate our mate when we express anger uncontrollably. Couples become polarized, living in two separate worlds, hurting and being hurt. Scripture commands us to remove this response to anger from our lives. Ephesians 4:31 — *Get rid of all bitterness, rage and anger, brawling and slander, along with every form of malice.*

Ephesians 4:31 — Get rid of all bitterness, rage and anger, brawling and slander, along with every form of malice.

Are you a expressor?

Wife: _____ Husband: _____

Is your mate?

Wife: _____ Husband: _____

What do you see in your life as a result of uncontrollably expressing anger?

Wife: _____

Husband: _____

How about the two lies expressors believe? They are just that — **lies**! Would God command you to get rid of rage and anger if it were impossible for you to do so? You grieve God's Spirit when you resist change. For when you resist change, you essentially resist His working within you. Ephesians 4:30 implores you to *not grieve the Holy Spirit of God....*

Ephesians 4:30 — And do not grieve the Holy Spirit of God, with whom you were sealed for the day of redemption.

Most of us respond to anger in one of these two ways. Which way do you respond? Are you a repressor...or an expressor? Aren't you tired of handling your anger in ways that don't work? Would you like to know...and put into practice ...ways that do work?

Write at least one personal application from today's study.

Wife: _____

Husband: _____

What does God want you to do to work out this application?

Wife: _____

Husband: _____

REFLECT TOGETHER: Read Hebrews 12:14-15. What do you think "bitter roots" grow into?

PRAY TOGETHER: Oh, Father, help us not to hold resentment against each other or our children. Help us obey You by controlling our anger.

The ways that WORK

CONTROL it — admit your anger, but keep your emotions under control. Proverbs 19:11 — *A man's wisdom gives him patience; it is to his glory to overlook an offense.* Ah, you knew there was a catch to it. It's going to take work!

Our tendency is to protest, "Forget it. I can't control my anger." Wait a minute. If a policeman stopped you to issue a traffic ticket, would you jump out of your car and beat him up? No, no, no...you would probably grin and bear it, at least until he left. You would control your anger, if only for a little while. And if you can control it, then you are ready for the next step.

I control my anger:

Wife: Never   Sometimes   Often   Almost always   Always
(Circle one)

Husband: Never   Sometimes   Often   Almost always   Always
(Circle one)

Does your mate agree with your response? Wife _____ Husband _____

PROCESS it — Admit you are angry, control it, then explore it to discover its **cause**. Remember, there is fear, hurt or frustration under that anger. These are the emotions that need attention. Only by dealing constructively with the **root cause(s)** of your anger can you find a **long term solution**.

Here are 6 steps in processing anger:

1. **CONTRACT** to **CONFESS** the moment you begin to feel angry. Say it out loud immediately. This will keep you from holding on to angry, resentful thoughts.

    We must warn you, this step is especially difficult for repressors. That is why a contract is imperative. You (repressors and expressors alike) are far more likely to achieve this step if you have made a covenant to do so.

2. **AGREE** to not attack. It is important that you not attack each other in anger. To achieve this — yes, it is possible — you simply need to agree to control your angry

Day 5

Proverbs 19:11 — *A man's wisdom gives him patience; it is to his glory to overlook an offense.*

Only by dealing constructively with the root cause of your anger can you find a long term solution.

Notes

Romans 12:18 — *If it is possible, as far as it depends on you, live at peace with everyone.*

responses. You don't need to attack, because you know there is a better way. You must refuse to hold thoughts of retaliation. Romans 12:18 commands, *If it is possible, as far as it depends on you, live at peace with everyone.*

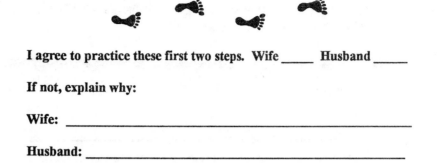

I agree to practice these first two steps. Wife _____ Husband _____

If not, explain why:

Wife: _____

Husband: _____

3. **REVIEW and REHEARSE.** After a **cooling off** period, **review** the situation that caused the anger, not with blame but with mutual concern. Then **rehearse** what you will do when a similar situation occurs in the future. In other words, it is possible for you to plan your behavior changes as a couple.

Do you and your mate fight about the same things over and over again? If so, you have developed a **pattern**. Now you need to develop a **plan**. The **review and rehearse** step provides a powerful tool to overcome **patterns of anger**.

The review and rehearse step provides a powerful tool to overcome patterns of anger.

Illustration: A while back, it seemed we got into an argument whenever Bette was driving. After one such heated ride, we did some **R and R** (Review and Rehearse). We discovered that the root of Bette's anger was my (Harold's) constant driving instructions: "get over in the next lane," "turn left up here," "don't stay in back of this truck, I can't see around it." She felt I was treating her like I thought she couldn't drive. And I admit, I had fallen into a bad habit of "back seat driving." We **reviewed what was happening** in our anger pattern and **why**.

Then we **rehearsed** what we would do in the future to dismantle that anger pattern. Bette suggested that I precede my *helpful* suggestions with a simple, "Need my help?" She would then have the option to reply, "Yes, help me," or, "No, thank you." This sounded reasonable to me, so we gave it a try.

It worked! What **was** an anger pattern in our relationship is **now** something we laugh at. I still forget once in a while and start to "back seat drive," but I usually catch myself in time to interrupt with, "OOPS, I mean, do you need my help?" Are there some patterns of anger you would like to remove from your relationship? Try some **R and R.**

Identify a recent anger episode that was not handled well. Review and Rehearse it now. Try to determine if there is an anger pattern involved.

Write at least one personal application from today's study.

Wife: _____

Husband: _____

What does God want you to do to work out this application?

Wife: _____

Husband: _____

REFLECT TOGETHER: Read Romans 12:9-21. Notice verse 16. Do you think "harmony" and "pride" can exist together?

PRAY TOGETHER: Help us admit when we're angry, Lord. Then give us the courage and determination to process our anger.

4. **Choose to FORGIVE.** We all blow it sometimes. We can not meet all our mates' expectations, nor they ours. However, when our partners fail, **we can choose to forgive** them.

Day 6

When you don't forgive, you lock yourself into a cage of your own making. You think you're putting your mate in a cage with your unforgiveness. They plead with you from the other side of the bars, but you lock the door and hide the key, ha, ha. But then...you look around; **you are the one inside**, not your mate. **You are locked in,** surrounded by bars of bitterness and resentment. You **have the key.** You can use it anytime you want to set yourself free. The key is **forgiveness,** but you must choose to use it. Have you ever considered that God **commands you to forgive** because He doesn't want **you** to be miserable?

Colossians 3:13 — *Bear with each other and forgive whatever grievances you may have against one another. Forgive as the Lord forgave you.*

Colossians 3:13 — *Bear with each other and forgive whatever grievances you may have against one another. Forgive as the Lord forgave you.*

5. **Seek SUPPORT.** We all need help from the Lord and from others. Immerse yourself in God's Word. Meditate on passages about how to handle anger. Pray. The Lord is eager to help you; He's waiting for you to ask. Tell Him you're ready to start obeying His commands about anger.

When you fail, ask for His and your mates' forgiveness. Then start over and keep on going. Remember, "Processing anger" is exactly that — a **process!** Ask your Christian friends to pray for you during this process. **God has promised to give you His power to change.**

Notes

6. **COVENANT to Change.** When you ask your partner for help, your anger becomes a problem to solve together instead of a wall of alienation between you. You can make a covenant to help each other change and grow out of your anger.

One effective method is granting each other permission to inform the other when you show signs of anger. (We often recognize our mates are getting angry before they do.) Develop a signal that will alert you to the fact that your anger doors are opening. Then you can begin the processing steps by recognizing your anger and keeping it under control. We recommend you choose a non-offensive signal. "You're getting angry again, you jerk," probably won't work well. Harold and I (Bette) have agreed to signal with "Please be wise." You'll see why shortly.

Of these last three steps in processing your anger (Choose to Forgive, Seek Support, and Covenant to Change), which would help you the most in dealing with your anger?

Wife: _____

Husband: _____

GOD'S PROMISE

Start at the bottom of these steps and work your way up. God promises a **progression** in Godly character. We start with being teachable and end with gaining self-control. This prepares us to begin the process of dealing with our anger. Meditate on the Scriptures that form these steps. As you apply them, you will develop the necessary tools to handle your anger.

Steps to

overcoming anger:

<u>**SELF-CONTROL**</u>
And will help you keep yourself under control. (Prov. 9:11b)

<u>**FORBEARANCE**</u> (Prov. 19:11b)
It will make you able to overlook offenses

<u>**PATIENCE**</u> (Prov. 19:11a)
And wisdom, in turn, will give you patience

<u>**WISDOM**</u> (Prov. 19:20b)
That will make you wise.

<u>**TEACHABILITY**</u> (Prov. 19:20a)
Listen to advice and accept instruction

Being teachable makes us wise and gives us patience, which makes us forbearing and helps us become self-controlled.

James 3:17-18 — *But the wisdom that comes from heaven is first of all pure; then peace loving, considerate, submissive, full of mercy and good fruit, impartial and sincere. Peacemakers who sow in peace raise a harvest of righteousness.*

Notes

James 3:17-18 — *But the wisdom that comes from heaven is first of all pure; then peace loving, considerate, submissive, full of mercy and good fruit, impartial and sincere. Peacemakers who sow in peace raise a harvest of righteousness.*

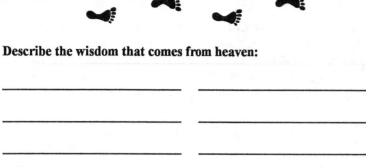

Describe the wisdom that comes from heaven:

_____	_____
_____	_____
_____	_____
_____	_____

Being _____ makes us _____ and

gives us _____, which makes us _____

and helps us become _____.

Write at least one personal application from today's study.

Wife: _____

Husband: _____

What does God want you to do to work out this application?

Wife: _____

Husband: _____

REFLECT TOGETHER: Again look carefully at the steps for overcoming anger. Notice each godly characteristic and what you must do to achieve it.

PRAY TOGETHER: Father God, we want to be teachable and wise, patient, forbearing and self-controlled. We open ourselves to You. Build Your character in us.

Notes

Day 7

Wrap Up: Read and answer the following questions individually. Then discuss each one.

1. I am naturally a (1) repressor or (2) expresser. I often respond to my anger by:

Wife: _____

Husband: _____

2. In the past, I have tended to become angry with you over:

Wife: _____

Husband: _____

 I think my underlying feeling is usually (hurt, fear, frustration):

Wife: _____

Husband: _____

 I confess this is wrong and take responsibility for my anger. Will you forgive me?

3. You could help me recognize and confess my anger by:

Wife: _____

Husband: _____

4. I enlist your help when you see that I am becoming angry. To help me, please give this signal:

Wife: _____

Husband: _____

I agree to this plan of action, and I have no right to be angry when you practice it.

REFLECT TOGETHER: Re-read James 3:17-18.

PRAY TOGETHER: Dear Lord, make us peacemakers.

GROUP DISCUSSION: If you are using this study with a group, you can use the following questions for group discussion.

Have a frank discussion

1. Of the six things sinful anger does to me, the most detrimental is
_____ because _____
_____.

2. Of the six truths about anger, the most difficult for me to accept is
_____ because _____
_____. The most helpful for me is
_____ because _____
_____.

3. Of the three primary emotions that are at the root of anger (fear, hurt and frustration), the one that causes most anger is probably
_____.

4. Talk about each of the steps for handling anger. Can you give illustrations of each step?

Make every effort to keep the unity of the Spirit through the bond of peace. (Eph. 4:3)

FIGHTING FAIR
THE ONLY WAY TO FIGHT
Chapter 4

Day 1

Do you ever fight? Maybe not the knock-down, drag out kind — but maybe so. Perhaps you hardly ever fight, but perhaps fighting is a serious problem in your marriage. Even if you are thinking, "We never fight," let us offer our definition of *fighting* to you. Using this definition, *everyone* fights sometimes.

Definition of *fighting*: Persisting in holding to your opinion in a disagreement rather than amiably, and without bias, working toward an acceptable solution you can both own. Does this definition of fighting include the two of you? We have a little exercise for you to do; but first, read James 4:1-12 together.

Now that you have read the passage in James, you are ready to mark each of the following 14 statements with a check indicating whether you agree or disagree with each statement. Yes, we know most of them are ambiguous, and some are even off the wall. They are meant to be. An agree/disagree's purpose is to make us **think**—not argue, **think**. So, with Philippians 2:14 in mind (*Do everything without complaining or arguing*), check each statement. No fence-riding — you must either **agree** or **disagree**. You each should define the terms in your own mind, and without consulting your mate's opinion, take a position on each statement.

Philippians 2:14 — *Do everything without complaining or arguing.*

No fence-riding — agree or disagree.

	AGREE	**DISAGREE**	
W	_____	_____	1. When fighting, we should tell the truth even if it hurts
H	_____	_____	our spouse.
W	_____	_____	2. When people become angry in their fights, they lose
H	_____	_____	control.
W	_____	_____	3. Fighting should be postponed when one or the other
H	_____	_____	spouse is tired.
W	_____	_____	4. When you criticize your mate in the heat of a fight, you
H	_____	_____	should make sure it's **constructive**.
W	_____	_____	5. Sometimes it may be necessary to yell in order to be heard
H	_____	_____	in the heat of a fight.
W	_____	_____	6. To bring a disagreement to a head, you may need to
H	_____	_____	confront your spouse, even if others are present.
W	_____	_____	7. You **can not** finish a fight without forgiveness.
H	_____	_____	
W	_____	_____	8. We fight only over symptoms, not actual causes.
H	_____	_____	

W _____ _____   9. Fights should **never** deal with more than one issue at a
H _____ _____   time.

W _____ _____   10. When labeling or categorizing your mate during a fight,
H _____ _____   you must make certain you are accurate.

W _____ _____   11. Bringing up the past *can* be helpful in settling today's
H _____ _____   fights.

No fence-riding — agree or
disagree.

W _____ _____   12. Quoting well-known authorities on the subject *can* give
H _____ _____   your side of the argument credibility.

W _____ _____   13. When your partner finally gives in or capitulates, and says
H _____ _____   "you're right," the fight is over.

W _____ _____   14. Physical contact while fighting should be avoided because
H _____ _____   of our human tendency to inflict hurt when we are angry.

**Now that you've marked whether you agree or disagree with each
statement, look back at the ones you and your partner have marked
differently. Discuss your reasons for marking them as you did.
Remember, don't fight, just discuss.**

Write at least one personal application from today's study.

Wife: _____

Husband: _____

What does God want you to do to work out this application?

Wife: _____

Husband: _____

REFLECT TOGETHER: Re-read James 4:1-12. Where do fights
come from?

PRAY TOGETHER: Dear Lord, thank You that You want to be our
friend. Help us humble ourselves before You and before one another.

Notes

Day 2

Ephesians 4:25 — *Therefore each of you must put off falsehood and speak truthfully to his neighbor, for we are all members of one body.*

Ephesians 4:15 — *Instead, speaking the truth in love, we will in all things grow up into him who is the Head, that is, Christ.*

Guidelines for Fighting Fair

Each Agree/Disagree statement matches with the following guideline of the same number. Only you can determine whether or not you answered correctly, because only you know **why** you answered as you did. Let's look at the guidelines and compare them with your answers to the Agree/Disagree statements.

1. **Keep it HONEST.** The Agree/Disagree statement was, "When fighting, we should always tell the truth even if it hurts our spouse." Ephesians 4:25 — *Therefore each of you must put off falsehood and speak truthfully to his neighbor, for we are all members of one body.* It **is** essential we commit ourselves to an honest relationship, so that we avoid the trap of acting or lying just to win over our partner. However, we must be tactful and speak the *truth in love* (Ephesians 4:15). If we speak the truth for truth's sake, we might say things which deeply hurt our mates. That's why God qualifies truth "with love." He wants us to **build each other up**, not tear each other down, even in the name of truth.

   We know a couple who love to tell each other the truth about themselves. It's gotten to the point where they now wrap the truth around emotional rocks and let 'em fly. When we ask them why they say things like that to each other, they shrug their shoulders and exclaim, "Well, it's the truth!" They must believe that somehow **that** makes it O.K. We don't ever want to wield the truth like that!

   How are you doing in keeping this guideline? Rate yourself *only* on a scale of 1 to 10, with "10" being "always."

   Wife: 1   2   3   4   5   6   7   8   9   10   (circle one)

   Husband: 1   2   3   4   5   6   7   8   9   10   (circle one)

   Discuss these ratings together for confirmation or adjustment.

   Unless you rate a "10," what would most help you improve in speaking the truth in love?

   Wife: _____

   Husband: _____

Ephesians 4:26a — *In your anger, do not sin.*

Proverbs 29:11 — *A fool gives full vent to his anger, but a wise man keeps himself under control.*

2. **Keep it under CONTROL.** The Agree/Disagree (from now on, we'll refer to it as A/D) statement number 2 was, "When people become angry in their fights, they lose control." Ephesians 4:26a — *In your anger, do not sin.* Proverbs 29:11 — *A fool gives full vent to his anger, but a wise man keeps himself under control.* Chapter 3 taught a lot about anger and the control of our natural responses to it — both repression and expression. You know as well as we do that it is essential to keep our reactions under control and to refrain from using **deadly weapons** on each other. Deadly weapons are words that trigger immediate defense: words like "always," "never," "You...," "If you really loved me..." Our simple rule is: always

avoid using "always," never say "never," and leave the rest of the deadly weapons alone!

I (Bette) have to watch myself because I tend to catastrophize a tad bit. "Always" and "never" are words I like to use for emphasis. I don't think I use them as much as I used to, but when Harold and I were first married, I'd often say clever things like, "I always say I'm sorry first. You never give in." "You never take out the trash. I always have to do it." And you know what? Harold could always think of an exception!

How are you doing in keeping this guideline? Rate yourself _only_ on a scale of 1 to 10, with "10" being "always."

Wife: 1   2   3   4   5   6   7   8   9   10   (circle one)

Husband: 1   2   3   4   5   6   7   8   9   10   (circle one)

Discuss these ratings together for confirmation or adjustment.

Unless you rate a "10", what would most help you keep your anger under control?

Wife: _____

Husband: _____

3. **Keep it TIMED RIGHT.** The A/D statement was, "Fighting should be postponed when one or the other spouse is tired." Ephesians 4: 26b-27 — _Do not let the sun go down while you are still angry, and do not give the devil a foothold._ The principle of this verse is to handle anger in a **timely manner**. It **can** mean we agree not to go to sleep before a fight is settled. Or it **can** mean we deal with it enough to mitigate some of its sting and agree to settle it later — in the morning or the earliest available time. Some of us can't sleep when we're angry, but many of us get so punchy at night that we couldn't settle a fight if our lives depended on it. We must mutually agree on how we as a couple will finish conflicts that drag on. But **when** we handle our fights is not as important as our mutual agreement **to handle them** in a timely manner, so the devil can **not** gain a foothold in our relationship.

    I (Harold) get too tired to settle our tiffs reasonably at night, while Bette stays up and fumes 'til the wee hours. We had to come to some sort of agreement about how to handle our conflicts when they dragged on into the night. Trying to abide by the principle of Ephesians 4:26, we developed the following plan which works for us. At the point we realize it is futile to continue discussing the problem due to fatigue, one of us says something like, "Look, we know we love each other and that we **will settle this**. Can we call a truce for now, and finish it in the morning?" That simple statement takes enough of the sting out of our conflict to enable each of us to get some rest and tackle it with better perspective the next morning.

Ephesians 4: 26b-27 — Do not let the sun go down while you are still angry, and do not give the devil a foothold.

Notes

How are you doing in keeping this guideline? Again, rate yourself *only* on a scale of 1 to 10.

Wife: 1 2 3 4 5 6 7 8 9 10 (circle one)

Husband: 1 2 3 4 5 6 7 8 9 10 (circle one)

Discuss these ratings together for confirmation or adjustment.

Unless you rate a "10," what would most help you to keep your fights timed right?

Wife: _____

Husband: _____

Write at least one personal application from today's study.

Wife: _____

Husband: _____

What does God want you to do to work out this application?

Wife: _____

Husband: _____

REFLECT TOGETHER: Read Ephesians 4:14-25. Notice how truth must be spoken.

PRAY TOGETHER: Lord God, help us put these guidelines into practice. Help us speak the truth in love. Help us remember not to use verbal deadly weapons on each other. And help us handle our disagreements in a timely manner.

Day 3

4. **Keep it POSITIVE.** The A/D statement: "When you criticize your mate in the heat of a fight, you should make sure it's constructive." Should we ever criticize our mate — whether we're in a fight or not? Does criticism have a legitimate place in a Christian marriage? To criticize means "to judge, to find fault, to censure." That sounds suspiciously like blame, doesn't it? And, like blame, it is counterproductive. Even with "constructive criticism," we must watch our motives carefully. We're often **quick** to criticize (even constructively), and **slow** to forbear the shortcomings of our mates. Colossians 3:12-13 — *Therefore, as God's*

*chosen people, holy and dearly loved, clothe yourselves with compassion, kindness, humility, gentleness and patience. **Bear with each other** and forgive whatever grievances you may have against one another.*

Sometimes there is an issue of sin we feel we must point out, but even in these situations, we must be quick to offer a positive suggestion. Paul exemplifies this principle in Ephesians 4:28 — *He who has been stealing must steal no longer, but must work, doing something useful with his own hands, that he may have something to share with those in need.* Notice that Paul did not simply tell the guilty persons to stop stealing, he immediately gave them a positive solution. However, in the midst of a fight, your motive probably would not be to help your mate free himself or herself from sin, but rather to condemn them for it. So save sin issues until a neutral time.

A couple approached us after the anger session at one of our conferences. Without any formalities, the wife blurted, "I only give **constructive** criticism. I **have** to give constructive criticism or he'd never know he was doing it wrong." The look on her husband's face told it all. We urged her, and we urge you, to be extremely cautious. What you consider "constructive" might be **destructive** to your mate. We're **not** saying constructive criticism is **never** needed in Christian marriages. We **are** saying it should be used **carefully** and **sparingly**. The better alternative is to practice the advise in Philippians 4:8 and concentrate on those things that are excellent and praiseworthy.

How are you doing in keeping this guideline? Again, rate yourself *only* on a scale of 1 to 10.

Wife: 1   2   3   4   5   6   7   8   9   10 (circle one)

Husband: 1   2   3   4   5   6   7   8   9   10 (circle one)

Discuss these ratings together for confirmation or adjustment.

Unless you rate a "10," what would most help you forbear instead of criticize?

Wife: _____

Husband: _____

5   **Keep it TACTFUL.** The A/D statement: "Sometimes it may be necessary to yell in order to be heard in the heat of a fight." Ephesians 4:29 — *Do not let any **unwholesome talk** come out of your mouths, but only **what is helpful** for building others up according to their needs, that it may benefit those who listen.* You must watch your words and guard your tone. The louder your voice, the less your mate will hear; the uglier the words, the less you will communicate. Want to get someone's attention? Whisper. It works even in a third grade classroom.

I (Bette) once knew a "yeller." She had yelled for so many years, she didn't even realize it anymore. She yelled at her children all day, and when her husband got home, she yelled at him too. I kept my visits to her home as short as possible; a couple of hours was the most I could handle. Each time I left exhausted, feeling as though all my emotions had been assaulted. I could hardly wait to return to the

Notes
Colossians 3:12-13 — *Therefore, as God's chosen people, holy and dearly loved, clothe yourselves with compassion, kindness, humility, gentleness and patience. Bear with each other and forgive whatever grievances you may have against one another.*

Ephesians 4:28 — *He who has been stealing must steal no longer, but must work, doing something useful with his own hands, that he may have something to share with those in need.*

Ephesians 4:29 — *Do not let any unwholesome talk come out of your mouths, but only what is helpful for building others up according to their needs, that it may benefit those who listen.*

Notes

quiet refuge of my own home and fall into bed for a recuperative nap. I decided then and there that **yelling** one's way through life was **no way to live.**

How are you doing in keeping this guideline? Again, rate yourself *only* **on a scale of 1 to 10.**

Wife: 1   2   3   4   5   6   7   8   9   10 (circle one)

Husband: 1   2   3   4   5   6   7   8   9   10 (circle one)

Discuss these ratings together for confirmation or adjustment.

Unless you rate a "10," what would most help you be more tactful?

Wife: _____

Husband: _____

6. **Keep it PRIVATE.** A/D statement number 6: "To bring a disagreement to a head, you may need to confront your spouse, even if others are present." Proverbs 13:3 — *He who guards his lips guards his soul, but he who speaks rashly will come to ruin.* Ephesians 4:31 — *Get rid of all bitterness, rage and anger, brawling and slander, along with every form of malice.* Never, never, never embarrass your mate in public. Whether an open potshot or a subtle "joke," verbal swings taken in public hurt much more deeply than private wounds. If you were reared in a family who teased each other unmercifully, we implore you to keep in mind that you **can not** treat your wife or husband the way you do your sister or brother. Too much of your mate's self esteem depends on **you.**

During one of our marriage enrichment conferences, just after teaching on this subject of all things, I (Harold) made what I thought was a harmless, humorous crack about Bette's cooking. Both Bette and the Holy Spirit *gently* reminded me that **cracks are never harmless** for "many a truth is said in jest." Being aware of the principle that private sin should be confessed privately and public sin confessed publicly, I knew what I had to do. When we stood before the group for the next teaching session, I had to swallow my pride and confess I had done what we told them **not** to do. Boy, was that humiliating! Since then, the memory of that experience has helped keep my roguish tongue a little more under control.

How are you doing in keeping this guideline? Again, rate yourself *only* **on a scale of 1 to 10.**

Wife: 1   2   3   4   5   6   7   8   9   10 (circle one)

Husband: 1   2   3   4   5   6   7   8   9   10 (circle one)

Discuss these ratings together for confirmation or adjustment.

Proverbs 13:3 — He who guards his lips guards his soul, but he who speaks rashly will come to ruin.

Ephesians 4:31 — Get rid of all bitterness, rage and anger, brawling and slander, along with every form of malice.

Unless you rate a "10," what would most help you remember to keep
your fights private?

Wife: _____

Husband: _____

Write at least one personal application from today's study.
Wife: _____
Husband: _____
What does God want you to do to work out this application?
Wife: _____
Husband: _____

REFLECT TOGETHER: Re-read Colossians 3:12-13.

PRAY TOGETHER: Oh, Father, take away our tendency to be
critical. Help us guard our words and tone of voice. And help us
never make one another the brunt of our jokes.

7. **Keep it CLEANED UP.** The A/D statement was: "You can not finish a fight
without forgiveness." Ephesians 4:32 — *Be kind and compassionate to one
another, forgiving each other, just as in Christ God forgave you.* The fight is over
when forgiveness has been asked for and given. **Don't assume** everything is all
right again. **Make sure** everything is all right again. Then you won't be burying
"ghosts" that will come back to haunt you. Notice — we are to forgive *just as in
Christ God forgave you.* How **does** God forgive us? He forgives completely, with
no remembrance of our sin. He *hurls all our iniquities into the depths of the sea*
(Micah 7:19). Cory Ten Boom used to add in her thick Dutch accent, "And then,
Beloved, He puts up a NO FISHING sign." He never brings them back up to hold
over our heads. How does He **do** that? He **chooses** to do that! He chooses to
thoroughly forgive, and He expects us to do the same.

When our children were youngsters, one of the hardest things to do was **ask their
forgiveness** when we were wrong. Want an exercise in humility? Try asking a
three-year old for forgiveness. However, we believe that as God's children, we are
called to be **humble** and to **confess** when we have wronged someone and seek their
forgiveness, even if that "someone" is our own child. So, as difficult as it was, we
tried to practice it. What do you think about this? Would such a practice cause
harm, or would it help children learn how to forgive? Our three children are all

Day 4

Ephesians 4:32 — *Be kind and
compassionate to one another,
forgiving each other, just as in
Christ God forgave you.*

Micah 7:19 — *You will again have
compassion on us; you will tread
our sins underfoot and hurl all our
iniquities into the depths of the
sea.*

Notes

You are your children's role model.

grown and married now. And as we observe them practice forgiveness in their marriages, we have come to the conclusion they must have learned **something positive** from it, even though we felt rather awkward at the time. **You** are your children's role model. How you **practice forgiveness** in your marriage and family relationships has a profound impact on them.

How are you doing in keeping this guideline? Again, rate yourself *only* **on a scale of 1 to 10.**

Wife: 1   2   3   4   5   6   7   8   9   10 (circle one)

Husband: 1   2   3   4   5   6   7   8   9   10 (circle one)

Discuss these ratings together for confirmation or adjustment.

Unless you rate a "10," what would most help you choose to forgive more quickly?

Wife: _____

Husband: _____

Proverbs 18:15 — *The heart of the discerning acquires knowledge; the ears of the wise seek it out.*

8. **Find out WHAT you're fighting about.** A/D statement number 8: "We fight only over symptoms, not actual causes." Proverbs 18:15 — *The heart of the discerning acquires knowledge; the ears of the wise seek it out.* In Chapter 3, we discussed how anger is a secondary emotion, and stressed the importance of discovering the feelings below the surface. This Scripture tells us that we are **wise** if we **seek to discern** the **underlying cause** of our — and our mate's — anger. If what starts things off is usually only the **symptom**, not the cause, then we need to *seek out* the **cause**.

Several years ago, a couple we know was experiencing continuous conflict over the husband's excessive work schedule. He rarely came home before their children were asleep. The wife was growing more and more bitter, and the husband was coming home later and later. As they discussed their conflict, they discovered the core of the problem. She felt he was valuing his job more than her and their children. After all, he lavished his time on his work, with little left over for his family.

For his part, he was delaying coming home each evening because he knew he would be facing her recriminations. They were trapped in a **deadlocked cycle** of conflict until they talked about the feelings under their anger. She was **hurt**; he was **afraid**. As they sought solutions, they knew they needed to **make some changes**. Because they finally understood the real reasons for their conflict, they were **willing** to make the necessary changes.

Because they finally understood the real reasons for their conflict, they were willing to make the necessary changes.

How are you doing in keeping this guideline? Again, rate yourself *only* on a scale of 1 to 10.

Wife: 1   2   3   4   5   6   7   8   9   10 (circle one)

Husband: 1   2   3   4   5   6   7   8   9   10 (circle one)

Discuss these ratings together for confirmation or adjustment.

Unless you rate a "10," what would most help you discover the underlying causes of your fights?

Wife: _____

Husband: _____

9. **Stick to the SUBJECT.** The A/D statement: "Fights should never deal with more than one issue at a time." Usually, this is true. We won't settle anything if one or both of us say things like, "And that reminds me...." If there are several issues disturbing us, we need to deal with one at a time. Throwing everything at your mate in one discussion just to get them off your chest **does not work**. You can overwhelm your mate and yourself. None of us can deal with five problems at the same time. It seems hopeless. But **one** problem at a time? **That** we can handle.

Have you ever heard of Green Stamps? Years ago, gas stations and grocery stores **gave** them to customers to encourage their business. They were great! We saved books and books of stamps, took them to the Green Stamp redemption center and "bought" TV trays or something equally worthless. As couples, we have our own kind of Green Stamps. We often save our hurts and unresolved anger and conflicts the same way people use to save Green Stamps. We don't announce it out loud, of course, but somewhere deep inside, we record our mates' *wrongs* against us, calculating the number of books it will take to "buy" our getting out. Let's see, if it takes twenty books of stamps to buy a separation, will it take forty for a divorce? **Don't save these stamps.** Don't keep even one or two of them, not a whole page, and certainly not an entire book. Handle issues as they arise — one at a time.

Are you saving resentment stamps?

How are you doing in keeping this guideline? Again, rate yourself *only* on a scale of 1 to 10.

Wife: 1   2   3   4   5   6   7   8   9   10 (circle one)

Husband: 1   2   3   4   5   6   7   8   9   10 (circle one)

Discuss these ratings together for confirmation or adjustment.

Notes

Unless you rate a "10," what would most help you handle issues as they arise instead of saving them up?

Wife: _____

Husband: _____

Write at least one personal application from today's study.

Wife: _____

Husband: _____

What does God want you to do to work out this application?

Wife: _____

Husband: _____

REFLECT TOGETHER: Read Micah 7:18-19. Notice how many action verbs describe what God does for us.

PRAY TOGETHER: Mighty God, teach us to forgive like You. And help us handle problems between us as they come up and not save and collect them.

Day 5

James 4:11 — *Brothers, do not slander one another. Anyone who speaks against his brother or judges him speaks against the law and judges it.*

10. **Avoid CATEGORIZING or name calling.** The A/D statement was, "When labeling or categorizing your mate during a fight, you **must** make certain you are accurate." James 4:11 — *Brothers, do not slander one another. Anyone who speaks against his brother or judges him speaks against the law and judges it.* Sometimes we say things in the heat of an argument like: "You're just saying that because you're a woman." "You men are all alike." "You're just like your mother!" Ooh, even if what we say is accurate, **name calling is deadly**. It's a habit we must avoid. And if you have gotten into this habit, you need to break it as quickly as possible.

I (Bette) was pushing my cart behind an elderly couple in our local market.

Their conversation went something like this:

"Why do you always get that brand of coffee? You know it burns my stomach."

"Oh, you old fool, everything burns your stomach."

"Well, I'd rather be an old fool than an old witch."

"Shut up, little baby, I'll get you the kind you want."

By this time, I was so embarrassed for them, I turned around and headed for another isle. Robert Browning's words crowded into my piteous thoughts: "Grow old along with me! The best is yet to be." I couldn't help but ponder how they had **bickered away** their 'best is yet to be.'

How are you doing in keeping this guideline? Again, rate yourself *only* **on a scale of 1 to 10.**

Wife: **1   2   3   4   5   6   7   8   9   10 (circle one)**

Husband: **1   2   3   4   5   6   7   8   9   10 (circle one)**

Discuss these ratings together for confirmation or adjustment.

Unless you rate a "10," what would most help you remember to never call your mate names?

Wife: _____

Husband: _____

11. **Leave out past HISTORIES.** A/D statement number 11: "Bringing up the past *can* be helpful in settling today's fights." 1 Corinthians 13:5 — *[Love] is not rude, it is not self-seeking, it is not easily angered, it **keeps no record of wrongs**.* If we've burned the Stamp Books we spoke of in guideline 9, then there will be no past histories to bring up. If we've truly settled yesterday's conflicts, then they're gone, **never** to be brought up again. There is a time, however, when past fights **must** be brought up — when they **were not** settled the first time. Even then, they must be brought up for **one reason** only — so that they **can** be settled. Old conflicts are like chains. The longer we carry them around, the heavier they get. We don't have to carry them any longer. We can lay them down; settle past wrongs; and get on with today.

Here's what the Apostle Paul had to say about how we should handle the past: *Brothers, I do not consider myself yet to have taken hold of it [becoming like Christ]. But one thing I do: **Forgetting what is behind** and straining toward **what is ahead**, I press on toward the goal to win the prize for which God has called me heavenward in Christ Jesus. All of us who are mature should **take such a view of things**.* (Philippians 3:13-15a)

1 Corinthians 13:5 — *[Love] is not rude, it is not self-seeking, it is not easily angered, it **keeps no record of wrongs**.*

Philippians 3:13-15a — *Brothers, I do not consider myself yet to have taken hold of it [becoming like Christ]. But one thing I do: **Forgetting what is behind** and straining toward **what is ahead**, I press on toward the goal to win the prize for which God has called me heavenward in Christ Jesus. All of us who are mature should **take such a view of things**.*

Notes

How are you doing in keeping this guideline? Again, rate yourself *only* on a scale of 1 to 10.

Wife: 1   2   3   4   5   6   7   8   9   10 (circle one)

Husband: 1   2   3   4   5   6   7   8   9   10 (circle one)

Discuss these ratings together for confirmation or adjustment.

Unless you rate a "10," what would most help you settle past conflicts and be done with them?

Wife: _____

Husband: _____

12. **Don't allow THIRD parties.** A/D statement: "Quoting well known authorities on the subject can give your side of the argument credibility." Don't bring in Dr. Dobson, Dr. Ruth or even your mother to support your position. Just fight it out on your own. If you keep in mind that you have **no other option** but to settle your conflicts, you **will find solutions** you can live with. By the way, it's only fair to warn you: if you use **us** to back up your position, we'll track you down.

Don't bring in Dr. Dobson, or even your mother, to support your position.

A husband we once knew used the "third party" weapon on his wife regularly. Whenever they had an argument, he called his mother for sympathy. She, of course, commiserated excessively with him. He would then inform his wife, like handing down a **verdict**, that his mother agreed with him. "She says you're wrong and I'm right!" We admonished him to immediately stop this practice. His mother had no business even knowing they had a fight, much less the details. Reluctantly at first, he gave up this crutch, and he and his wife are now finding better ways to handle their conflicts. But guess who still thinks her baby is being used and abused?

How are you doing in keeping this guideline? Again, rate yourself *only* on a scale of 1 to 10.

Wife: 1   2   3   4   5   6   7   8   9   10 (circle one)

Husband: 1   2   3   4   5   6   7   8   9   10 (circle one)

Discuss these ratings together for confirmation or adjustment.

Unless you rate a "10," what would most help to not use others to support your side of arguments?

Wife: _____

Husband: _____

Notes

> Write at least one personal application from today's study.
>
> Wife: _____
>
> Husband: _____
>
> What does God want you to do to work out this application?
>
> Wife: _____
>
> Husband: _____

REFLECT TOGETHER: Read 1 Corinthians 13:4-7. Note each characteristic of love as you read.

PRAY TOGETHER: Dear Lord, help us truly love one another. We want all the characteristics of love You list in Your Word to be true of us.

Day 6

1 Corinthians 13:5 — [Love] is not rude, it is not self-seeking....

James 4:1-2 — What causes fights and quarrels among you? Don't they come from your desires that battle within you? You want something but don't get it.

13. **Remember it's the one you LOVE you're fighting with.** The A/D statement for this guideline was, "When your partner finally gives in or capitulates, and says, 'you're right,' the fight is over." 1 Corinthians 13:5 — *[Love] is not rude, it is not self-seeking....* Why do we have a driving need to win? Why do we believe so fervently we are right and our partners are wrong? James 4:1-2 explains our problem. *What causes fights and quarrels among you? Don't they come from your desires that battle within you? You want something but don't get it.* We are out to win, even if we must step on our mates to do so. We fail to realize that when we win this way, we **lose**. We **both** lose.

Have you ever tried **praying together** when you're in a heated discussion? Oh, yes, we know — it's the **last** thing you feel like doing at the time. But it is also the **best** thing you could do! It will remind you that you're on the **same team**. When your **team wins, you both win**. When only one of you wins, your team can still lose. Consider the November 1, 1992, game between the Los Angeles Rams and the Atlanta Falcons. Jim Everett threw four touchdowns and completed 18 more passes for a total of 253 yards. Jim played a great game, but his team (the Rams) still lost. The record book isn't going to record Jim Everett's victory, it's going to record his team's loss. **Your team—your marriage relationship—needs to win the fights.** Not you...not your spouse...your **team!**

How are you doing in keeping this guideline? Again, rate yourself *only* on a scale of 1 to 10.

Wife:	1	2	3	4	5	6	7	8	9	10 (circle one)
Husband:	1	2	3	4	5	6	7	8	9	10 (circle one)

Discuss these ratings together for confirmation or adjustment.

Unless you rate a "10," what would most help you remember it's the one you love you're fighting with?

Wife: _____

Husband: _____

14. **Hold HANDS while fighting.** The final A/D statement was, "Physical contact while fighting should be avoided because of our human tendency to inflict hurt when we are angry." When we have conflict, our natural tendency is to retreat from one another. We feel alienated from our partners, because we believe they must not love us as much as they say. Otherwise they wouldn't treat us like this. Our real need during conflict, however, is the complete opposite of our usual behavior. We **need** touch. Touching reminds us that **WE** are more important than any issue. And as you will discover, it is difficult to fight while touching. The trick in following this guideline is to make a mutual decision to hold hands during your next fight...but make this decision now while you're **not** fighting. You can't wait until an argument has started, and then remember, "Oh, we're supposed to hold hands." By then, it's too late. So why not decide **today** to give it a try?

The first few times we taught this guideline at GTO conferences, it was only a theory to us. It **sounded** good, but we had never tried it. (True confession.) Then at one conference, a young couple excitedly expressed the profound difference this guideline had made in their relationship. **They sold us!** We began a conscious effort to hold our hands out to each other as soon as we realized a discussion was creating more heat than light. And **it worked!** It's not easy...but it works! We challenge you to try it.

If you fight about the same things over and over again, you must start doing something different....

Our need during conflict is **touch**.

How are you doing in keeping this guideline? Again, rate yourself *only* on a scale of 1 to 10.

Wife: 1   2   3   4   5   6   7   8   9   10 (circle one)

Husband: 1   2   3   4   5   6   7   8   9   10 (circle one)

Discuss these ratings together for confirmation or adjustment.

Unless you rate a "10," what would most help you hold hands while fighting?

Wife: _____

Husband: _____

Notes

> Write at least one personal application from today's study.
>
> Wife: _____
>
> Husband: _____
>
> What does God want you to do to work out this application?
>
> Wife: _____
>
> Husband: _____

REFLECT TOGETHER: Read 1 Corinthians 13:4-7 again. See if you can list the characteristics of love without looking.

PRAY TOGETHER: Dear God, help us remember we are a team, even when we're fighting. Help us commit to holding hands and praying during our fights.

Day 7

WRAP UP: Answer the following questions. Answer the first two individually before you start discussing.

1. The guideline I will need the most help in applying is

   Wife: _____

   Husband: _____

   You have my permission to help me apply this by:

   Wife: _____

   Husband: _____

2. The guideline I would most like you to apply in our fights is

   Wife: _____

   Husband: _____

79

3. **Review the 14 guidelines together asking each other the following questions about each one:**

    (1) Do we need this guideline in our fighting?

    (2) Are we applying this one regularly?

    (3) Do I need to concentrate on this one as one of my top three guidelines?

    (4) Do I need help in applying this one? Will you help me by:

    Wife: _____

    Husband: _____

REFLECT TOGETHER: Read James 4:1-12 one more time.

PRAY TOGETHER: Father, help us be lovingly honest with each other in discussing which guidelines we need to use more. Teach us to be humble enough to accept help from each other.

GROUP DISCUSSION: If you are using this study in a group setting, the following may be used as group discussion questions.

1. Are any of these guidelines new to you?

2. Which guideline do you feel is the most difficult to apply? Why?

3. Which **three** guidelines do you feel would be the most helpful to you in fighting fairer?

4. Which one of these three will you need the most help in applying?

Have a frank discussion

CONSTRUCTIVE CONFLICT
Chapter 5

Day 1

What is Conflict?

If we obeyed — **really obeyed** — two simple verses in Scripture, we would have **very little conflict** in our homes. These two verses describe what conflict is made of and how to rid ourselves of it. What are these miracle verses? Ephesians 4, verses 31 and 32 — *Get rid of all bitterness, rage and anger, brawling and slander, along with every form of malice. Be kind and compassionate to one another, forgiving each other, just as in Christ God forgave you.*

We, as God's children, are commanded to **get rid** of certain thoughts and behavior. *Get rid* indicates action. This means it will **take work.** Let's explore how these elements of conflict might look in our lives.

> **BITTERNESS** = the harboring of hurts, disappointments, rejections and unresolved conflicts.

Has your mate hurt and disappointed you? Are you keeping a stamp book filled with memories of the times you felt rejected by your partner? Do you replay unresolved conflicts in your mind and think of things you should have said? When your mate does something negative, do you think, "I knew he/she was going to do that. Why am I the one who always gets hurt?" This pattern of bitterness trips up both anger repressors and expressors (Chapter 3). Is there some bitterness in your life you need to *get rid* of?

Ephesians 4, 31, 32 — Get rid of all bitterness, rage and anger, brawling and slander, along with every form of malice. Be kind and compassionate to one another, forgiving each other, just as in Christ God forgave you.

> **RAGE** (or wrath) = a temper flare up which causes us to act without considering the consequences.

Do you get angry quickly, like striking a match? Do you slam doors and walk out? Do you yell at anyone unfortunate enough to be within hearing? If so, you are an anger expressor, and need to *get rid* of an uncontrolled temper.

> **ANGER** = a strong response of irritation; an abiding condition of the mind, frequently with a view to taking revenge.

Are you often irritated with your spouse and children? Do you make them pay (or think about making them pay) for the things they do to irritate you? Do you say things like, "This is all your fault"? If these patterns of anger are in your life, then God says you are responsible to *get rid* of them.

> **BRAWLING** (or clamor) = a response without regard for the feelings of our mates; the tumult of controversy.

Do you spit out opinions just to get a reaction from your mate? Do you disregard your mate's feelings and blurt out things that could hurt them? Do you say things like, "You look awful! Why can't you fix yourself up?" Do you argue for the sake of arguing? If you do these things, you practice brawling and must *get rid* of such hurtful behavior.

> **SLANDER** = a response intended to defame and show contempt; verbal abuse.

Do you purposefully say things to hurt your mate? Do you call them names and question their character? Do you ever put them down or tell them they can't do something as well as you or someone else can? Do you sometimes say things like, "Why can't you ever do anything right?" These are slanderous actions and God wants you to *get rid* of them.

MALICE = spite and ill-will; resentment which holds a grudging desire to see our mates suffer.

Have you ever thought, "I'll treat them the way they treat me, and then they'll know how much it hurts"? Or, "It serves them right"? Do you withhold affection as punishment for your mate? Do you use sarcasm frequently — or is silence your weapon of choice? These are all forms of malice. You are commanded to *get rid* of them all.

God urges us to *get rid* of these six traits from our lives. Perhaps you are thinking, "Well, when God said that, He hadn't met MY spouse!" Sorry. If any or all of these are a part of your life, you can not blame your spouse. You are responsible for your thoughts and behavior regardless of how your partner acts. You probably find it as hard as we do to accept this truth. The commands in verse 32 won't be much easier, but we'll save that for later. First, we need to explore Conflict a little deeper.

List the six characteristics God commands we get rid of:

1_____ 4_____

2_____ 5_____

3_____ 6_____

HUSBAND: circle the two characteristics you need to get rid of most.

WIFE: Put an asterisk beside the two characteristics you need to get rid of most.

Why We Have Conflict

DIFFERENCES

We fight for three basic reasons. The first is our differences. Differences cause a great deal of conflict because **we are different**.

Wow! That's profound, isn't it? You'd think this would be so obvious, none of us could miss it, wouldn't you? It's not. Our expectations drive us on in unrealistic anticipation that our mates will be **who** we want them to be...usually that means being more like ourselves. But, at the risk of repeating profundity, our mates **are not like us**, and they **can not** meet all our expectations. Hey, we can't even meet all our own expectations. Somehow, though, we hang on to them, unwilling to let our expectations slip from our grasp. When they are not fulfilled (which is pretty often), we become frustrated. Frustration ignites anger; anger sparks demands; demands activate defense systems. Our mates dig in their heels, loudly protesting, "No way!" The result? CONFLICT.

Notes

The Differences that can lead to Conflict:

We are different because of the way we were BROUGHT UP. Your families of origin were different. Your mate's parents might have been strict, while yours were lenient. Your family might have made a big deal about birthdays and holidays, but your mate's didn't. Your families probably handled anger and problem-solving in unique ways, and used different methods of child-rearing. They may even have had conflicting value systems.

<u>With all this diversity, being from different families is almost like being from different countries</u>. All of this means that you and your mate are sometimes going to see things from opposite points of view. You might as well expect it.

Are you and your mate different in the way you were brought up?

Talk about this difference together.

We are different because of our BIRTH ORDER. Every child born into a family is actually born to a different family. Hold on...let us explain. The first born comes into a family of two, usually inexperienced, adults. The second born enters a family of two more experienced adults and one sibling. The third child is born into a family of two tired adults and two siblings. <u>Family dynamics change with the addition of each child.</u>

Every child born into a family is actually born into a different family.

Can you see how this could affect the way you approach life? First born's are often driven by success and control because they may have been pushed to walk, talk and do everything else early. Second born's usually adopt traits exactly opposite of the first born in order to establish their own identity. Third born children seem to either vie with the others for some individuality and distinction or idolize one sibling and dislike the other. It gets a bit complicated, but hopefully this offers some insight into how birth order can conspire to make you and your mate different.

Are you and your mate different in birth order?

Talk about this difference together.

We are different because some of us are THINKERS and some are FEELERS. Thinkers use details and logic to form their conclusions and want their feeler mates to logically express what they **think** about things. Feelers process information through their emotions and want their thinker mates to express how they **feel** about things.

Differences are good!

The problem is, thinkers may never be able to share their feelings the way their feeler mates desire them to. The same problem exists for feelers trying to stay detached and logical in the way their thinker mates want. Actually, this is not bad news. It's really **good news**! Your marriage...your family...needs both a thinker and a feeler to find a good balance.

Are you and your mate different in this area?

Talk about this difference together

Write at least one personal application from today's study.

Wife: _____

Husband: _____

What does God want you to do to work out this application?

Wife: _____

Husband: _____

REFLECT TOGETHER: Read Acts 10:9-23 and vv. 34-36. Notice how Peter changed his mind about what he thought was good and what God thought was good.

PRAY TOGETHER: Lord, thank you for making us different. Help us never call each other's characteristics "weaknesses" when You have made them "strengths."

We are different because some of us are **INNER** and some are **OUTER** people. Inner people are introspective and thorough, but rarely the life of the party. Outer people are gregarious and open in their communication, but often fail to think everything through carefully. If inner and outer people focus on each other's weaknesses, they become irritated. If, however, they focus on each other's strengths, they realize they need each other. If one of you is an inner person and the other an outer person, you actually **complete** one another.

Day 2

Differences can be strengths.

Are you and your mate different in this area?

Talk about this difference together.

We are different because some of us are **ORGANIZED** and some are **SPONTANEOUS.** Organized people like to plan their lives down to the hours and minutes. Spontaneous people enjoy letting life simply happen to them. Organized people are usually steady and dependable, while spontaneous people are usually flexible and fun.

Do you remember The Odd Couple? Felix and Oscar drove one another crazy on a

Notes

rather consistent basis just like many organized vs. spontaneous mates do. But both have valuable and beneficial qualities which the other actually **needs**.

Are you and your mate different in this area?

Talk about this difference together.

We are different because some of us are MALE and some are FEMALE. You noticed? This in itself accounts for huge differences. Our bodies are different, both in looks and function. We tend to express our emotions in different ways. We even process thoughts differently. We are gloriously different! Although God could have made Eve a **clone** of Adam, He chose to make her the **complement** of Adam.

God could have made Eve the clone of Adam, instead He chose to make her the complement of Adam.

Why do men and women strive to conform each other to themselves? If we succeeded, this world would be a pretty **boring** place, don't you think? Unfortunately, we keep trying. Here's a list of what men and women wish were different about the opposite sex, according to Joe Taunebaum in his book, Male and Female Realities.

MEN THINK WOMEN SHOULD:

1. Talk less
2. Be less emotional
3. Be more physical
4. Be less romantic
5. Be more sexual
6. Be less involved with others
7. Laugh less
8. Be more rational
9. Be more serious
10. Stay home more
11. Change less
12. Pay less attention to clothes
13. Be less sensitive
14. Pay more attention to time

WOMEN THINK MEN SHOULD:

1. Talk more
2. Be more emotional
3. Be less physical
4. Be more romantic
5. Be less sexual
6. Be more involved with others
7. Laugh more
8. Be less rational
9. Be less serious
10. Go out more
11. Change more
12. Pay more attention to clothes
13. Be more sensitive
14. Pay less attention to time

O.K. — you two are different! The question is: What can you do about your differences so they will bring **completion** instead of **conflict** to your relationship?

Since you and your mate are obviously different in this area, talk about this difference.

How to handle your Differences

Forbear them. Ephesians 4:1-3 — *I urge you to live a life worthy of the calling you have received. Be completely humble and gentle; be patient, **bearing with***

Ephesians 4:1-3 — *I urge you to live a life worthy of the calling you have received. Be completely humble and gentle; be patient, bearing with one another in love. Make every effort to keep the unity of the Spirit through the bond of peace.*

*one another in love. Make **every effort** to keep the unity of the Spirit through the bond of peace.* Colossians 3:12-14 — *Therefore, as God's chosen people, holy and dearly loved, clothe yourselves with compassion, kindness, humility, gentleness and patience. **Bear with** each other and forgive whatever grievances you may have against one another. Forgive as the Lord forgave you.*

Forbear...a forgotten word in our culture. Society says, "Don't put up with anybody!" But God says, "Put up with each other compassionately." Actually, "forbear" or "bear with" means more than simply "putting up" with someone. The Greek word literally means "to hold up." Therefore, to forbear is "to endure with gentleness, clemency, and a sweet reasonableness." (Vine's Expository Dictionary of New Testament Words)

We need to "hold up" one another in our **uniqueness**. (Yes, that means differences.) You looked for differences when you sought your mate. You might not have known it at the time, but you craved completion — someone like you, but not like you; someone who fit your "nooks and crannies." But over time our perspective tends to become distorted. What we once saw as our mates' unique qualities, we can begin to see as their unbearable differences. If this has happened to you, you must choose to obey God's command to forbear and once again appreciate your mates' uniqueness.

What is a difference between you and your mate you need to forbear?

Wife: _____

Husband: _____

See your partners' unique characteristics as STRENGTHS instead of WEAKNESSES. 1 Thessalonians 5:11 — *Therefore encourage one another and build each other up....* Romans 12:10 — *Be devoted to one another in brotherly love. Honor one another above yourselves.* We tend to think, "**My** characteristics are strengths. So my partner's characteristics — the ones different from mine — **must be weaknesses.**" It's hard for us to comprehend that our differences **are** our strengths. We need to abide in these two Scriptures, so that we will **build up** our mates and **honor their differences** as strengths.

Would you say logical thinking is a strength? Sure it is, and so is intuition. Open communication is a strength, as is thoroughness of thought. The ability to organize is a wonderful characteristic, but the ability to be flexible is too.

If you **pool your strengths**, instead of stubbornly viewing your differences as weaknesses, your relationship will reap great rewards. You can accomplish projects together you could never achieve on your own. You can also make better, stronger decisions. Harold and I (Bette) make our best decisions when we both bring our strengths to the process. Harold's a thinker. He makes his pro and con lists and does projections on his computer. I like to read, so I research the books and magazines. And because I'm a feeler, I also rely heavily on my intuition. When we pool all our strengths, we make great decisions. We **need** each other's differences.

Notes

Colossians 3:12-14 — *Therefore, as God's chosen people, holy and dearly loved, clothe yourselves with compassion, kindness, humility, gentleness and patience. Bear with each other and forgive whatever grievances you may have against one another. Forgive as the Lord forgave you.*

1 Thessalonians 5:11 — *Therefore encourage one another and build each other up....*

Romans 12:10 — *Be devoted to one another in brotherly love. Honor one another above yourselves.*

Notes

What differences in your mate do you need to see as strengths instead of weaknesses?

Wife: _____

Husband: _____

Do not try to REMAKE your partner to be like yourself. Ephesians 5:1-2a — *Be imitators of God, therefore, as dearly loved children and live a life of love....* The plan is — we **both** imitate God. He never suggests we should expect our mates to imitate us. Our mates can't possibly imitate God and us at the same time anyway!

Our desire for our mates to be like ourselves is very subtle. Most of the couples we've counseled didn't realize they even had this problem. But they made statements like, "She's the one who needs to change, not me." And, "He should have handled the situation like I told him." What are they really saying? "I want my mate to do things like **I** do, to think like **I** do, to handle situations like **I** do, to see things from **my** point of view. And I won't be satisfied until **he/she** changes." This attitude poses an important question: what if your mate doesn't change? Are you going to go around being frustrated the rest of your life?

You know, if God had wanted **two** of **you**, He would have made **two** of **you**. Instead, He made you with **unique strengths**, and He made your mate with **unique strengths**. He knows, with His help, you can blend your differences, so that **together you are stronger** than each of you are separately. It's up to you. You can use your differences to bring **completion** to your marriage — or you can allow them to bring **conflict**.

Have you tried to remake your mate to be like yourself?

WIFE: _____   HUSBAND: _____

In what ways?

Wife: _____

Husband: _____

Ephesians 5:1-2a — Be imitators of God, therefore, as dearly loved children and live a life of love....

Blend your differences.
Together you're stronger.

Write at least one personal application from today's study.

Wife: _____

Husband: _____

What does God want you to do to work out this application?

Wife: _____

Husband: _____

REFLECT TOGETHER: Read Ephesians 4:1-6. Notice how the first step to 'living a life worthy of your calling' is to be "completely humble."

PRAY TOGETHER: Dear Lord, thank you that we are Your unique creations. Help us never be so proud as to try to remake one another to be like ourselves.

Power Struggles

Day 3

What are Power Struggles?

POWER = the ability of one spouse to influence or control the other.

STRUGGLE = the battle for power.

Therefore, a **power struggle** is the battle to gain influence or control of your mate.

We want to control and we fear being controlled. These attitudes create an atmosphere of competition. We begin to view our marriage as a contest...a contest we *have* to win. Have you ever seen two puppies fighting over a rag? They sink their teeth into opposite ends and growl and shake their heads and growl some more. They wrestle and struggle for the rag, but usually end up so tired, they fall asleep with the rag between them, neither having won. That is a perfect picture of how we act in a power struggle. We sink our teeth into our own agenda, growl and wrestle with our mates, but never really win. The more we struggle for control, the less control we have.

We begin to view our marriage as a contest...a contest we have to win.

James, the brother of our Lord Jesus, was right when he said, *What causes fights and quarrels among you? Don't they come from your desires that battle within you? You want something but don't get it....* (James 4:1-2a). How aptly that describes power struggles: we *want something but don't get it.* We'd be far better off to believe the truth. And that is: we are not in competition with one another; we are interdependent with one another. We are not two fists, fighting for control. We are one fist made of two hands, fingers interlocked.

James 4:1-2a — *What causes fights and quarrels among you? Don't they come from your desires that battle within you? You want something but don't get it....*

Power Struggle Role-play: Here is a skit we'd like you to read. You'll notice part way through, a mediator interrupts this couple's power struggle to ask

Notes

We are not two fists, fighting for control. We are one fist made of two hands, fingers interlocked.

important questions. Now, we don't have mediators to referee our power struggles, but once we know the right questions to ask, we can act as our own mediators and stop the conflict before it goes too far.

Helen: I've had it with you! You come home, say a few words to me and the kids and then head for the tube. Honestly, I think you're addicted to it! And the weekends are the worst. If anything even smells like sports, you're buried in front of that TV!

Mark: Well, it's the only relaxation I ever get! If I even look up for a minute, you're there with that stupid list of projects you've been saving. I need to unwind!

Helen: I don't mind your unwinding, but there's a limit. You're so unwound, you....

Mark: (Interrupts) Stow it, will you! I've heard it all before. You always go on and on. I want some relief from your constant griping!

Mediator: Whoa, you two! Don't you see what you are doing? This power struggle is getting you nowhere. Let me ask you a few questions. Helen, when he retreats to the TV, what do you do?

Helen: That really makes me angry, so I try to get his attention and find out when he can help or even talk to us. I bang around in the room and try to disturb his old TV show as much as I can.

Mediator: What is it you really want? Do you simply want his attention and involvement?

Helen: Yes. Is that too much to ask?

Mediator: How about you, Mark? What do you do when she gets after you?

Mark: I tune her out and watch more TV. I just got home from work. I need to let down a little.

Mediator: It sounds like all you really want is for her to back off and give you some peace and quiet when you first get home. Is that right?

Mark: That's right. I wouldn't try to ignore her so much if she'd just give me a little space.

Let's explore what happened in this role-play. Both Helen and Mark have developed a strategy to get each other to do what they want. Was it working? Not only did it **not** work, it created **more** problems. Each wanted the other to change, but the more they tried to force the change, the worse things got. How strange! They both want this conflict out of their lives. Yet they both seem to be working extremely hard to intensify it, don't they?

A vicious cycle dominates their relationship, but neither seems even aware of it, let alone able to control it. These two puppies need to let go of their rag long enough to examine their power struggle and find a way to stop it. After all, why should they work **so hard** to get what they **don't want**?

Why should you work so hard to get what you don't want?

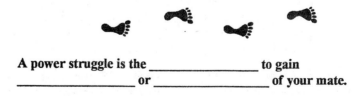

A power struggle is the _____ to gain _____ or _____ of your mate.

We engage in power struggles (circle one):

WIFE: Never   Seldom   Sometimes   Often   Too Much

HUSBAND: Never   Seldom   Sometimes   Often   Too Much

Ways to BREAK the power of Power Struggles.

1. ADMIT what you have been doing does not work. This is absolutely necessary. If you believe your struggle for power has been successful, you probably won't abandon it.

2. OPEN your mind enough to see your spouse's point of view. In the power struggle role-play, Helen could have said to herself (apply a little Thot-Talk here), "It seems like the more I bug him about this, the more he backs away. He must be backing off for a reason. What is it?" And Mark could say to himself (more Thot-Talk), "She keeps telling me she wants me to talk to her instead of watching TV. Hmm, maybe she really **does** need my attention."

3. LOOSEN your hold on your own point of view. Just because your point of view is **right** does not mean your partner's is **wrong**. You might be fighting a battle that doesn't need to be fought. Both spouses could continue their Thot-Talk, "Perhaps I'm not seeing this whole thing in perspective. I guess my point of view isn't the only one to consider here."

4. ASK your mate what he/she really wants in a situation. Mark could say, "Sweetheart, you keep handing me that 'honey-do' list of yours. Do you want me to get that list done, or do you resent my watching TV, or what? Tell me what you really want me to do." Helen could say, "Honey, I feel like you don't want to spend time with me and our kids anymore. Can I ever approach you about my needs? Or is it only when you're watching TV that you don't want to hear about them? Tell me what you really want me to do." What a simple statement, "Tell me what you want me to do." When said in a **quiet, loving** way, it works miracles. And after your mate awakens from a dead faint, you can move on to the next step.

"Tell me what you want me to do."

5. ALLOW your mate the freedom to choose whether he/she will abide by your request. (that's *request* not *demand*). You might be asking the impossible of your mate. Or he/she might be feeling too stubborn at the moment to acquiesce. Either way, the choice is your spouse's, not yours. Are you willing to **not** get your way about this? Perhaps it's time to read James 4 again and take a motive check.

6. DECIDE what you are going to do. You've given your mate a choice about your request; now it's time to choose whether **you** will abide by **your mate's** request. Before you decide, consider Romans 12:18 — *If it is possible, **as far as it depends on you**, live at peace with everyone* [even your mate].

Romans 12:18 — *If it is possible, as far as it depends on you, live at peace with everyone.*

There is no mystery to these suggested steps; they're plain, simple, and easy. Well...easier than struggling for power that you never get...easier than being agitated most the time...easier than trying to manipulate your mate to do what you want...easier than conflict. **Power struggles are a lose/lose effort.** These simple steps can help you and your mate create a **win/win** situation.

Power struggles are a lose/lose effort.

Look back at the 6 steps. Choose the one that would be the most help for you to apply in order to break the power of your power struggles.

Notes

Wife: _____

Husband: _____

Talk over this step with your mate.

> **Write at least one personal application from today's study.**
>
> Wife: _____
>
> Husband: _____
>
> **What does God want you to do to work out this application?**
>
> Wife: _____
>
> Husband: _____

REFLECT TOGETHER: Read Romans 12:9-21. Notice how many commands have to do with love, honor, blessing and harmony.

PRAY TOGETHER: Father, we release our right to have our own way. Humble us enough to see each other's needs before we see our own.

Day 4

Faulty Communication

The third cause of conflict is our faulty communication patterns. What do we mean by this? Don't we talk right? Well, maybe not. Let's look at six patterns of communication that fuel the fires of conflict. In a sense, these are six ways we don't talk —or listen —right.

1. Faultfinding. This is a habit...a bad habit. When we practice habits over a long period of time, they wear ruts into our lives. We'll call this one the **"gripe rut."** A "gripe rut" is full of criticism, complaints, whining, and accusations. Some of us grew up in homes where the deep rut of criticism tripped everyone in the family. It was an uncomfortable rut and we hated it. Yet we perpetuate it. Why? Because it is a habit. But habits can be **broken** — with work.

Faultfinding leads to retaliation and conflict. That's why the whole family trips and falls into the "gripe rut." No one wins with criticism. Not the one criticizing, not the one being criticized, and not the children, who learn to be critical from their parents — their role models. Scripture gives us a better way.

Ephesians 4:29-32 — *Do not let **any unwholesome talk** come out of your mouth, but only what is helpful for **building others up**...Get rid of...every form of malice. Be kind and compassionate to one another....*

2. Avoiding Talking About Concerns For Fear Of Conflict. When one partner fears conflict, he or she often avoids talking about any matter of concern or

Ephesians 4:29-32 — Do not let any unwholesome talk come out of your mouth, but only what is helpful for building others up...Get rid of...every form of malice. Be kind and compassionate to one another....

frustration. Their motive is to keep the peace by **avoiding the issues**. They don't want to "rock the boat." But as unresolved issues pile up, a storm of resentment begins to brew inside that spouse. And resentment, if not handled correctly, can produce **indifference**. Sooner or later, the one who avoids conflict at any cost may no longer **care** about the relationship at all.

We're speaking especially to those of you who tend to swallow your anger. It would be good to review Chapter 3 and compare the section on repressing anger with this faulty communication pattern. Avoiding conflict can, in the long run, actually **fuel the fires** of conflict. Scripture reminds us to ...*put off falsehood and speak truthfully...for we are all members of one body* (Ephesians 4:25). To say nothing is bothering you when there **is** something wrong, is falsehood. Remember, you are commanded to speak truthfully *in love* (verse 15).

3. Talk-Talk-Talking Instead Of Listening. We have the crazy idea the more we talk to our mates about a particular concern or situation, the more we will influence them to do what we want. The truth is — the **more** we talk, the **less** our mates listen. When we verbally overload them, they tune us out. Someone has said: women are prone to **nag**, and men are prone to **badger**. Both nagging and badgering come down to the same thing, don't they? — Talking instead of listening. Solomon said it was like Chinese water torture (Proverbs 19:13, liberally paraphrased). We need to practice what James 1:19 exhorts, *Everyone should be quick to listen, slow to speak....* In other words, we need to put a sock in it!

4. Speaking In A Strange Language—Yours—Instead Of Your Mate's. Remember one difference which causes conflict is being from different families of origin? This difference is seldom more conspicuous than in our communication patterns. Because we were reared with different values, beliefs and customs, we can use the same words but interpret them in entirely different ways. In some aspects, we talk to each other in a foreign language. We must study our mate as we would Latin or Greek. We need to concentrate on understanding that **deep person** we've promised to love, honor and cherish. This is one reason God intends marriage to be for life. We need our whole life time to discover the intricate person to whom we are married.

For years, Bette nagged (gently, of course) me (Harold) about things I needed to do around the house. I particularly remember the loose backs on our dining room chairs. She reminded me many times to glue those chairs. I didn't avoid fixing them on purpose; I simply didn't remember them at convenient times. Then Bette discovered how visual I am. I write everything I need to do or remember on 3x5 cards and keep them in my shirt pocket for reference. I love striking through the written reminder when I've accomplished a task. She learned that if she wrote a "to do" list on a 3x5 card for me, I couldn't resist it. I fixed those chairs within a week, just to be able to check them off my list. Bette no longer needed to nag — which didn't work — because she discovered my "language."

5. Expressing Yourself In Negative Terms Instead Of Positive. When someone asked a man what his favorite wine was, he replied, "Why don't you ever listen to me?" (Wine — whine?) Many of us have developed the habit of expressing ourselves negatively. We say things like, "You don't have time to talk with me right now, do you?" Or, "Why don't you ever...?" Each of our negative whines can be rephrased in a positive way. Instead of, "You don't have time to talk with me right now, do you?" you can say, "I would really like to talk with you right now. Do you have time?" "Why don't you ever listen to me?" can become, "I have something important to tell you. I would really like you to listen to me for a moment."

Ephesians 4:15,25 — *Instead, speaking the truth in love, we will in all things grow up into him who is the Head, that is, Christ. Therefore each of you must put off falsehood and speak truthfully to his neighbor, for we are all members of one body.*

James 1:19 — *Everyone should be quick to listen, slow to speak....*

Notes

Yes, it will take **thought** and **practice**. But think of all the years you've practiced the negative; and think of all the conflicts your negative communications have incited. Isn't it time to start practicing positive ways of communicating? If you practice positive communication **as long** as you've practiced negative, and it still doesn't work, **then** you can quit trying.

6. Using Silence As A Weapon. Norm Wright states more marriages today are dying from silence than from violence (<u>Making Peace With Your Partner</u>). We would have to agree with him. Silence is extremely **flammable** and feeds the fires of conflict.

Silence is a shield. However, the problem with shields is that they have two sides.

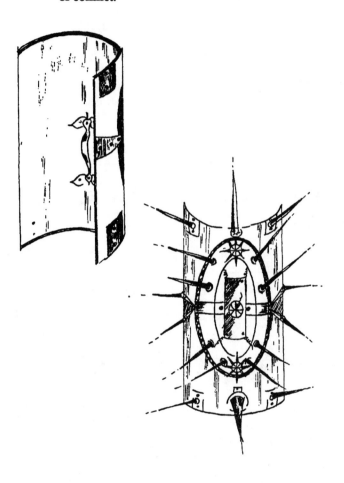

We think especially of a couple who talked with us about the silence in their marriage. The husband insisted his silence was not a weapon but merely a shield he used for protection. However, the problem with shields is that they have two sides. He saw the inside which looked like smooth, polished metal to him. But his wife saw the outside of the shield, and it had long, sharp spikes of isolation that were very painful to her. Silence is a deadly weapon that can destroy your relationship. Lay the **shield** down, and use instead the **oil** of Ephesians 4:32. *Be kind and compassionate to one another....*

Ephesians 4:32. *Be kind and compassionate to one another....*

Rate yourself on each of the six Faulty Communication Patterns (circle for each):

Faultfinding

		Never	Seldom	Sometimes	Often	Too Much
1. WIFE:		Never	Seldom	Sometimes	Often	Too Much
HUSBAND:		Never	Seldom	Sometimes	Often	Too Much

Avoiding talking about concerns

		Never	Seldom	Sometimes	Often	Too Much
2. WIFE:		Never	Seldom	Sometimes	Often	Too Much
HUSBAND:		Never	Seldom	Sometimes	Often	Too Much

						Notes
						Talking instead of listening
3. WIFE:	Never	Seldom	Sometimes	Often	Too Much	
HUSBAND:	Never	Seldom	Sometimes	Often	Too Much	
4. WIFE:	Never	Seldom	Sometimes	Often	Too Much	Not speaking your mate's language
HUSBAND:	Never	Seldom	Sometimes	Often	Too Much	
5. WIFE:	Never	Seldom	Sometimes	Often	Too Much	Negative communication
HUSBAND:	Never	Seldom	Sometimes	Often	Too Much	
6. WIFE:	Never	Seldom	Sometimes	Often	Too Much	Silence as a weapon
HUSBAND:	Never	Seldom	Sometimes	Often	Too Much	

From the above analysis, pick one Faulty Communication Pattern you need to focus on correcting.

Wife: _____

Husband: _____

Write at least one personal application from today's study.

Wife: _____

Husband: _____

What does God want you to do to work out this application?

Wife: _____

Husband: _____

REFLECT TOGETHER: Re-read Ephesians 4:29-32.

PRAY TOGETHER: Thank you, Lord, for the power to change. Help us be kind and compassionate as we communicate with one another.

How to Handle Conflict

Conflict can be as simple as a difference of opinion, but when it erupts into anger, we need to know what to do. Let's look at how to handle it from both sides: first from the viewpoint of the one receiving the anger, and then from the viewpoint of the one who is angry.

What to do when your SPOUSE is angry and ready for conflict.

1. Give your partner PERMISSION to be angry with you. This is probably the most important step you can take to accept your mate when he/she is angry. By

Day 5

Notes

reminding yourself it is **all right** for them to be angry, you not only accept your partner in their anger, you also accept the **fact** they **are** angry. When you see anger kicking open your mate's emotional doors, you need to practice positive Thot-Talk such as, "It is O.K. for my mate to be angry. He/she isn't a horrible person just because he's angry." You'd be surprised how much of the conflict this will diffuse, because it helps keep you from jumping into the fray. Philippians 2:4 is a good reminder that your mate's concerns (even if they are shrouded in anger) are worthy of your interest: *Each of you should look not only to your own interests, but also to the interests of others.*

2. Don't REINFORCE your spouse for becoming angry with you. That is, don't jump right into battle with your dukes up. This may sound crazy, but that in itself somehow rewards your mate for expressing anger. Instead, say something like, "I can understand your being angry and upset." That sentence alone may stop the whole confrontation, for when your mate regains consciousness, he or she may not remember he was even angry. Ecclesiastes 7:9 is wise counsel: *Do not be **quickly provoked** in your spirit, for anger resides in the lap of fools.*

3. Ask your partner to speak in a REASONABLE manner. It's O.K. to respond to your partner's yelling in a calm and neutral way, such as, "Would you please restate that in a lower voice so I can better understand you?" Your spouse has the right to be angry, but not the right to yell. The key words here are **calm** and **neutral.** We could also add: **nonjudgmental.** A gentle and nonjudgmental answer at this time will go a long way in calming your spouse's anger. Proverbs 15:1— *A gentle answer turns away wrath.*

4. DON'T BECOME ANGRY just because your mate is angry. Are you thinking, "I'm not made of stone. I can't do that!"? We encourage you to give it a try. If you decide now, while you are **calm, not to respond in anger** the next time your spouse is angry, you just might surprise yourself. You may be stronger than you think. God knows you are capable of pulling this off with His help, or He wouldn't have said things like Proverbs 12:16 — *A fool shows his annoyance at once, but a prudent man overlooks an insult,* and James 1:19 — *Everyone should be quick to listen, slow to speak and slow to become angry.*

5. Identify your BEHAVIOR that contributes to the conflict. Analyze your conflicts. Is there a **pattern** to them? Do you say or do the same kind of things over and over again; things that seem to push your partner's buttons? Focus only on **your** actions. Don't allow yourself to start throwing blame at your mate. The goal here is for you to discover **your part** in the conflicts. If you think conflict is a serious problem in your marriage, keep a notebook of your fights to help analyze the problem. Record what you say and do, and what your partner says and does. You might even need to tape record one or two of your arguments to analyze later when you are calm.

It's important that you concentrate on **your contribution** to the fight, **not your mate's**. It's your mate's job to analyze his/her own contribution — not yours. This sounds like a lot of work, doesn't it? But if you are really serious about finding **solutions** to your conflict, this could be a very important step. Remember, God promises to give you understanding if you are teachable. Proverbs 15:32b — *...whoever heeds correction gains understanding.*

Proverbs 15:32b — *...whoever heeds correction gains understanding.*

Review the 5 steps, and identify the step that would help you most when your spouse is angry.

Wife: _____

Husband: _____

Talk together about how you might put this step into practice.

Write at least one personal application from today's study.

Wife: _____

Husband: _____

What does God want you to do to work out this application?

Wife: _____

Husband: _____

REFLECT TOGETHER: Read James 1:19-21. What does anger not produce?

PRAY TOGETHER: Oh, God, help us put these steps into practice. Teach us to respond to each other's anger the right way.

What to do when YOU are angry and ready for conflict.

Day 6

1. DELAY. The old saying about "counting to ten" is not as trite as you might think. When you feel anger rising up inside you, put on the brakes, wait a little and think about how you should handle it. Listen to Nehemiah's wise counsel: *I was very angry when I heard their cry and these words.* ***I thought it over, then rebuked the nobles and officials....*** (Nehemiah 5:6-7, Amplified Version).

Nehemiah 5:6-7 — *I was very angry when I heard their cry and these words.* ***I thought it over, then rebuked the nobles and officials....*** (Amplified Version).

Remember those three underlying emotions of anger: fear, hurt and frustration? Take time to look inside yourself and ask, "**Why am I so angry** about this? Am I afraid?...hurt? ...or frustrated?"

Notes

2. Express your anger in a NEUTRAL way. You can say something like, "I'm getting angry," or "I'm losing control." When you make a neutral statement like that, you are not issuing a challenge to fight. You are being honest and acknowledging your feelings. This step is imperative if you are going to handle your anger effectively. It isn't easy. You will have to guard your emotions and keep them under control. You will also have to keep your **mouth** under control. Proverbs 21:23 — *He who guards his mouth and his tongue keeps himself from calamity.*

Proverbs 21:23 — He who guards his mouth and his tongue keeps himself from calamity.

3. COMMIT yourself to not yell or raise your voice. This is another commitment you must make while you are **calm**. It's best to talk about it as a couple, and make a **mutual commitment** to not raise your voices or lose self-control during a fight. However, if one or both of you begins to spin out of control during a conflict, the best course of action may be to **stop** the fight until after you both have calmed down. This is called *suspending the anger*. Proverbs 17:27 reminds us of the importance of such discipline: *A man of knowledge uses words with restraint, and a man of understanding is even-tempered.*

Proverbs 17:27 — A man of knowledge uses words with restraint, and a man of understanding is even-tempered.

It is important to keep in mind you are not moving away from the issue forever. You must resolve it in a timely manner, because you don't want to bury it alive. Issues buried alive grow stronger under ground and have the annoying habit of resurrecting at the most inconvenient times.

4. RENOUNCE your anger. You could say, "I'm angry with you right now. I don't want to be angry with you. I love you. I don't like myself in this condition." There! You've stated you are angry in a neutral manner and renounced your anger.

You don't want to be angry, but you are. Instead of a declaration of war, you have issued an invitation to negotiate. Proverbs 20:3a declares this is the honorable thing to do: *It is to a man's honor to avoid strife....*

Proverbs 20:3a — It is to a man's honor to avoid strife....

5. Ask your partner for HELP. This might be hard on your pride, but it will certainly make things easier on your relationship. The issue of conflict becomes a problem for the two of you to solve, rather than a wall of alienation to separate you. You can take this one step further by giving your partner **permission** to let you know when he/she sees you becoming angry. (See Chapter 3 for more details.) It is essential to humbly acknowledge your need for help in this area. Proverbs 19:20 — *Listen to advice and accept instruction, and in the end you will be wise.*

Proverbs 19:20 — Listen to advice and accept instruction, and in the end you will be wise.

6. After the conflict, do some R AND R—Review and Rehearse.

Review — After you both have **cooled down**, do some discovery together about the conflict. This is not for the purpose of placing blame, but simply to find out what **triggered** it. Was the conflict part of a pattern? What contributed to your feelings of anger? What emotion was hidden under your anger? This is review.

Rehearse — Talk about what you could do differently when a similar situation occurs. Suggest things to do to make the situation less volatile. This is especially helpful for **patterns** of conflict. If you fight about the same things over and over again, you must start doing something **different**, or that pattern will develop into a very thick wall.

If you fight about the same things over and over again, you must start doing something different....

We sat down with a couple a while back to **R and R** a pattern of conflict with them. Claudia felt John continually put down her opinions when they were making a decision. John felt Claudia tried to push her opinions on him. In **review**, they discovered she said things like, "I know I am right in this. After all, I am the one who did the research." This made him feel threatened, and, in defense, he retaliated with an insult. They realized they were both pushing too hard and decided to stop being afraid of one another's opinions.

When they **rehearsed** their plan for making decisions in the future, Claudia offered not to use the word "I" as frequently as in the past. Instead, she promised to use "you" more often: "What do **you** think about this? How would this effect **you**?" And John, confessing that he probably resorted to insults because he felt she **did** know more than he did about some of their decisions, promised to **compliment** her suggestions instead of insulting them.

Now, this couple isn't perfect. They will **fail** sometimes in the plans and promises they have rehearsed. But they will **succeed** at least part of the time, and get **better** at it as they work together. Eventually, this pattern of conflict will be eradicated from their lives. Isn't that what you want? To eliminate your patterns of conflict? The rewards are **worth** the work. Proverbs 19:8 — *He who gets wisdom loves his own soul; he who cherishes understanding prospers.*

Proverbs 19:8 — *He who gets wisdom loves his own soul; he who cherishes understanding prospers.*

Review these 6 steps and identify the step that would help you most when you are angry.

Wife: _____

Husband: _____

Talk together about how you might put this step into practice.

Write at least one personal application from today's study.

Wife: _____

Husband: _____

What does God want you to do to work out this application?

Wife: _____

Husband: _____

REFLECT TOGETHER: Read Proverbs 19:8-11 and 19-22. Notice how beneficial it is to gain wisdom.

PRAY TOGETHER: Dear God, thank you for these new ways to handle our conflicts right. Help us see our conflicts as problems we can solve with your help.

God's formula for RESOLUTION:

Ephesians 4:32 — *Be kind and compassionate to one another, forgiving each other, just as in Christ God forgave you.* We promised you this verse, remember? It begins by imploring you to be kind and compassionate to one another. If you really had this attitude, most of your fights would never happen, would they? **Kindness — compassion** — such simple words. But we see so little of them in conflictive relationships.

Day 7

Ephesians 4:32 — *Be kind and compassionate to one another, forgiving each other, just as in Christ God forgave you.*

Notes

In fact, their absence is a distinctive trait of couples who have a lot of conflict. Oh, how **we all need** kindness and compassion! And oh, how your mate needs **your** kindness and compassion!

The second appeal in verse 32 is that we **forgive** like God forgives us. We've talked about forgiveness several times already...and we'll talk about it more before we're finished. <u>Forgiveness is one of the most important subjects in Scripture</u>. There are at least one-hundred-and-twelve verses that talk about it (we counted). It's profoundly important to God, and profoundly important to us. **We can't live without it**—now or eternally. We need God's forgiveness; we need each other's. And we need to forgive as God forgives — **unconditionally**.

God doesn't forgive us because we deserve it. He doesn't look at us and say, "Well, you're a nice person, and seem repentant enough, so I'll forgive you." He forgives unconditionally because Christ's blood covers **all** the sins for which we need forgiveness. <u>God gives us the power to forgive others the same way, for the same reason.</u>

God gives us the power to forgive others the way He forgives.

If we choose to nurse our resentments and withhold forgiveness from our mates or family, that choice will **cripple** us. And if we need to seek forgiveness from those we love but stubbornly refuse, that choice will also **cripple** us. That's why God urges us to forgive. He loves us too much to see us crippled by unforgiveness. Are you withholding forgiveness from your mate? You will succeed at handling your anger and conflict **only if you choose to forgive**.

Whew! We don't know about you, but these three chapters on anger have been hard. We've had to admit to truths we would rather not accept, face responsibilities we'd rather not face, and make decisions for change we know won't be easy. But if anger and conflict **are** the major causes of marriage failures, as David Mace claims, then we must do all we can to handle this area of our lives correctly.

We can not afford for our Holy Wedlock to become Holy Deadlock. Unless we determine to do something about the way we handle conflict, we may find ourselves alone, on opposite sides of a wall neither of us can climb over. We don't want the German poet Gerta's words to be true of us: *Every time I hear the wedding march, I think of soldiers going off to war.* We want the **Holy Spirit's words** to describe our marriage: *Peacemakers who sow in peace raise a harvest of righteousness* (James 3:18).

James 3:18 — *Peacemakers who sow in peace raise a harvest of righteousness .*

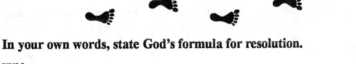

In your own words, state God's formula for resolution.

Wife: _____

Husband: _____

WRAP UP: Answer all the following questions individually first, then discuss them together.

1. I feel our greatest difference is

Wife: _____

Husband: _____

Of the 3 suggestions for handling differences, the one I need to apply the most is:

Wife: _____

Husband: _____

2. Our power struggles seem to center around:

Wife: _____

Husband: _____

Of the six suggestions for breaking the power of power struggles, this is the one I most need to apply:

Wife: _____

Husband: _____

3. When you are angry with me, the suggestion I will try hardest to apply is:

Wife: _____

Husband: _____

4. When I am angry with you, the suggestion I will try hardest to apply is

Wife: _____

Husband: _____

REFLECT TOGETHER: Re-read Ephesians 4:31-32. What are the three things God commands us to be?

PRAY TOGETHER: Father God, teach us how to be peacemakers. We choose to forgive each other the way You forgive us.

GROUP DISCUSSION: If you are using this study in a group, the following may be used as group discussion questions.

Have a frank discussion

1. Case Study: Let's pretend for a moment that Mike and Joanie are your friends. Their marriage has always seemed stable and happy, but now they are coming to you for help. They spill out their troubles and ask for your advice. See if you can spot their **real problems.**

   Mike and Joanie were married three years ago and have a one year old baby girl. Mike grew up in a Christian home. His mother was rather domineering. His father usually allowed her to control things up to a certain invisible point, at which time he would "set his foot down." Joanie's father was an alcoholic. Her mother was a Christian and the glue that held the family together. Joanie left home when she was seventeen, shortly after her mother died.

   Mike and Joanie are Christians who faithfully attend church, but their marriage has always been a little rocky. Mike tends to be a bit arrogant and dominating. Joanie is a part-time office manager and full-time mother. She tries hard to please Mike, but feels outraged when he attempts to control her and their relationship. Mike tells you he is sick and tired of Joanie never seeing things his way. Joanie says she is fed up with Mike always criticizing her and telling her what to do. With all the knowledge you've gained about anger and fighting thus far, what advice would you give to Mike and Joanie?

2. Which of the five DIFFERENCES do you think cause the most conflict? How?

3. Of the six faulty communication patterns, which do you tend to practice?

4. Of the five suggestions for handling your spouse's anger, which do you feel would be the most difficult to apply? Why?

5. Of the six suggestions for handling your anger, which one will you need the most help applying? Why?

GOOD DECISIONS ARE
COUPLE DECISIONS
Chapter 6

Day 1

Marcia sighed a tired sigh and looked over at Ted. "Honey, we have been under such stress lately. How about our getting away this weekend? We could leave Friday after work and relax for two whole days. What do you say?"

Ted looked up from his newspaper, "Umm...it *does* sound good, but I told Larry I'd take his Sunday School class for him Sunday."

"You did?" Marcia's eyebrows arched with surprise. "I didn't know that. Well, then we could come back home Saturday night. At least we could get away for one day. How about it?"

"Well..." Ted paused sheepishly, "that'd be great, except I promised Ted Jr. I'd sit in on his band's jam session Saturday afternoon. You want me to support our son's dream, don't you?"

Marcia shook her head in unbelief, "I didn't know you had made plans for Saturday afternoon. Ted Jr.'s band practices *every* weekend. O.K." she finally concluded, "What if we just go away overnight Friday night? Even one night away would be better than nothing."

Ted scratched his head nervously, "I wish you'd said something earlier. I just now arranged with Tom to work on the church's sound system with him early Saturday morning."

"You what?" Marcia yelped. "You've made plans for this whole weekend, and I didn't know one thing about them!"

"Well," Ted shrugged his shoulders helplessly, "they didn't involve you; they just involved me."

"I beg your pardon," Marcia retorted with hands on her hips. "They do involve me! It's my weekend too. You've scheduled our entire weekend, and I didn't have a thing to say about it!"

Couples often behave like this — like they were room mates instead of a team. They make decisions that affect each other or their relationship without even consulting their partners. The key word? — *partners*. We could never get away with making solitary decisions in a business partnership. What makes us think it's good, sound policy for our marriage partnership? First of all, let's discuss **why** we should make decisions together.

Why Make Decisions Together?

1. Because we are ONE.

They shall leave father and mother and be UNITED.

Genesis 2:23-24 — *The man said, "This is now bone of my bones and flesh of my*

Genesis 2:23-24 — *The man said, "This is now bone of my bones and flesh of my flesh; she shall be called 'woman,' for she was taken out of man." For this reason a man will leave his father and mother and be united to his wife, and they will become one flesh.*

flesh; she shall be called 'woman,' for she was taken out of man." For this reason a man will leave his father and mother and be united to his wife, and they will become one flesh.

The beginning of verse 24 refers back to verse 23. What is this reason we are to be **united**? Because we are bone of each other's bone and flesh of each other's flesh. We have a unique relationship. You might say, God took **one** person (Adam) and made from him **two** persons (Adam and Eve), so together they could make **one** UNIT. God took **one** to make **two** to make **one**.

The uniqueness of the marriage relationship emphasized by CHRIST.

Matthew 19:4-6 — *"Haven't you read," He replied, "that at the beginning the Creator 'made them male and female,' and said, 'For this reason a man will leave his father and mother and be united to his wife, and the two will become one flesh'? So they are no longer two, but one. Therefore what God has joined together, let man not separate."* Jesus refers to the same mystery of the marriage relationship (one - two - one), and adds, *So they are no longer two, but* **one.** God looks at us as a married couple and sees **One Unit.**

The uniqueness of the marriage relationship reiterated by PAUL.

Ephesians 5:31-32 — *'For this reason a man will leave his father and mother and be united to his wife, and the two will become one flesh.' This is a profound mystery — but I am talking about Christ and the church.*

This is the third time this verse appears in Scripture. Do you get the impression it must be important? Paul says the oneness which occurs between marriage partners is a **profound mystery** — like the oneness which occurs between Christ and the church. Both relationships are **profound mysteries.**

Our oneness is also like the oneness of the GODHEAD.

Deuteronomy 6:4—*Hear, O Israel: The Lord our God, the Lord is one.* The Hebrew word here for *one* is the same word used in Genesis. We as a married couple are **one;** the triune God is **one.** Can you grasp that? Our husband-wife oneness is like the relationship shared by the Trinity. No wonder Paul calls it a **profound mystery.**

Can you imagine God the Son making a decision without God the Father and God the Holy Spirit being involved? It boggles the mind, doesn't it? And if, as the Scripture says, we are one **like** the Godhead is one, then shouldn't we make decisions **like** the Godhead? Oneness demands we make decisions together.

Do you agree with the statement: "Oneness demands we make decisions together."

Wife: _____ Husband: _____

Why or why not?

Wife: _____

Husband: _____

Matthew 19:4-6 — *"Haven't you read," He replied, "that at the beginning the Creator 'made them male and female,' and said, 'For this reason a man will leave his father and mother and be united to his wife, and the two will become one flesh'? So they are no longer two, but one. Therefore what God has joined together, let man not separate."*

Ephesians 5:31-32 — *'For this reason a man will leave his father and mother and be united to his wife, and the two will become one flesh.' This is a profound mystery — but I am talking about Christ and the church.*

Deuteronomy 6:4—*Hear, O Israel: The Lord our God, the Lord is one.*

Notes

Proverbs 11:14 — *For lack of guidance a nation falls, but many advisers make victory sure.*

Proverbs 13:10 — *Pride only breeds quarrels, but wisdom is found in those who take advice.*

Proverbs 15:22 — *Plans fail for lack of counsel, but with many advisers they succeed.*

2. Because it is SAFER.

Proverbs 11:14 — *For lack of guidance a nation falls, but many advisers make victory sure.* 13:10 — *Pride only breeds quarrels, but wisdom is found in those who take advice.* 15:22 — *Plans fail for lack of counsel, but with many advisers they succeed.* Get the picture? **It's too risky to make decisions on your own.** It's safer to have counsel from others. And the very best counselor you could ever have...specially made for you...uniquely qualified...is your mate.

3. Because we both need to OWN the decision and the RESULT.

If you **both** don't own the decision, can you **both** own the results? Is it fair for you to expect your mate to live with the results — sometimes disastrous results — of **your** decisions?

Several years ago, some friends of ours were looking for a good buy on a used car. They had looked unsuccessfully for several weeks, when the husband (we'll call him Harry) brought home a comfortable sedan he had snapped up from a co-worker. Lucy was enraged. How dare Harry buy that car without consulting her! Their car-shopping was supposed to be a mutual project. She felt so hurt and left out, that for the three years they owned that vehicle, she refused to ride in it. Lucy would not **own the results** of Harry's decision, because she could not **own the decision.** Granted, she went a little overboard. But the point is: if you **both** have to live with the results, you had better **both** own the decision.

What are three reasons for making decisions as a couple?

_____

_____

_____

> Write at least one personal application from today's study.
>
> Wife: _____
>
> Husband: _____
>
> What does God want you to do to work out this application?
>
> Wife: _____
>
> Husband: _____

REFLECT TOGETHER: Re-read Matthew 19:4-6. Notice again what Jesus says after He quotes Genesis 2.

PRAY TOGETHER: Oh, God, thank You that You created us to be one. Help us understand what being one really means.

What Making Couple Decisions Does <u>NOT</u> Mean:

Day 2

- It does <u>not</u> mean you lose your individual PERSONALITIES.

    We are **one**, but we are still **two**. Like the personalities of the Godhead, we can, at the same time, be **two persons forming one unit**.

    Your partner is not an extension of yourself. You are not two chunks of wax melted into one candle. You remain **two** candles, but stand securely in **one** candlestick. It's not unusual for one partner in a marriage to have a more dominant personality, thinking and speaking faster than the other. However, if the dominant partner swallows up the non-dominant one, that's not oneness. That's being a **bully**. There might be agreement, but that is **not** couple decision making.

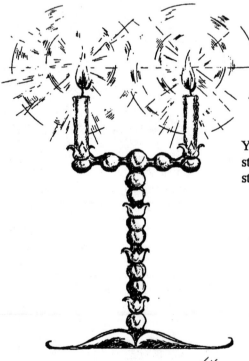

You remain two candles, but stand securely in one candlestick.

Notes

Husbands and wives who sit on the sidelines usually end up losing interest in the game.

- **It does <u>not</u> mean you both THINK alike.**

  If you both think exactly alike about everything, then one of you isn't necessary...or perhaps one of you isn't thinking. Or maybe one of you is playing the martyr and letting the other think for both of you. This is not oneness. Marriage is not a spectator sport. Every team member plays. No one sits on the bench. Husbands and wives who sit on the sidelines usually end up losing interest in the game.

  We know you can't possibly think alike about everything. And that's good, because you shouldn't if you are going to make good couple decisions. You need to consider more than one side of any issue. So, you don't have to think **alike**, but you do have to **think**; and you need to **share** what you're thinking with each other.

- **It does <u>not</u> mean you will never have CONFLICT.**

  Uh-oh, did we shock you? Because you do not think exactly alike, you might experience some conflict along the way to making good decisions together. We never said making couple decisions was **easy**; we just said it was **best**.

  After the last three chapters, you are already aware of the many reasons why conflict might sneak into your couple decision making. So don't get discouraged if there's some conflict along the way. **In the long run**, making decisions together will produce **less conflict** in your relationship.

Complementary = compromise

The majority of couples (around 60%) learn to adjust to one another in a **complementary relationship**. There is give and take: they have differences and sometimes see things from opposite viewpoints, but in general, they **respect** each other's differences and **support** one another. The word **"compromise"** typifies their relationship. These couples know that couple decision making is not as easy as falling off a log, but they **can** do it. They experience successes and make their relationship better in the process.

Congruent = commonality

A small percentage of couples (around 10%) are in a **congruent relationship**. Their backgrounds, values, needs, and even personalities are **similar**. **"Commonality"** typifies their relationship. These couples have very little trouble making decisions together, because they think so much alike. But, as we said, there's not many of them around.

Conflictive = clashing

The final 30% of couples are in a **conflictive relationship**. They experience continual **struggle**, handling their conflicts in destructive ways, hurting and being hurt. **"Clashing"** typifies their relationship. These couples find it extremely difficult to make decisions together, but they **can** change. There is **hope** and **help** for conflictive couples. If they are **open** and **willing to change** by the power of the Holy Spirit, in time they can develop a **complementary** relationship.

Classify your present relationship. Are you congruent, complementary or conflictive?

Wife: _____ Husband: _____

- **It does <u>not</u> mean decisions which do not AFFECT BOTH must be made by both of you.**

If a decision doesn't affect you as a couple or as a family, then, by all means, make it yourself. Don't call your husband to help you decide what underarm deodorant to use. And don't call your wife to help you decide whether to have lunch at Burger King or Arby's. We're really not *too* worried that you'll go overboard and make every little decision together. That's usually not the problem, is it? Our problems normally stem from the simple fact that we are **independent** creatures. We like to do things **our way** without consulting someone else.

Of the four things Couple Decision-Making does not mean which is the biggest relief to you?

Wife: _____ Husband: _____

Write at least one personal application from today's study.

Wife: _____

Husband: _____

What does God want you to do to work out this application?

Wife: _____

Husband: _____

REFLECT TOGETHER: Re-read Ephesians 5:31-33. Notice Paul's comments after he quotes Genesis 2.

PRAY TOGETHER: Dear Father, thank You that You have designed our relationship to be founded on love and respect. (Husband) Help me love my wife as if she were myself. (Wife) Help me respect and revere my husband.

What Couple Decision Making DOES Mean.

Day 3

• It means you talk over ANY decisions that affect both BEFORE either of you makes up your own mind about the matter.

How many times do you come together to discuss a decision, already knowing what **you** want? Your goal for the discussion is actually to talk your partner into seeing things **your** way. Be honest, now. Isn't that your agenda sometimes?

Making decisions as a couple assumes you keep your mind open to what your mate thinks.

Notes

But making decisions **as a couple** assumes you keep your mind **open** to what your mate thinks. Neither of you should make up your mind before you talk about it. That's the only way you can truly make decisions together.

Remember the yellow station wagon we talked about in Chapter 2? The "lemon" that began falling apart within minutes of our buying it? I (Harold) **wanted** that car. After considering all our options, I **knew** that was the right car for us. Under the guise of making a couple decision, I talked with Bette for hours about what we should do. The problem was, I already had **my mind made up**. The time we should have spent discussing a mutual decision was wasted on my efforts to persuade her to agree with my choice. I finally wore her down; she agreed, and we bought the car. But it was **not** a good decision...and it was certainly **not** a couple decision.

Identify a decision you made when you did not apply this principle. What were the results or effect on your family?

Wife: _____

Husband: _____

How would this principle have changed things?

Wife: _____

Husband: _____

Identify a decision, if you can, in which you applied or would apply this principle.

Wife: _____

Husband: _____

• **It means both of you discuss and agree on decisions that affect both BEFORE INFORMING others or ACTING on a decision.**

Have you ever noticed how kids like to play one parent against the other? "Daddy says it's all right with him if it's all right with you." Teenagers are especially adept at this. One evening, our daughter, then sixteen, asked Bette for permission to date a certain young man on Saturday night. Her Mom said, "Sure, I don't see any problem with it." Later, at the dinner table, Dena leaned over to me (Harold) and whispered, "Mom said it would be all right for me to go out with Carl Saturday night. O.K.. Dad?" I looked up in surprise, "No, it's not O.K."

I had been secretly planning a surprise for the whole family for Saturday. I was going to spring my surprise early that morning, kidnap everyone, and head for the miniature golf course. This could have worked if (1) I had let Bette in on my surprise, and if (2) our three kids were still under 8 years old. Unfortunately, all three were teenagers, which made my plans seem like foolish strategy indeed. There I was...on the spot because Bette and I had failed to make **two** decisions as a couple. I should have consulted her about my desired surprise and decided together about it. That way, it would have stood at least a **slim** chance of succeeding.

Couple decision making is a great protection against being "divided and conquered."

And I (Bette) shouldn't have let myself be put on the spot. I should have told Dena that I needed to talk with Daddy before I could give her permission. After all, as her father, the decision affected him, too. I don't know where kids learn this tactic, but it doesn't seem to take them long to perfect their "divide and conquer" technique. As parents, we have to learn to present a united-couple front to our children. Couple decision making is a great protection against being "divided and conquered."

When someone wants your answer on a decision that should be made by both of you, don't be embarrassed to say simply, "Since that affects my spouse too, I'll talk it over with him/her and get back with you." Even if you're given a great opportunity to invest money in the deal of a life time, wait and talk it over with your mate. It's his/her money too. Or if a friend asks you to dinner, tell them you'll check with your mate and call them back.

Don't assume to know your partner's desires until you've spoken with them. To request your mate's help to decide about something that affects him/her too is just **common courtesy**. And you are being **courteous** when you postpone your answer until you have given your mate that consideration.

> To request your mate's help to decide about something that affects him/her too is just common courtesy.

Identify a decision you made when you did not apply this principle. What were the results or effect on your family?

Wife: _____

Husband: _____

How would this principle have changed things?

Wife: _____

Husband: _____

Identify a decision, if you can, in which you applied or would apply this principle.

Wife: _____

Husband: _____

Write at least one personal application from today's study.

Wife: _____

Husband: _____

What does God want you to do to work out this application?

Wife: _____

Husband: _____

Notes

REFLECT TOGETHER: Read Genesis 2:20-24. Notice what "For this reason" refers to.

PRAY TOGETHER: Dear Lord, we want to face decisions with an open mind. Help us treat each other with courtesy as we make decisions together.

Day 4

- **It means a satisfactory solution is reached that can be OWNED by both.**

    Owning the **decision** and **results** is not just a reason for making decisions together, it is an absolute necessity. We must take **ownership** of our decisions. If we don't, we will live a life of resentment and blame.

When a couple fails to make a joint decision about a matter that affects them both, there are **two people** who are **wrong**.

What happens when one spouse makes a decision without consulting the other, and it results in disaster? Even if the other spouse gave a cursory "O.K.," what do you think will happen? That's right...**blame**. When a couple fails to make a joint decision about a matter that affects them both, there are **two** people who are **wrong**. One spouse is wrong for being selfish and making the decision arbitrarily. The other spouse is wrong for abdicating his or her responsibility in decision making. When this happens, both must **take responsibility** for their decisions.

An attractive, young couple sat across from us, the wife in tears. Andrea had been harboring resentment against David for two long years. She had resisted a move back East, but finally gave in, swallowing a lot of bitterness in the process. Their relocation was not the once-in-a-life-time opportunity David had envisioned, so they moved back in less than a year. Andrea, who had just settled into their new home, didn't want to move the second time either. But she took only a superficial role in the decision to return.

We could almost reach out and touch the thick wall of resentment they had built between them. Neither David nor Andrea wanted to take ownership of their decisions. David blamed circumstances and rationalized that there was nothing else they could have done. Andrea blamed David for making two unwise decisions that made her unhappy. They were so busy blaming, they couldn't see they were **both** wrong. David had ramrodded the decisions through without listening to Andrea or caring about how these moves would affect her. They could have discovered **other options** if they had taken the time to look for them **together**. David needed to take responsibility for his choice to be arbitrary. Andrea, on the other hand, abdicated her responsibility to tell David how she thought and felt about the moves. She needed to understand that choosing **not** to discuss the decisions thoroughly with David before they were made, **was** her decision. **She** chose to handle the decisions in that manner, and now she needed to **own** her choice. Their problem was neither circumstances nor David's misjudgment, it was their decision making practices.

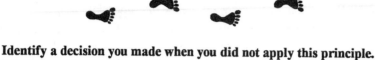

Identify a decision you made when you did not apply this principle. What were the results or effect on your family?

Wife: _____

Husband: _____

How would this principle have changed things?

Wife: _____

Husband: _____

Identify a decision, if you can, in which you applied or would apply this principle.

Wife: _____

Husband: _____

- **It means the goal becomes GOD'S WILL and our COUPLE ONENESS.**

  The **first** question a couple should ask when trying to make a decision is, "What would **God** have us do?" The **second** question they should ask is, "Will this **increase** our oneness or **decrease** it?" So often, we approach decisions without giving God or our coupleness a second thought. But if we are to make good couple decisions, we need to recognize that **God's will** and **our coupleness** are the two **most important considerations**.

  What if David and Andrea had gone to the Lord first, honestly seeking His guidance in their moves? What if they had then considered what would be best for their coupleness? A move away from interfering parents might have been the best decision for their oneness. And God may have wanted to open other job and location possibilities to them.

  If you honestly and humbly seek first God's will and then your couple oneness when faced with a decision, you will find **solutions** you didn't even know existed. You may want to make the decision your way. Your mate might have another way in mind. But if you follow this principle, you will usually be able to find a **third way** — the one God has for you — the one that will further your oneness.

  Larry and Gloria were young and madly in love, with one toddler and another baby on the way. Because of their family's imminent expansion, they decided they needed a bigger house. They bought a house twice as big as their old one, with a twice-as-big mortgage payment. At first, Larry worked overtime to afford the increased payment. Eventually, Gloria reluctantly quit being a full-time Mom and

The first question a couple should ask when trying to make a decision is, "What would God have us do?"

The second question they should ask is, "Will this increase our oneness or decrease it?"

Notes

Look for a third way.

Proverbs 3:5-6 — *Trust in the Lord with all your heart and **lean not on your own understanding**; in **all your ways** acknowledge him, and he will make your paths straight [will direct your paths].*

house they didn't have time to enjoy. They hardly had time for one another any more, spending the small amount left over from their work schedules on their two children. They had made a decision without considering God's will or their coupleness.

Their smaller home might not have provided enough space, but it certainly provided enough **time** for their coupleness. It afforded them the luxury of time and energy for one another. If they had faced the decision of buying a larger house with **benefit to their coupleness** in mind, they might have decided against the move. And if they had approached the decision with **God's will** in mind, He might have shown them a **third way**, such as a larger house for less money. If their goal had been God's will and their couple oneness, they would have grown closer instead of apart.

Proverbs 3:5-6 are such well known verses, we quote them without even thinking how profound they are. They can change forever the way we approach decisions. *Trust in the Lord with all your heart and **lean not on your own understanding**; in **all your ways** acknowledge him, and he will make your paths straight [will direct your paths].*

Identify a decision you made when you did not apply this principle. What were the results or effect on your family?

Wife: _____

Husband: _____

How would this principle have changed things?

Wife: _____

Husband: _____

Identify a decision, if you can, in which you applied or would apply this principle.

Wife: _____

Husband: _____

Write at least one personal application from today's study.

Wife: _____

Husband: _____

What does God want you to do to work out this application?

Wife: _____

Husband: _____

REFLECT TOGETHER: Re-read Proverbs 3:5-6.

PRAY TOGETHER: Oh, Lord, we want Your direction in all our decisions. Help us make decisions that draw us closer to You and closer to each other.

SUBMISSION — What's it all about?

Day 5 - Wife
(Husband, you have a separate reading for day 5.)

Submission, what a word! We've seen people react to it like angry dogs and like limp doormats. What does the Bible really teach about it? Who's suppose to be submissive? And what does it have to do with making decisions?

What does the Bible teach?

1 Peter chapters 2 and 3 teach specifically about submission. In 2:9 and following, the Apostle Peter labels us a chosen people, a called people...called to live like Jesus...called to live a life of submission. Throughout the rest of chapter 2 and most of chapter 3, Peter paints pictures of what "called people" look like in different walks of life.

In verses 13-17, he starts with Christian citizens, instructing them to *submit yourselves for the Lord's sake to every authority instituted among men.* We, as citizens, are called to exercise our citizenship like Jesus. We are called, like Him, to a life of submission.

In verses 18-20, Peter addresses slaves. We can up-date the word *slaves* to *employees.* (After all, we sometimes feel like slaves, don't we?) Here is God's command to employees: *submit yourselves to your masters with all respect.* Therefore, if we as Christian employees are to look like chosen, called people, we too must live a life of submission.

In verses 21-25, Peter focuses our attention on Jesus Christ, and explains **why we** are called to a life of submission: *because Christ suffered for you, leaving you an example, that you should follow in his steps.* What is the example Jesus left us? *...No deceit was found in his mouth....When they hurled their insults at him, he did not retaliate; when he suffered, he made no threats. Instead, he entrusted himself to him who judges justly [the Father].* This is the example we are to follow...the steps of Jesus...the steps of submission.

When I (Bette) walked as a little girl with my Mom through the snows of West Virginia, I would have to step very carefully in her footprints or I'd sink in the snow and get stuck (not to mention, getting *gobs* of snow in my boots!). That's how carefully we have to follow Jesus' footprints on this path of submission. He showed us the steps to take. It is now our calling to **walk in them.**

Now we come to chapter 3. This is not a separate teaching but a continuation of what Peter started in chapter 2, that is, Christians are called to a life of submission. Verse 1 begins with *Wives, in **the same way** be submissive to your husbands.* In what "same way" is Peter talking about? The way Jesus exemplified. The way

1 Peter 2:9-3:9 — *But you are a chosen people, a royal priesthood, a holy nation, a people belonging to God, that you may declare the praises of him who called you out of darkness into his wonderful light....*

Submit yourselves for the Lord's sake to every authority instituted among men: whether to the king, as the supreme authority, or to governors, who are sent by him to punish those who do wrong and to commend those who do right....

Slaves, submit yourselves to your masters with all respect, not only to those who are good and considerate, but also to those who are harsh....

To this you were called, because Christ suffered for you, leaving you an example, that you should follow in his steps. He committed no sin, and no deceit was found in his mouth. When they hurled their insults at him, he did not

Notes

retaliate; when he suffered, he made no threats. Instead, he entrusted himself to him who judges justly....

Wives, in the same way be submissive to your husbands so that, if any of them do not believe the word, they may be won over without talk by the behavior of their wives, when they see the purity and reverence of your lives....

Husbands, in the same way be considerate as you live with your wives, and treat them with respect as the weaker partner and as heirs with you of the gracious gift of life, so that nothing will hinder your prayers.

Finally, all of you, live in harmony with one another; be sympathetic, love as brothers, be compassionate and humble. Do not repay evil with evil or insult with insult, but with blessing, because to this you were called so that you may inherit a blessing.

Christian citizens and employees are commanded to live. We, as wives, like Sarah of old, are called to a life of submission. We are called to walk in the steps of Jesus.

Peter doesn't stop there. In verse 7, he speaks to husbands about how to live as well. *Husbands,* **in *the same way*** *be considerate as you live with your wives, and treat them with respect....* In what "same way"? The way Jesus walked. The way Christian citizens, employees and wives are to live. So husbands also are called to a life of submission.

Who is supposed to be submissive?

Peter wants to make absolutely sure he doesn't leave anyone out, so he continues in verses 8 and 9 with, *Finally,* **all of you,** *live in harmony with one another; be sympathetic, love as brothers, be compassionate and humble. Do not repay evil with evil or insult with insult, but with blessing, because to this you were called so that you may inherit a blessing.* Do these verses remind you of the description of Jesus in chapter 2? Did you notice the words *to this you were called*? **As Christians, no matter who we are or what we do, we are called to a life of submission...just like Jesus.**

You see, God cannot *conform us to the likeness of his Son* (Romans 8:29) in a vacuum. He has to work that miracle within us through the practical experiences of our daily lives — whoever we are, whatever we do.

Submission simply means *to defer or yield to the wishes of another.* It's basically a military term, referring to rank or job position. There's no thought in it of one person being better or smarter than another. Submission is simply a **non-rebellious attitude** of life.

It is day-by-day living with nothing to prove. We don't have to make sure we get our rights. We can *trust ourselves to Him who judges justly* — the Father — just like Jesus. Submission is learning to walk in the steps of Jesus, letting God the Father make us like His Son as we submit to Him and to one another.

Most of my life, I (Bette) was taught that, as a wife, I must be submissive to my husband. I was rather confused about what that meant, but I tried. I must admit, it ruffled my feathers when I heard some preachers describe how wives should be their husbands' doormats. I felt that **couldn't** be what God was actually saying, but I wasn't quite sure until I studied 1 Peter 2 and 3 for myself. Then it became so clear to me, I couldn't believe I had missed it all those years. Being submissive is simply **being like Jesus**; being like Jesus is **being submissive**. Yes, my heart still kicks up its rebellious heels, but being submissive is something I **want** to be, because I **want** to be like **Jesus**. Besides now, when I'm rebellious and refuse to have an attitude of submission, I know against whom I rebel...Jesus Himself.

Wife:

How does this picture of submission compare with what you've been taught?

_____

In what ways do you agree with this picture?

_____

_____

In what ways do you disagree with this picture?

_____

_____

Write at least one personal application from today's study.

Wife: _____

What does God want you to do to work out this application?

Wife: _____

Discuss with your husband your insights from today's study.

What does the Bible teach?

The apostle Paul echoes Peter's theme of submission in Ephesians 5 and 6. (Ask your wife about 1 Peter 3:7 when you're finished here.) Verses 22 and 23 state, _Wives, submit to your husbands as to the Lord. For the husband is head of the wife as Christ is the head of the church...._ We've heard these verses misused to prove that husbands are **kings** and wives their **subjects**. But let's look more closely, because this Scripture teaches something completely different from that.

First of all, this section of Ephesians 5 actually begins with often-overlooked verse 21: _Submit to one another out of reverence for Christ._ Paul, like Peter, then describes what submission looks like in different walks of life. He instructs wives, husbands, children, fathers, slaves and masters.

We husbands especially cherish verse 23, though we usually only memorize the first phrase: _the husband is the head of the wife...._ When I (Harold) was a young man, I took this verse and ran with it. Bette was to submit to me, because I was the head! I wasn't quite sure what a head was supposed to be, but **I was it**. One day, I finally looked at the rest of the verse, _For the husband is the head of the wife as Christ is the head of the church, his body, of which he is the Savior._ I decided if I am supposed to be _the head_ **like Christ**, then I'd better find out what kind of _head_ Christ is. The rest of this passage gave me some clues. Verse 25 urged me to love my wife sacrificially like Christ loves the church. Verse 28 commanded me to love her like I love my own body. And verse 33 said I must love her as if she were me.

DAY 5 —
Husband
(Wife, you have a separate reading for day 5.)

Ephesians 5:21-33 — _Submit to one another out of reverence for Christ. Wives, submit to your husbands as to the Lord. For the husband is the head of the wife as Christ is the head of the church, his body, of which he is the Savior. Now as the church submits to Christ, so also wives should submit to their husbands in everything._

Husbands, love your wives just as Christ loved the church and gave himself up for her to make her holy, cleansing her by the

Notes

washing with water through the word, and to present her to himself as a radiant church, without stain or wrinkle or any other blemish, but holy and blameless. In this same way, husbands ought to love their wives as their own bodies. He who loves his wife loves himself. After all, no one ever hated his own body, but he feeds and cares for it, just as Christ does the church — for we are member of his body.

For this reason a man will leave his father and mother and be united to his wife, and the two will become one flesh. This a profound mystery — but I am talking about Christ and the church. However, each one of you also must love his wife as he loves himself, and the wife must respect her husband.

Philippians 2:5-11 — Your attitude should be the same as that of Christ Jesus: Who, being in very nature God, did not consider equality with God something to be grasped, but made himself nothing, taking the very nature of a servant, being made in human likeness. And being found in appearance as a man, he humbled himself and became obedient to death — even death on a cross!

Therefore God exalted him to the highest place and gave him the name that is above every name, that at the name of Jesus every knee should bow, in heaven and on earth and under the earth, and every tongue confess that Jesus Christ is Lord, to the glory of God the Father.

Searching further, I found that Philippians 2:5-11 presented an even clearer picture of the kind of *head* Christ is, and therefore, the kind of *head* I am to be: *Your attitude should be the same as that of Christ Jesus: Who, being in very nature God, did not consider equality with God something to be grasped, but made himself nothing, taking the very nature of a servant, being made in human likeness. And being found in appearance as a man, he humbled himself and became obedient to death — even death on a cross....* That doesn't sound like a **dictator** to me. Christ was a **servant-leader** whose strength was displayed in **humility**.

What does this mean?

A certain picture comes to mind. The scene? The last supper. *Jesus knew that the time had come for him to leave* (John 13:1). But before He left, He wanted to impress His disciples with a picture so vivid, they could never forget it. He tied a towel around His waist, knelt on the floor before the disciples and, one by one, took their dirty feet in His hands and washed them. He showed them what a servant-leader looks like...what a servant-leader acts like. He had no fear of losing status, no rebellion in performing such a menial task, no authority to prove, no rights to demand. Oh, He had rights. He had the right to demand that the disciples wash *His* feet. But, instead, He washed theirs.

A servant-leader leads by example (1 Peter 2:21). So, husbands, if we want to be the right kind of *heads,* then we must learn to be **servant-leaders** like Jesus Christ.

Husbands and wives have been called to **mutual submission** to the Lord and to one another (Ephesians 5:21). **We have both been called to be like Jesus.**

Husband:

How does this picture of headship compare with what you've been taught?

_____

In what ways do you agree with this picture?

_____

_____

In what ways do you disagree with this picture?

_____

_____

> Write at least one personal application from today's study.
>
> Husband: _____
>
> **What does God want you to do to work out this application?**
>
> Husband: _____
>
> Discuss with your wife your insights from today's study.

REFLECT TOGETHER: Read 1 Peter 3:1-9 and Philippians 2:1-5. Notice how every Christian is called to live a life of submission.

PRAY TOGETHER: Blessed Lord, we want to have Your attitude in every aspect of our lives. Help us be just like You to each other.

What does all this have to do with decision making?

The only way for God to direct us into His will is for us to **submit** ourselves to Him. It follows then, that when you make decisions as a couple, you must come to Him in **mutual submission**. Here are some **guidelines** to follow in making couple decisions the right way.

1. **PRAY** together for God's direction, submitting your wills to Him. Philippians 4:6 — *Do not be anxious about anything, but in everything, by prayer and petition, with thanksgiving, **present your requests to God.***

2. **RELEASE** your rights. If you approach a decision while demanding your own rights, you essentially jam the process. Philippians 2:3 — *Do nothing out of **selfish ambition or vain conceit,** but in humility consider others better than yourselves.*

3. Maintain an attitude of **MUTUAL SUBMISSION**: to God and to one another. James 4:7a — ***Submit** yourselves, then, to God.* Ephesians 5:21 — ***Submit to one another** out of reverence for Christ.*

4. **SEARCH** God's Word for direction. If the Bible says something definitive about your specific decision or plans, obey that directive. Psalm 119:105 — *Your Word is a lamp to my feet and a **light for my path.***

5. **COMPILE** a pro and con list.

Day 6

Philippians 4:6 — *Do not be anxious about anything, but in everything, by prayer and petition, with thanksgiving, **present your requests to God.***

Philippians 2:3 — *Do nothing out of selfish ambition or vain conceit, but in humility consider others better than yourselves.*

James 4:7a — ***Submit** yourselves, then, to God.*

Ephesians 5:21 — ***Submit to one another** out of reverence for Christ.*

Psalm 119:105 — *Your Word is a lamp to my feet and a **light for my path.***

Notes

Luke 14:28 — *Suppose one of you wants to build a tower. Will he not first sit down and estimate the cost to see if he has enough money to complete it?*

Proverbs 19:20 — *Listen to advice and accept instruction, and in the end you will be wise.*

Proverbs 19:2 — *It is not good to have zeal without knowledge, nor to be hasty and miss the way.* Psalm 37:34a — *Wait for the Lord and keep his way.*

At the top of a page, write down a possible solution to the decision before you, and draw a vertical line down the middle of the paper. Then list all the reasons **for** following that solution down one side of the page, and all the reasons **against** down the other side. Remember to consider the affect on your relationship. Of course, even if you and your mate have ten reasons against and only two for, it may still be what **God** wants you to do. This exercise, however, should help you gain perspective about the decision.

Luke 14:28 — *Suppose one of you wants to build a tower. Will he not first **sit down and estimate the cost** to see if he has enough money to complete it?* We are urged to "sit down and estimate" before we decide.

6. If you still can't reach a decision, **ASK** a godly friend (someone you respect) to help you discover together all the options open to you. Proverbs 19:20 — ***Listen to advice** and accept instruction, and in the end you will be wise.*

7. **WAIT** for God's answer.

We've come to the point in our marriage where, if we cannot agree on a decision, we put it off until we can, if at all possible. For if we have followed all these guidelines and still don't have the answer, we know by now it is dangerous to forge ahead without the three of us (God, Harold and Bette) agreeing.

Proverbs 19:2 — *It is not good to have zeal without knowledge, nor to be **hasty** and miss the way.* Psalm 37:34a — ***Wait for the Lord** and keep his way.*

Which of these 7 guidelines do you like the most?

Wife: _____ Husband: _____

Why?

Wife: _____

Husband: _____

Which do you like the least?

Wife: _____ Husband: _____

Why?

Wife: _____

Husband: _____

Which one would help you most in making couple decisions?

Wife: _____ Husband: _____

Something wonderful will happen in you and in your marriage when you stop digging in your heels and fighting to get your own way...when you **stop** acting like two independent individuals living together and **start** acting like a team. **You are a team. Jesus Himself calls you a team.** Matthew 19:6 — *So they are no longer two, but one.* **Let's start acting like it!**

Matthew 19:6 — *So they are no longer two, but one.*

Write at least one personal application from today's study.

Wife: _____

Husband: _____

What does God want you to do to work out this application?

Wife: _____

Husband: _____

REFLECT TOGETHER: Read Jeremiah 6:16. Notice God's promise if we walk in His good ways.

PRAY TOGETHER: Father God, help us make decisions as a team. Help us obey the guidelines for decision making You have given in Your Word.

Notes

Day 7

WRAP UP: Complete the first question individually, then discuss both questions together.

1. How do I feel about the way we now make decisions? According to the principles we have just studied, I would like to start (list at least one new practice from the decision-making guidelines):

Wife: _____

Husband: _____

2. Were some of our decision-making practices reflected in the illustrations of Andrea and David or Larry and Gloria? Which ones? How can we change them?

Wife: _____

Husband: _____

REFLECT TOGETHER: Read Matthew 19:4-6 again. Notice God's plan for a couple's oneness was clear from the very beginning.

PRAY TOGETHER: Lord, we want to be more like You. You showed us how to be servants. We want to be Your servants and servants to one another. Help us learn to be mutually submissive—to You, Lord, and to one another. And help us make decisions Your way.

GROUP DISCUSSION QUESTIONS: If this study is being used in a group setting, the following are for group discussion.

Have a frank discussion

1. **Case Study #1**

    Pretend this couple is coming to you for advice: A Christian husband and wife have lived in the same town for 10 years and are very active in their church. The husband has a fine position with a good company, but he does not like his work. He has been offered another position — 3,000 miles away, in a colder climate and at less pay. He wants to accept the position because it is the type of work he has always wanted to do. He talks with his wife and tells her he is thinking of taking the job. She does not want him to accept it and gives her reasons. She says she definitely won't move. What would you advise them to do?

2. **Case Study #2**

    Here is another couple coming to ask for your wise counsel: A Christian couple has been very active in an evangelical church. For some time, though, the husband has been interested in the Mormon church and finally decides to join that church and becomes a Mormon. His wife does not know what to do. The Scriptures say to submit, but does that mean she should follow her husband, leave her church and take the children with her to the Mormon church? What would you advise her to do? How would you advise the husband?

3. From your observation of other couples and your own experience, list some common decision-making practices among couples that ought to change. How would the principles we've learned make a difference in them?

I am my beloved's, and my beloved is mine....(Song of Sol. 6:3 KJV)

ROMANCE & SEX
Chapter 7

Day 1

Has the Sexual liberation movement succeeded?

In the last two or three decades there has been a drastic change in the public acceptance of the subject of sex.

There are sexual connotations in display ads on billboards, newspapers, magazines, television — it's almost impossible NOT to be confronted by a scantily clothed, beautiful-to-look-at female or "buff" male on a daily basis from one source or another.

The subject is so freely discussed that you can hear it talked about in almost any surrounding — any, that is, except the church.

Older parents and most grandparents were raised in an environment so different from this that even the subject was verboten — you couldn't even say the word — you spelled out "S-E-X" in sort of a whisper.

It was not taught in churches or in schools and one rarely learned about it in the home environment. The misinformation gathering techniques of the locker room provided the primary source of sex education for young people.

The media has joined the locker room in the misinformation business.

No indeed, no one can deny that the Sexual Liberation Movement has succeeded in raising sexual consciousness. The media has now joined the locker room in the misinformation business.

This movement has failed dismally in the most important part of sexuality: keeping romance and commitment part of the sexual experience. "Shacking up" together for a time or having one night flings with no "ties" or even romance, has become common.

Unfortunately, the only thing that seems to be deterring this trend is the AIDS scare. But it's sad, isn't it, that people are turning from casual sex because they're afraid of catching a terminal disease instead of seeing it as a matter of right and wrong.

What effect did the sexual liberation movement have on your family of upbringing (or origin)?

Wife: _____

Husband: _____

How open was the subject of sex in your home?

Wife: _____

Husband: _____

The love people yearn for includes ROMANCE

The following is a quote from an Ann Landers' survey in FAMILY CIRCLE magazine on June 11, 1985:

Last January I published a letter from a woman who lives in Oregon. In it she wrote: "If you were to ask 100 women how they feel about sexual intercourse, I'll bet 98 would say, 'Just hold me close and be tender. Forget about the act.' If you don't believe it, why not take a poll? How about it, Ann?"

I replied, "You're on." I then asked my women readers to send a postcard or letter replying to the question: "Would you be content to be held close and treated tenderly and forget about 'the act'? Reply YES or NO and please add one line: 'I am over (or under) 40 years of age.'"

Four days later our mailroom looked like a disaster area — apparently the question had become a lively topic of conversation in barrooms, boardrooms, bedrooms, classrooms, wherever people gathered.

After tabulating 90,000 responses, we published the results. The verdict was clear: A solid 72% of the women said "Yes," they would be content to be held close and treated tenderly and forget about the act. Of those 72%, 40% were under 40 years of age.

A solid 72% of the women said "Yes," they would be content to be held close and treated tenderly and forget about the act.

What does this say to us men? It should at least shock us into a little romancing and make us open our ears to the rest of this session! Marriages are dying for lack of romance. We all need to invest ourselves in being more romantic.

Why do you think so many women would be willing to "forget about the act"?

Wife: _____

Husband: _____

Romance is not foreign to the Bible. Have you read the Book of Ruth? Pretty romantic. Proverbs is full of insights into romance. And, of course, the Song of Solomon is devoted solely to marital romantic and sexual love. In fact, marital romance and love must be a very important subject to our Father. He dedicated an entire book in His Word to it. Can you think of any other subject besides salvation that He does that for?

A teacher asked her second grade Sunday School class this question, "What can you tell me about Lot's wife?

The children's little foreheads knit tightly as they pondered the deep theological question. Finally, one brave little boy raised his hand. "Wasn't she the lady who was a pillar of salt by day and a ball of fire by night?"

Well, he was half right. Mrs. Lot was a pillar of salt by day (and night), but it was Shulamith (Mrs. Solomon) who was a ball of fire by night (and day). We have included a portion of the Song of Solomon at the end of each day's study. Each portion of the Scripture text is scripted so that you can read Solomon's and Shulamith's words to one another.

Notes

1 Corinthians 13:4-7 — *Love is patient, love is kind. It does not envy, it does not boast, it is not proud. It is not rude, it is not self-seeking, it is not easily angered, it keeps no record of wrongs. Love does not delight in evil but rejoices with the truth. It always protects, always trusts, always hopes, always perseveres.*

This type of love — love that includes romance and commitment — demands that we grow in INTIMACY. Listen to the kind of love God wants for your marriage.

1 Corinthians 13:4-7 — *Love is patient, love is kind. It does not envy, it does not boast, it is not proud. It is not rude, it is not self-seeking, it is not easily angered, it keeps no record of wrongs. Love does not delight in evil but rejoices with the truth. It always protects, always trusts, always hopes, always perseveres.*

If you practice this kind of love, you can be **sure** of intimacy in your marriage relationship. There are different kinds of intimacies. We're going to mention just four. And remember, we need to grow in each of these.

Emotional Intimacy: Actually, this is what we have been talking about up to this point. Sharing the *real you* with your *real partner*. The following is a poem entitled "Walls." Read carefully, because this is what you DO NOT want in your relationship. But it is what you will end up with if you do not work on your emotional intimacy.

"Walls"

Their wedding picture mocked them from the table, these two
whose minds no longer touched each other.

They lived with such a heavy barricade between them that
neither battering ram of words nor artilleries of touch
could break it down.

Somewhere, between the oldest child's first tooth and the
youngest daughter's graduation, they lost each other

Throughout the years, each slowly unraveled that tangled ball
of string called self, and as they tugged at stubborn
knots each hid his searching from the other.

Sometimes she cried at night and begged the whispering darkness
to tell her who she was.

He lay beside her, snoring like a hibernating bear, unaware
of her winter.

Once, after they had made love, he wanted to tell her how
afraid he was of dying, but fearing to show his naked
soul, he spoke instead about the beauty of her breasts.

She took a course in modern art, trying to find herself in
colors splashed upon a canvas, and complaining to other
women about men who were insensitive.

He climbed a tomb called "the office," wrapped his mind in
a shroud of paper figures and buried himself in customers.

Slowly, the wall between them rose, cemented by the mortar
of indifference.

One day, reaching out to touch each other, they found a barrier
they could not penetrate, and recoiling from the coldness
of the stone, each retreated from the stranger on the other side.

*For when love dies, it is not in a moment of angry battle,
nor when fiery bodies lose their heat.*

*It lies panting, exhausted, expiring at the bottom of a wall
it could not scale.*

(Source unknown)

Aesthetic Intimacy: This is sharing the "we" experiences of our lives, like watching a sunset or your child's ball game together. It's taking a walk along the beach or sharing a special moment in time. But it doesn't even have to be a positive moment. It can be the agonizing times, such as clinging to one another, waiting for a doctor's diagnosis. It's creating history together, and it is powerful in the bonding process.

Spiritual Intimacy: This is the sharing together of our lives and faith in Christ. This intimacy, more than any other, breeds trust in our relationship as husband and wife. In fact, according to a Harvard Study, couples who are committed to reading the Bible together, praying together and attending church together, have a divorce rate of 1 out of 1,287. Not bad, huh? We'll be talking a lot more about this in chapter 12. So, hang in there.

Physical Intimacy: Ah, this is what you've been waiting for. But you know what? Physical intimacy is the culmination of all the other intimacies. For the two bodies that come together physically house two persons who should be in process of becoming intimate in every way. That's why we say physical intimacy is the *celebration* of your relationship.

Physical intimacy is the celebration of your relationship.

Discuss together how these intimacies inter-relate.

Write at least one personal application from today's study.

Wife: _____

Husband: _____

What does God want you to do to work out this application?

Wife: _____

Husband: _____

REFLECT TOGETHER: Song of Solomon passages are provided in script form at the end of each day's study. The wife should read Shulamith's parts and the husband should read the King's parts. The other parts can be divided between you as desired. Today read Song of Solomon 1:1-14.

PRAY TOGETHER: Lord, help us understand how important romance is in our relationship. Please keep us from ever looking like the couple spoken of in "Walls."

Notes

The Most Beautiful Love Song Ever Written
Shulamith's First Days in the Palace (1:2-11)

The King's fiancee, Shulamith, in soliloquy

How I wish he would shower me with kisses for his exquisite kisses are more desirable than the finest wine. The gentle fragrance of your cologne brings the enchantment of springtime. Yes, it is the rich fragrance of your heart that awakens my love and respect. Yes, it is your character that brings you admiration from every girl of the court. How I long for you to come take me with you to run and laugh through the countryside of this kingdom. (You see, the King had brought me to the kingdom's palace.)

Women of the court to the King

We will always be very thankful and happy because of you, O King. For we love to speak of the inspiring beauty of your love.

Shulamith in soliloquy

They rightly love a person like you, my King.

Shulamith to women of the court

I realize that I do not display the fair and delicate skin of one raised in the comfort of a palace. I am darkened from the sun—indeed, as dark as the tents of the humble desert nomads I used to work beside. But now I might say that I am also as dark as the luxurious drapery of the King's palace. Nevertheless, what loveliness I do have is not so weak that the gaze of the sun should make it bow its head in shame. And if the glare of the sun could not shame me, please know that neither will the glare of your contempt. I could not help it that my stepbrothers were angry with me and demanded that I work in the vineyard they had leased from the King. It was impossible for me to care for it and for the vineyard of my own appearance.

Shulamith to King

Please tell me, you whom I love so deeply, where you take your royal flock for its afternoon rest. I don't want to search randomly for you, wandering about like a woman of the streets.

Women of the court to Shulamith

If you do not know, O fairest among women, why not simply go ahead and follow the trail of the flocks, and then pasture your flock beside the shepherds' huts?

King to Shulamith

Your presence captivates attention as thoroughly as a single mare among a hundred stallions. And how perfectly your lovely jewelry and necklace adorn your lovely face.

Women of the court to Shulamith

We shall make even more elegant necklaces of gold and silver to adorn her face.

In a Palace Room (1:12-14)

Shulamith in soliloquy

While my King was dining at his table, my perfume refreshed me with its soothing fragrance. For my King is the fragrance and my thoughts of him are like a sachet of perfume hung around my neck, over my heart, continually refreshing me. How dear he is to me, as dear as the delicate henna blossoms in the oasis of En-Gedi. What joy I have found in that oasis!

The Art of Romance

Definition of Romance: The state in which one is captivated with the "wooing," winning or keeping another's affection by practicing other than ordinary words and actions intended to display and convey an attitude of heart and mind which is focused on and oriented to the one being "romanced."

In other words, romance is **love made visible.**

Why romance DECLINES.

Day 2

Romance is love made visible.

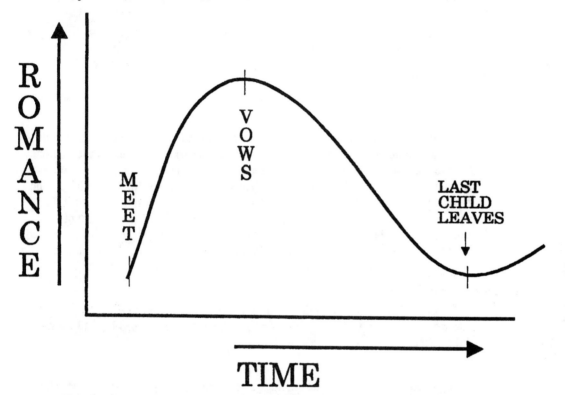

This is the average, or typical, romance curve. This curve depicts what happens in a couple's relationship when life is left to run its own course. Why do you think it peaks at the time the "knot is tied?"

One explanation is that during courtship both parties are in a **WIN** mode of operation. They are attempting to WIN the affections of the other. Naturally their focus of attention is on the other person.

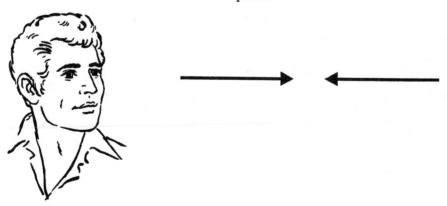

Notes

At the Wedding the VOWS are said and the "KNOT IS TIED," and we begin to feel we have now **WON**. But we get a little mixed up on the spelling of WON and start treating our partner as though we **OWN** them. Our attention turns inward to self and we begin to **expect** our mates to meet **our** needs instead of the other way around. The focus is on **SELF**.

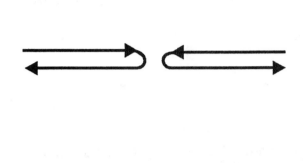

Romance naturally declines in such an atmosphere because romance demands that attention be placed on the other partner. Romance must be "other" centered not self centered. If we would keep romance alive in our relationship, we must get out of the **OWN** mode and get back into the **WIN** mode.

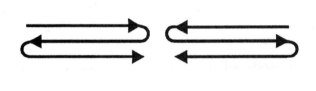

You can change the direction of your romance curve at any point you **choose to refocus your attention on your mate's needs instead of your own**. The romance curve can be altered at any point such a decision is made and carried through. In fact, romance can exceed the level experienced at the point of VOWS — there is no upper limitation.

Romance can exceed the level experienced at the point of VOWS — there is no upper limitation.

Does this romance curve describe your relationship to date?

Wife: _____

Husband: _____

If not, draw what you think your romance curve would look like and put an "X" where you are now. (If the romance curve we provided typifies your relationship put an X where you are on that curve.)

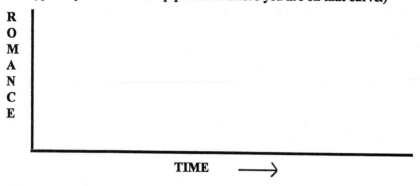

How to help your ATTITUDE make your marriage romantic.

POSITIVE attitude -- remember all that stuff about THOT-TALK? Go back and look at that chapter again, and apply it to the bedroom. No, on second thought, apply it all day long, and see the difference it will make in your bedroom. Philippians 4:8 instructs, *Finally, brothers, whatever is true, whatever is noble, whatever is right, whatever is pure, whatever is lovely, whatever is admirable—if anything is excellent or praiseworthy—think about such things.* Now, read that Scripture again, applying it to your marriage. *Finally, brothers and sisters, whatever is true **about your mate**, whatever is noble **about your mate**, whatever is right **about your mate**, whatever is pure **about your mate**, whatever is lovely **about your mate**, whatever is admirable **about your mate**—if anything **about your mate** is excellent or praiseworthy—think about such things.* Nothing kills romance faster than criticism. Nothing builds romance faster than the positive THOT-TALK commanded in this verse. Remember, what you <u>say</u> and what you <u>do</u> are the direct results of what you <u>think</u>!

Philippians 4:8 — *Finally, brothers, whatever is true, whatever is noble, whatever is right, whatever is pure, whatever is lovely, whatever is admirable—if anything is excellent or praiseworthy—think about such things.*

COMPLIMENTS build strong romantic attitudes. When is the last time you

gave your mate a compliment? If you are sitting there thinking, "Yeah, but when's the last time he/she gave me one," then you need to redirect your focus off yourself onto your mate (remember why romance declines?).

Give your mate a compliment every day. In fact, we recommend you make a list of 30 things you like about your spouse. Know what you will have? A compliment resource. Each day you can choose one characteristic you like and give your husband or wife a compliment about it. You see, compliments don't have to be spontaneous, they just have to be sincere.

The guy in the cartoon needs to work on his compliments!

Charlie Shedd, author of *Letters to Karen* and *Letters to Phillip*, and his wife Martha pastored and counseled couples for many years. Charlie used to give Martha a compliment every day of their lives. And he said he gave her a new one

Notes

— one he had never used before — once a week. Wow! That's a lot of compliments. But it must have worked, because they had many happy years together. And now that Martha has gone to be with the Lord, Charlie doesn't have to live with the regret of not telling her how much she meant to him.

COMMUNICATION helps build romance. You know this by now, don't you? There is nothing quite so romantic as sharing your hopes and dreams together. That's probably what stirred up the fires of romance between you two in the first place. Remember those long talks when you were courting?

THOUGHTFULNESS — doing those things that you know your mate enjoys and appreciates creates romantic feelings. Taking her hand, catching his eye across the room, opening her door, wearing his favorite nightie are just a few examples.

A few months ago, Harold brought me (Bette) the cutest little bouquet of flowers. But what made it so special was that it was arranged in a beautiful little pitcher. I collect pitchers, so this gift was especially precious to me, because he remembered that and wanted to add a pretty one to my collection. His thoughtfulness made me feel very special and romantic.

The nubs and the grubs!

Some time ago we heard a radio DJ do a spontaneous survey among his listeners. The question they were to respond to was, "What bugs you the most about your mate?" The number one answer from the wives? "My husband doesn't shower often enough." And the number one complaint from Husbands? "My wife doesn't shave her legs often enough." We call it "The nubs and the grubs." Sometimes, we just plain forget to take the trouble to be thoughtful, don't we?

Which of these attitudes would contribute the most right now to romance in your relationship?

Wife: _____

Husband: _____

Why?

Wife: _____

Husband: _____

Write at least one personal application from today's study.

Wife: _____

Husband: _____

What does God want you to do to work out this application?

Wife: _____

Husband: _____

REFLECT TOGETHER: Read Song of Solomon 1:15-2:17 provided below.

PRAY TOGETHER: Dear Lord, help us obey Your Word by thinking about each other's positive characteristics instead of the negatives. We want to learn to communicate with each other in positive, thoughtful ways.

In the Countryside (1:15-2:7)

King to Shulamith

You are so beautiful, my love. You are so beautiful. Your soft eyes are as gentle as doves.

Shulamith to King

And you are handsome, my love, and so enjoyable. It's so wonderful to walk through our home of nature together. Here the cool grass is a soft couch to lie upon, to catch our breath and to gaze at the beams and rafters of our house—the towering

Notes

cedars and cypresses all around. Lying here I feel like a rose from the valley of Sharon, the loveliest flower in the valley.

King to Shulamith

Only the loveliest flower in the valley? No, my love. To me you are like a flower among thorns compared with any other woman in the world. Shulamith to King

And you, my precious King, are like a fruitful apple tree among the barren trees of the forest compared with all the men in the world.

Shulamith in soliloquy

No longer do I labor in the heat of the sun. I find cool rest in the shade of this apple tree. Nourishment from its magical fruit brings me the radiant health only love brings. And he loves me so much. Even when he brings me to the great royal banquets attended by the most influential people in this kingdom and beyond, he is never so concerned for them that his love and his care for me is not as plain as a royal banner lifted high above my head.

How dear he is to me! My delightful peace in his love makes me so weak from joy that I must rest in his arms for strength. Yet such loving comfort makes me more joyful and weaker still. How I wish he could lay me down beside him and embrace me! But how important it is I promise, with the gentle gazelles and deer of the countryside as my witnesses, not to attempt to awaken love until love is pleased to awaken itself.

On the Way to the Countryside (2:8-17)

Shulamith in soliloquy

I hear my beloved. Look! He is coming to visit. And he is as dashing as a young stag leaping upon the mountains, springing upon the hills. There he is, standing at the door, trying to peer through the window and peep through the lattice. At last he speaks.

King to Shulamith

Come, my darling, my fair one, come with me. For look, the winter has passed. The rain is over and gone. The blossoms have appeared in the land. The time of singing has come, and the voice of the turtledove has been heard in the land. The fig tree has ripened its figs, and the vines in blossom have given forth fragrance. Let us go, my darling, my lovely one; come along with me. O my precious, gentle dove. You have been like a dove in the clefts of the mountain rocks, in the hidden places along the mountain trails. Now come out from the hidden place and let me see you. Let me hear the coo of your voice. For your voice is sweet and you are as gracefully beautiful as a dove in flight silhouetted against a soft blue sky. My love, what we have together is a valuable treasure; it is like a garden of the loveliest flowers in the world. Let us promise each other to catch any foxes that could spoil our garden when now at long last it blossoms for us.

My love, what we have together is a valuable treasure....

Shulamith in soliloquy

My beloved belongs to me and I belong to him—this tender King who grazes his flock among the lilies.

Shulamith to King

How I long for the time when all through the night, until the day takes its first breath and the morning shadows flee from the sun, that you, my beloved King, might be a gazelle upon the hills of my breasts.

Day 3

Things you can DO to make your marriage more romantic

Recapture the mystery and excitement of earlier days.

What was your dating like in early marriage? Be that way again! What experiences were special? They were probably **planned** — not **spontaneous.** Plan for "special times" now.

Good romantic relationships take PLANNING: Baby-sitting, scheduling, setting the mood with flowers, candlelight, clothing, music, perfume — appeal to all five senses to please your mate.

Good romantic relationships take planning.

Be CREATIVE about your dates —Going to a nice restaurant, a play, or the movies — regular kinds of dates are great, but don't stop there. A walk on the beach, a trip to the mountains, a picnic on the floor of your bedroom after the kids are in bed, a scenic drive with a special lunch hidden in the trunk, a scenic hike, a walk around the block, a milk shake at McDonald's — these can also be special and romantic.

Take the time and effort to plan surprises for each other. The planner has the most fun.

On our 10th Anniversary, Bette thought I (Harold) was simply taking her out to a nice dinner at a restaurant overlooking the beach in Ventura, California. The baby-sitter that had been arranged was not one we would leave our kids with for an extended period of time. Bette didn't know I had arranged for a more mature woman to come in several hours later to stay the night while I whisked her off to a romantic getaway. I had arranged for a hotel room on the Beach near the restaurant where we had reservations.

The suitcase was packed and safely in the trunk of the car. Packing her make-up and personal care stuff would have been a nightmare for me. Luckily her sister, Linda, dropped by that day. While Bette was involved with the kids, Linda excitedly helped me pack what she thought Bette would need out of all her paraphernalia. The only thing I forgot was her night-gown—but that oversight worked out fine. (To this day she still thinks it was intentional.)

Be creative.

After dinner we took a walk on the beach toward the pier. It happened to take us by "our" hotel. There Bette played right into my scheme as she mentioned she needed to find a restroom. I replied that the hotel should have restrooms in their lobby, so we walked in. While Bette was otherwise occupied, I checked in at the Front Desk and picked up our room key.

When she came out, I was sitting innocently in the lobby waiting for her. As we started out to complete our walk, I complained about how far we would have to trudge back to the car once we got to the pier. I suggested we get the car and park closer. She agreed, but when I drove the car into the hotel's parking lot (which was really close to the pier), she cried, "But the sign says they'll tow the car away if we park here! This lot is for hotel guests only."

I continued to park the car while I calmly pulled the key from my jacket and said, "Well — **we are** hotel guests, here's our room key. Let's go celebrate our 10th."

Need some ideas on surprises and creative dates? Get ahold of the small, paper back book called <u>Creative Dating</u>, by Doug Fields. He lists hundreds of great ideas for you to "steal."

Notes

What is the last surprise you sprung on your mate?

Wife: _____

Husband: _____

Talk about the types of surprises you each most enjoy.

Within the next week, plan a new surprise for your mate.

Spend TIME together regularly.

Quality time. If the only time you give your mate is left-over time when you're too tired to think, much less communicate, then you are going to end up with a "left-over" relationship.

It takes quantitiy of time to make quality time.

We know for some of you, quality time has become a rare commodity in your marriage. Your lives and schedules are frantic. You may have to make some painful changes. But if you want a quality relationship, you are going to have to schedule quality time and plenty of it, because it takes quantity of time to make quality time.

Schedule it and keep it! Surely your marriage is as important as a business appointment or dental appointment. So schedule time together, and don't let anything usurp it!

Alone. Sure, it's nice sometimes to be with other couples for fun, but make sure you take dates alone too. This is especially important if you have children. The best thing you can do for your children is ensure they have a Mommy and Daddy who love each other!

Get away from the everyday — the hum-drum. Get away from the phone, from interruptions and everyday stress. **This is our prescription:**

Our prescription:

Once per week — a date. It doesn't have to be fancy or expensive. Be creative.

Once per quarter — an overnight. Save your pennies for a hotel, trade houses with some friends, or camp under the stars, but get away overnight once every three months. What a zing it will add to your romantic relationship!

Once every 6 months — a weekend. Twice a year, get away alone for a whole weekend. Again, it doesn't have to be fancy — but it has to *be*. If you don't follow this prescription, you run the risk of forgetting how to have fun to-gether. And that's a mighty dangerous position for any married couple to be in.

One of these weekends can be invested in a yearly marriage enrichment retreat. But the other one should be spent with no other agenda than to relax and enjoy one another: eat, sleep, make love, talk, walk, relax, make love, talk.... Get the picture?

Talk about this prescription together.

What has to happen in order for you to practice this prescription?

Wife: _____

Husband: _____

Together plan a weekend away within the next 6 months.

When: _____

Where: _____

Arrangements needed:

_____

_____

Romance is a part of making love. Men and women both need romancing. Each of us needs to feel like we are very special to our mates. Romance is love made visible, so you need to let your mate know in visible ways how special he or she is to you. And don't forget, the romancing **STARTS** when you wake up in the morning and **CONTINUES** through the day. A popular book about marriage is entitled SEX BEGINS IN THE KITCHEN. Think about it.

Romancing starts when you wake up in the morning and continues through the day.

Write at least one personal application from today's study.

Wife: _____

Husband: _____

What does God want you to do to work out this application?

Wife: _____

Husband: _____

REFLECT TOGETHER: Read Song of Solomon 3:1-5:1 provided below.

PRAY TOGETHER: Oh, Father, help us remember how special we are to each other. Show us new ways we can give our relationship the time we need.

Notes

Shulamith Waits for Her Fiancé (3:1-5)

Shulamith in soliloquy

How I miss the one I love so deeply. I could not wait to see him. I thought to myself, "I must get up and find him. I will get up now and look around the streets and squares of the city for him. Surely I'll be able to find this one I love so much." But I could not find him. When the night watchmen of the city found me, I immediately asked them if they had seen this one I loved so deeply. But they had not. Yet no sooner did I pass from them than I found my beloved. I held on and on and would not let him go until I could bring him to my home. I still held on until my fearful anxieties left me and I felt peaceful once again. How hard it is to be patient! You women of the court, we must promise ourselves, by the gazelles and deer of the field, not to awaken love until love is pleased to awaken itself.

The Wedding Day (3:6-11)

Poet

What can this be coming from the outskirts of the city like columns of smoke, perfumed clouds of myrrh and frankincense, clouds of the scented powders of the merchant? Look! It is the royal procession with Solomon carried upon his lavish couch by his strongest servants. and take a look at all those soldiers around it! That is the imperial guard, the sixty mightiest warriors in the entire kingdom. Each one is an expert with his weapon and valiant in battle. Yet now each one has a sword at his side only for the protection of the King and his bride. Look at the luxurious couch Solomon is carried on. He has had it made especially for this day. He made its frame from the best timber of Lebanon. Its posts are made of silver, its back of gold, and its seat of royal purple cloth. And do you see its delicate craftsmanship! It reflects the skill of the women of the court who gave their best work out of love for the King and his bride. Let us all go out and look upon King Solomon wearing his elegant wedding crown. Let us go out and see him on the most joyful day of his life.

The Wedding Night (4:1-5:1)

King to Shulamith

You are so beautiful, my love, you are so beautiful. Your soft eyes are as gentle as doves from behind your wedding veil. Your hair is as captivating as the flowing movement of a flock descending a mountain at sunset. Your full and lovely smile is as cheerful and sparkling as pairs of young lambs scurrying up from a washing. And only a thread of scarlet could have outlined your lips so perfectly. Your cheeks flush with the redness of the pomegranate's hue. Yet you walk with dignity and stand with the strength of a fortress. Your necklace sparkles like the shields upon the fortress tower. But your breasts are as soft and gentle as fawns grazing among the lilies. And now at last, all through the night—until the day takes it first breath and the morning shadows flee from the sun—I will be a gazelle upon the hills of your perfumed breasts. You are completely and perfectly beautiful, my love, and flawless in every way. Now bring your thoughts completely to me, my love. Leave your fears in the far away mountains and rest in the security of my arms.

You excite me, my darling bride; you excite me with but a glance of your eyes, with but a strand of your necklace. How wonderful are your caresses, my beloved bride. Your love is more sweetly intoxicating than the finest wine. And the fragrance of your perfume is better than the finest spices. The richness of honey and milk is under your tongue, my love. And the fragrance of your garments is like the fragrance of the forests of Lebanon.

You are a beautiful garden fashioned only for me, my darling bride. Yes, like a garden kept only for me. Or like a fresh fountain sealed just for me. Your garden is

Leave your fears in the far away mountains and rest in the security of my arms.

overflowing with beautiful and delicate flowers of every scent and color. It is a paradise of pomegranates with luscious fruit, with henna blossoms and nard, nard and saffron, calamus and cinnamon with trees of frankincense, myrrh and aloes with all the choicest of spices. And you are pure as fresh water, yet more than a mere fountain. You are a spring for many gardens—a well of life-giving water. No, even more, you are like the fresh streams flowing from Lebanon which give life to the entire country-side.

Shulamith to King

Awake, O north wind, and come, wind of the south. Let your breezes blow upon my garden and carry its fragrant spices to my beloved. May he follow the enchanting spices to my garden and come in to enjoy its luscious fruit.

King to Shulamith

I have rejoiced in the richness of your garden, my darling bride. I have been intoxicated by the fragrance of your myrrh and perfume. I have tasted the sweetness of your love like honey. I have enjoyed the sweetness of your love like an exquisite wine and the refreshment of your love like the coolness of milk.

Poet to couple

Rejoice in your lovemaking as you would rejoice at a great feast, O lovers. Eat and drink from this feast to the fullest. Drink, drink and be drunk with one another's love.

Some Practical DO'S of Making Love

We would like to give you some practical points about marital love. We are going to try our best to be forthright and honest with you, because we believe that is how God handles the subject. We have already shared some Scriptures with you, especially the book of Song of Solomon. There is one more we would like to bring to your attention.

Hebrews 13:4 — *Marriage should be honored by all, and the marriage bed kept pure, for God will judge the adulterer and all the sexually immoral.*

God says the marriage bed is "pure" or "undefiled," which means *completely free from any contamination.* The Holy Spirit, through the writer of Hebrews, uses this same word back in chapter 7 to describe Jesus Christ Himself. This means that according to God, the creator of sex, we can no more call marital intimacy dirty than we can call Jesus Christ dirty .

The other reason we want to be straightforward and candid about sex with you is that you probably don't have any other Christian environment in which to hear this stuff. There are some excellent Christian books about marital sexuality, but too few read them. So we hope the following information will help you in this very important area of your marriage.

- **Be COURTEOUS**

Never DEMAND. We never have that right. It can do so much harm.

The more aggressive spouse can actually lower the more passive mate's sex drive by being too pursuing. Don't play the Approach-Avoidance game. One of you has a higher sex drive than the other. Are we right? Sometimes you, as the Approacher, feel like you have to ask or hint for sex five or six times in order to get it once. Have you thought about how that looks from your mate's (the Avoider's) point of view? Approach...approach......approach....approach......approach...approach. It's human

Hebrews 13:4 — *Marriage should be honored by all, and the marriage bed kept pure, for God will judge the adulterer and all the sexually immoral.*

Approach-Avoidance game.

Notes

nature to back off from someone who is over-aggressive. That's self protection. This applies to our sexual relationship too. The natural response for the mate with the lower sex drive is to back away — that is, avoid — when the more aggressive mate over-pursues.

Keep this in mind, if you are the Approacher. You may be working very hard at getting the exact opposite of what you want. If you will back off lovingly, not in a guilt producing way (and you know what we mean), you will find that, given time, your more passive partner has a chance to feel safe.

If you are the Avoider in this little game, you too have a responsibility in stopping this dangerous cycle. Affirm your mate for lovingly backing off and remind yourself daily that you no longer have to back away in self protection. Be courageous. Try being the Approacher a few times. You may find it's actually fun!

What are the dangers in playing the Approach-Avoidance Game?

Wife: _____

Husband: _____

Have you been playing this game?

Wife: _____

Husband: _____

What will you do to stop this dangerous game?

Wife: _____

Husband: _____

Biblical guidelines for sexual behavior:

The partner who wants to try new things must not demand these of the other. Here are some guidelines to follow as you consider any sexual behavior:

1. Does the Bible say anything about it? If so, that is definitive. But if the Bible is silent about a particular behavior, the rest of these general biblical guidelines apply.

2. Is it loving? Do you want to do it out of love for your mate or for self gratification?

3. Do you feel peace or guilt after you have finished? There is true guilt — feeling guilty when we should feel guilty. But there is also false guilt — feeling guilty because someone told us we should. Most of us have had well-meaning people tell us things like, "Sex is nasty." "Only bad girls and boys actually enjoy it." "Don't touch yourself there; you'll hurt yourself." These kinds of messages plant false guilt, so source your guilt. Ask God to help you discern whether it is *true* or *false*. You have the responsibility to push yourself beyond your comfort zone, but you never have the right to push your mate beyond theirs.

Notes

4. Is it mutually agreed upon without pressure of any kind? No nagging, no badgering, no begging, no pressure of any kind.

5. Are you being gentle with each other?

6. Is it constructive? Will it add to your oneness and mutual fulfillment, or will it take away from it? 1 Corinthians 10:23 — *Everything is permissible — but not everything is beneficial. Everything is permissible — but not everything is constructive.*

1 Corinthians 10:23 — *Everything is permissible — but not everything is beneficial. Everything is permissible — but not everything is constructive.*

7. Will it enslave one or both of you? If you come to depend on an object in order to have orgasm, you have been enslaved by that object. It is for this reason we strongly discourage the use of vibrators and similar equipment. You don't want to become so dependent on a particular behavior or object that you can't reach orgasm without it. 1 Corinthians 6:12b — *Everything is permissible for me — but I will not be mastered by anything.*

1 Corinthians 6:12b — *Everything is permissible for me — but I will not be mastered by anything.*

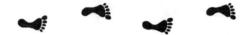

Discuss a sexual behavior you have questions about in light of each guideline.

- **Do not MANIPULATE your mate into making him or her have sex because of guilt or fear or some negative emotion.** That makes the memories of making-love negative and actually lowers the sex drive of the more passive spouse. Your memories of sex are extremely powerful. If the memories are good, the sex drive will improve.

- **Do not INTERRUPT once the fun begins. Don't begin to talk about something UNRELATED,** i.e. "Did you remember to take the trash out?" "Oh, I forgot to put gas in the car today." "Did you air up that tire that was low when you were out with the car this afternoon?" Enough said.

- **CONCENTRATE on your mate.** Focus on them. Show them how important they are to you by becoming engrossed with them and them alone.

- **Do not make FUN of one another.** Needless to say, while you are making love is not the time to point out a spare tire, a new wrinkle or pimple, small breasts, a small penis or anything that would remotely resemble making fun of your mate.

  To laugh at, or be unkind to, your partner at anytime can be devastating, but especially when they are at their most vulnerable. We are such fragile creatures, but never more fragile than when we are naked. Scripture says *Be kind to one another* (Ephesians 4:32) — this applies to the bedroom as well as every other room in the house.

Ephesians 4:32 — *Be kind to one another....*

- **Give COMPLIMENTS and affirmation freely.** Imagine that! You can actually talk while you're making love! In fact, giving compliments during love-making will free you to be a better lover, because it will take your focus off your own perceived inadequacies. Instead, focus your attention on your wife or husband and their pleasure. You can say things like, "I really like to hold you." "I am so thankful for you." "Your body feels so good to me." "I like the way you do that." "I love touching you there." "I love you touching me there."

Notes

> **Write at least one personal application from today's study.**
>
> Wife: _____
>
> Husband: _____
>
> **What does God want you to do to work out this application?**
>
> Wife: _____
>
> Husband: _____

REFLECT TOGETHER: Read Song of Solomon 5:2-6:3 provided below.

PRAY TOGETHER: Lord God, help us talk about this very important subject even when it's hard. We want to learn to enjoy your gift of sex more. Teach us how.

A Problem Arises (5:2-6:3)

Shulamith in soliloquy

I was half asleep when I heard the sound of my beloved husband knocking gently upon the door of our palace chamber. He whispered softly, "I'm back from the country-side, my love, my darling, my perfect wife." My only answer was a mumbled, "I've already gone to sleep, my dear." After all, I had already prepared for bed. I had washed my face and put on my old nightgown.

But then my beloved gently opened the door and I realized I really wanted to see him. I had hesitated too long though. By the time I arose to open the door, he had already walked away, leaving only a gift of my favorite perfume as a reminder of his love for me. Deep within my heart I was reawakened to my love for him. It was just that the fatigue and distractions of the day had brought my hesitating response. I decided to try to find him. I threw on my clothes, went outside the palace and began to call out to him.

But things went from bad to worse. The night watchmen of the city mistook me for a secretive criminal sneaking about in the night. They arrested me in their customarily rough style, then jerking my shawl from my head they saw the face of their newly found suspect—a "great" police force we have!

O, you women of the court, if you see my beloved King, please tell him that I deeply love him, that I am lovesick for him.

Women of the court to Shulamith

What makes your husband better than any other, O fairest of women? What makes him so great that you request this so fervently of us?

Shulamith to women of the court

My beloved husband is strikingly handsome, the first to be noticed among ten thousand men. When I look at him, I see a face with a tan more richly golden than gold itself. His hair is as black as a raven's feathers and as lovely as palm leaves atop the stately palm tree. When I look into his eyes, they are as gentle as doves peacefully resting by streams of water. They are as pure and clear as health can make them.

When he places his cheek next to mine, it is as fragrant as a garden of perfumed flowers. His soft lips are as sweet and scented as lilies dripping with nectar. And how tender are his fingers like golden velvet when he touches me! He is a picture of strength and vitality. His stomach is as firm as a plate of ivory rippling with sapphires. And his legs are as strong and elegant as alabaster pillars set upon pedestals of fine gold. His appearance is like majestic Mt. Lebanon, prominent with its towering cedars.

But beyond all this, the words of his heart are full of charm and delight. He is completely wonderful in every way. This is the one I love so deeply, and this is the one who is my closest friend, O women of the palace court.

Women of the court to Shulamith

Where has your beloved gone, then O fairest among women? Where has he gone? We will help you find him.

Shulamith to women of the court

Oh, I know him well enough to know where he has gone. He likes to contemplate as he walks through the garden and cares for his special little flock among the lilies. I know him, for I belong to him and he belongs to me—this gentle shepherd who pastures his flock among the lilies.

- **Respect one another's need for PRIVACY** — put a lock on the bedroom door. If you are compartmentalized, you may be thinking, "What in the world for? It's not a problem for me." But if you are global, you're probably saying, "Right on." Of course, both of you may be thinking, "Global, compartmentalized — what are they talking about?"

  Compartmental — each event, happening, emotion and thought can be segregated into separate areas or "compartments." The fight in the morning was a separate event from the lovemaking at night and so does not need to be confused or mixed together. For the compartmentalized person, everything is in a different "emotional drawer." You can pull out one, then shut it and pull out a different one. They are each neatly labeled and don't get mixed together.

  Global — all outside and internal events, happenings, emotions and thoughts are intermingled. The fight or harsh words in the morning are brought into the bedroom that night—they can't be separated out into a different compartment. For the global person, everything is in one "emotional drawer." One thing in the "drawer," even if it's stuck in the corner, affects everything else in the entire "drawer."

  For the global partner a lock on the bedroom door when children or other people are in the house is essential. It doesn't matter whether it is only one chance in a million that you might be interrupted in the act of making love — it's still **one,** and a big concern for the global partner that affects her or his ability to enter into the experience fully.

  Not so for the compartmentalized mate — he/she sees the probability as so remote they just shut that "drawer" or compartment of their mind. Often men get stereotyped as compartmentalized and women as global—but this is not always so. We know many couples where the male is global and the female is compartmentalized.

This is the one I love so deeply, and this is the one who is my closest friend.

Day 5

Compartmental

Global

Notes

Find out where the two of you stand in regard to this. If you have a global partner, then tend to their need for the protection of their privacy, even though you see no real need for it. Go get a lock and install it on your bedroom door. That kind of thoughtfulness and consideration is an investment that will reap big dividends.

Wife: **Are you (a) compartmental or (b) global? (Circle one)**
                Your husband is (a) compartmental or (b) global? (Circle one).

Husband: **Are you (a) compartmental or (b) global? (Circle one)**
                Your wife is (a) compartmental or (b) global? (Circle one).

Discuss these opinions and determine the greatest distraction during love-making for the more global partner and try to determine a solution.

_____

_____

- **Come DRESSED for the occasion — or undressed.** Wear what pleases each other — sexy men's underwear, slinky nightgowns, leather, fur, skin, whatever. Be clean and shaved (remember the nubs and the grubs).

What do you most like your partner to wear?

Wife: _____

Husband: _____

- **Make the ATMOSPHERE conducive to love-making.** Candles, soft music, a clean bedroom, perfume on the sheets — all create a romantic atmosphere. Your bedroom is your special place; it should be the prettiest room in the house. Take a little trouble and time to make your intimate time together truly romantic. Both men and women crave romance. The SONG OF SOLOMON proves that. Read about some of the romantic places they made love!

> *Your bedroom should be the prettiest room in the house.*

What could you do to improve the atmosphere of your bedroom?

Wife: _____

Husband: _____

- **Pay ATTENTION** — You are probably thinking, "Well, of course I pay attention!" But what we are talking about is active touching, sensual message, or as the pros call it, sensate focus. Sensate focus is allowing yourself to be aware of the pleasure found in touch. It's giving yourself permission to admit that when your partner touches you in certain places, it feels good.

Sensate focus (or "Pleasuring" as we like to call it) also teaches you that giving your partner pleasure is pleasurable. We will be giving you a pleasuring exercise as a Wrap Up option on Day 7. So, if you choose this option, you will be able to understand what we're talking about in a "hands-on" (pun intended) experience.

Look for Option #2 — Pleasuring.

Agree on a time to do DAY 7 Option #2 (Minimum of one uninterrupted hour needed)

- **Be CREATIVE** — not the same way, the same place, the same time. Change the place, position, time, etc. — Don't be afraid to try new things and new ways.

A professional counseling couple at one GTO Conference suggested making love under the dining room table. We had never thought of doing it *THERE*. But we said, "Who knows what kind of experience it would be unless we try it." Well, we are here to tell you that our dining room table, viewed from underneath, is no great romantic place. It's not finished like the top and there are staples with little pieces of cardboard under them scattered around. There were even some pieces of gum stuck here and there. It was definitely not one of our better ideas.

Now, you may have a totally different kind of table — maybe one with mirrors or glass. Your experience may prove to be entirely different from ours, and you may find yourself going back to your dining room table for more than meals. But whether you make love under your dining room table or not, find some creative places and new "come on" ways to enjoy your sexual intimacy.

Think about the most creative love-making experience with your mate. Talk together about it.

God gave sexual intimacy to you as a married couple as His gift of pleasure to be enjoyed to its fullest potential within the bonds of marriage. He designed it to be enjoyable to both the husband and the wife, and that enjoyment includes romance. Keep the Ann Landers' survey in mind as you continue to court each other. Get back into that **WIN** mode and **stay** there.

Get back in the WIN mode and stay there.

Remember love-making is a **skill**, and skills get better when we **practice** them. Especially when we have fun practicing them. One of the most wonderful aspects of sex is that God created it in the context of safety and permanence. You see, God expects us to work on perfecting our love-making skills with our mates our whole lives through, protected inside the boundary of marriage. This means we can be honest and trust one another with our sexuality. It also means we have the liberty within this God-ordained boundary to try different and new intimacies, for we know if one idea does not work for us, we can throw it out and try something else. This is God's plan: that our sexual intimacy be safe and free and celebrative!

This is God's plan: that our sexual intimacy be safe and free and celebrative!

Notes

> **Write at least one personal application from today's study.**
>
> Wife: _____
>
> Husband: _____
>
> **What does God want you to do to work out this application?**
>
> Wife: _____
>
> Husband: _____

REFLECT TOGETHER: Read Song of Solomon 6:4-13 provided below.

PRAY TOGETHER: Thank You, Lord, for creating sexual intimacy and giving it to us to celebrate our oneness. Help us learn to enjoy one another more in new intimate ways.

The Problem Resolved (6:4-13)

King to Shulamith

My darling, did you know that you are as lovely as the city of Tirzah glittering on the horizon of night? No, more than that you are as lovely as the fair city of Jerusalem. Your beauty is as breathtaking as scores of marching warriors. (No, do not look at me like that now, my love; I have more to tell you.)

Do you remember what I said on our wedding night? It is still just as true. Your hair is as captivating as the flowing movement of a flock descending a mountain at sunset. Your lovely smile is as cheerful and sparkling as pairs of young lambs scurrying up from a washing. And your cheeks still flush with the redness of the pomegranate's hue.

King in soliloquy

The palace is full of its aristocratic ladies and dazzling mistresses belonging to the noblemen of the court. But my lovely wife, my dove, my flawless one, is unique among them all. And these ladies and mistresses realize it too. They too must praise her. As we approached them in my chariot, they eventually perceived that we were together again.

Women of the court to one another

Who is that on the horizon like the dawn, now fair as the moon but now plain and bright as the sun and as majestic as scores of marching warriors?

Shulamith in the chariot in soliloquy

I went down to the garden where I knew my King would be. I wanted to see if the fresh flowers and fruits of spring had come. I wanted to see if our reunion might bring a new season of spring love for my husband and me. Before I knew what happened, we were together again and riding past the palace court in his chariot. I can still hear them calling out, "Return, return O Shulamith; return that we may gaze at the beloved wife of the King."

King to Shulamith

How they love to look upon the incomparable grace and beauty of a queen.

Quickly scan the "Most Asked Sex Questions" at the end of this chapter (pages 149-156). Pick 2 or 3 of interest, read the answers and discuss them with your mate.

Wife: #'s _____ Husband: #'s _____

Day 6

REFLECT TOGETHER: Read Song of Solomon 7:1-10 provided below.

PRAY TOGETHER: Father, some of these questions are embarrassing to read and even more so to talk about. But help us talk about them, and help us apply truth to our sexual relationship where we need it.

In the Royal Bedroom (7:1-10)

King to Shulamith

How delicate are your feet in sandals, my royal prince's daughter! The curves of your hips are as smooth and graceful as the curves of elegant jewelry, perfectly fashioned by the skillful hands of a master artist. As delectable as a feast of wine and bread is your stomach—your navel is like the goblet of wine, and your stomach is the soft warm bread. Your breasts are as soft and gentle as fawns grazing among lilies, twins of a gazelle, and your neck is smooth as ivory to the touch. Your eyes are as peaceful as the pools of water in the valley of Heshbon, near the gate of the populous city.

Yet how strong you walk in wisdom and discretion. You are, indeed, as majestically beautiful as Mt. Carmel. Your long flowing hair is as cool and soft as silken threads draped round my neck, yet strong enough to bind me as your captive forever. How lovely and delightful you are, my dear, and how especially delightful is your love! You are as graceful and splendrous as a palm tree silhouetted against the sky. Yes, a palm tree—and your breasts are its luscious fruit.

I think I shall climb my precious palm tree and take its tender fruit gently into my hand. O my precious one, let your breasts be like the tender fruit to my taste, and now let me kiss you and breathe your fragrant breath. Let me kiss you and taste a sweetness better than wine.

How strong you walk in wisdom and discretion.

Shulamith to King

And savor every drop, my lover, and let its sweetness linger long upon your lips, and let every drop of this wine bring a peaceful sleep.

Shulamith in soliloquy

I belong to my beloved husband and he loves me from the depths of his soul.

Notes

Day 7

WRAP-UP: There are two Wrap Up options to choose from. Option 1 is a sexual intimacy discussion which will give you the opportunity to talk about areas of your sexual intimacy you may never have discussed before. Option 2 is the pleasuring exercise we mentioned on Day 5. Remember you will need a whole hour of uninterrupted time for this option. You may decide to do both options, one now and one later. It's up to you. Just be sure you make a couple decision about how you are going to do this day's interaction.

OPTION #1

<u>SEXUAL INTIMACY DISCUSSION</u>

<u>Directions</u>: Complete the thoughts individually and alone, then share and discuss them with your spouse. If some of the questions are too intimidating, save them until later. But discuss as many as you can.

1. Before we were married, what I looked forward to most as I thought about our future sexual relationship was:

2. Before we were married, my greatest fantasy about you (or us) was:

3. In my mind, the best time(s) we have had sexually have been in (location):

4. To me, sex would be even more inviting if I:

5. To me, sex would be even more inviting if you:

6. The best time of day for me to "make love" is:

7. The worst time of the day for me to be sexually excited is:

8. At times when my sexual responses are slow, or I'm not in the mood, I'd generally like for you to:

9. The way (or words) I'd like to hear from you when you want to "make love" is (are):

10. When other people are around and you are thinking about "making love" let me know by:

11. When preparing for "making love," the most exciting things you can do for me are:

12. You turn me "on" the most when you:

13. I'd like you to touch me in the following ways when we "make love":

14. I'd like you to say the following things when we "make love":

15. With only positive growth in mind, the areas I believe we need to work on improving in our sexual relationship are:

OPTION #2

<u>PLEASURING</u>

This optional exercise should be fully agreed upon on a transparent level, otherwise it should be postponed until both spouses feel free to participate. This option is the experiencing of "pleasuring." Make sure your room is comfortably warm and you allow yourself the luxury of time (one hour minimum). Remember that continual feedback on the level of pleasure experienced is essential for your spouse to know what "pleasures" you the most. COMMUNICATE, COMMUNICATE, COMMUNICATE.

This exercise is primarily a communication exercise. Sex therapists often use it with couples having to agree beforehand that there will be no intercourse associated with the experience. Whether or not you are open to this ending in sexual intercourse is something you should discuss **prior** to entering into the exercise. Either is O.K.

To begin, both partners need to disrobe to nudeness. One partner, either one, should lie face down on the bed while the other starts touching at the feet and slowly works his/her way up the back side of their partner's body. Continual feedback is needed as to the amount of "pleasure" the pleasuree is receiving. We suggest a range of 1 to 10 with 10 being the greatest pleasure. The genitals are not to be included in this exercise — you **know** they're a 10!

The partner doing the touching, the pleasurer, should vary the touch from light to medium to heavy and should experiment with front of hands, back of hands and even cheeks and tongue for a variety of touch. Pay attention to the 6's and above — these are areas you should remember for future reference.

When the first partner has traversed the entire length of the body, then trade positions. If you cover the whole length of your partner's body in less than 10 minutes, you are going too fast! Slow down! When the process is complete for the second pleasuree, then the one who started lying face down should again lie down, this time on his/her back.

The process again should proceed with the first pleasurer starting at the feet and working his/her way to the top of the partner's head (don't be too quick in leaving the feet!). Again allow around 15 minutes for this one process and get continual feedback concerning the amount of pleasure given. Once this portion is complete then again trade positions and have the second pleasurer traverse from toe to head getting feedback all the while.

This whole four-part process should take around an hour to accomplish. If you cannot devote that much time to this option before one or both of you is overly tired, then schedule this option for another time when you can.

REFLECT TOGETHER: Read Song of Solomon 7:11-8:14 provided below.

Pray together: Thank you for the model of married love you have given us in Song of Solomon. Help us learn to enjoy one another like these two lovers.

In the Countryside (7:11-8:14)

Shulamith to King

Spring's magic flowers have perfumed the pastel countryside and enchanted the hearts of all lovers. Come, my precious lover; every delicious fruit of spring is ours for the taking. Let us return to our springtime cottage of towering cedars and cypresses where the plush green grass is its endless carpet and the orchards are its shelves for every luscious fruit. I have prepared a basketful for you, my love, to give you in a sumptuous banquet of love beneath the sky.

I wish we could pretend you were my brother, my real little brother. I could take you outside to play, and playfully kiss you whenever I wished. But then I could also take your hand and bring you inside and you could teach me and share with me your deep understanding of life. Then how I wish you would lay me down beside you and love me.

Shulamith to women of the court

I encourage you not to try to awaken love until love is pleased to awaken itself. How wonderful it is when it blossoms in the proper season.

Shulamith to King

Do you remember where our love began? Under the legendary sweetheart tree, of course, where every love begins and grows and then brings forth a newborn child, yet not without the pain of birth. Neither did our love begin without the pain, the fruitful pain of birth. O, my darling lover, make me your most precious possession held securely in your arms, held close to your heart. True love is as strong and irreversible as the onward march of death. True love never ceases to care, and it would no more give up the beloved than the grave would give up the dead.

The fires of true love can never be quenched because the source of its flame is God himself. Even were a river of rushing water to pass over it, the flame would yet shine forth. Of all the gifts in the world, this priceless love is the most precious and possessed only by those to whom it is freely given. For no man could purchase it with money, even the richest man in the world.

King to Shulamith

Do you remember how it was given to us?

Shulamith to King

My love, I truly believe I was being prepared for it long before I even dreamed of romance. I remember hearing my brothers talking one evening. It was shortly after my father died, and they were concerned to raise me properly, to prepare me for the distant day of marriage. They were like a roomful of fathers debating about what to do with their only daughter. They finally resolved simply to punish and restrict me if I were promiscuous but to reward and encourage me if I were chaste. How thankful I am that I made it easy for them. I could see even when I was very young that I wanted to keep myself for the one dearest man in my life.

And then you came. And everything I ever wanted I found in you. There I was, working daily in the vineyard my brothers had leased from you. And you "happened" to pass by and see me. That's how our love began.

I remember when I worked in that vineyard that a thousand dollars went to you and two hundred dollars for the ones taking care of its fruit for you. Now I am your vineyard, my lover, and I gladly give the entire thousand dollars of my worth to you; I give myself completely, withholding nothing of my trust, my thoughts, my care, my love. But my dear King, let us not forget that two hundred dollars belongs to the ones

How wonderful it is when [love] blossoms in the proper season.

147

who took care of the fruit of my vineyard for you. How thankful we must be to my family who helped prepare me for you.

King to Shulamith

My darling, whose home is the fragrant garden, everyone listens for the sound of your voice, but let me alone hear it now.

Shulamith to King

Hurry, then, my beloved. And again be like a gazelle or young stag on the hills of my perfumed breasts.*

*Taken from A SONG FOR LOVERS by S. Craig Glickman. c 1976 by Inter-Varsity Christian Fellowship of the USA and used by the author's permission.

GROUP DISCUSSION: If this study is being used in a group setting, the questions and answers on pages 149-156 can be discussed in the group. If this is too threatening, the questions can simply be used as a home assignment. These same questions are the ones referred to in Day 6.

Have a frank discussion

MOST ASKED SEX QUESTIONS
WITH ANSWERS

1. It's been said that "It doesn't matter where you get your appetite as long as you eat at home." If it really doesn't matter, then is it okay to get one's sexual appetite revved up by X-rated movies, Playboy, Cosmopolitan, etc. as long as you only "do it" with your spouse?

We disagree with the statement quoted. It **does matter** where you get your appetite; it matters a great deal. Jesus explicitly forbade pornography in His teaching in Matthew 5:27-28 — *You have heard that it was said, 'Do not commit adultery.' But I tell you that anyone who looks at a woman lustfully has already committed adultery with her in his heart.* Pornography's **design** is to encourage the people who watch it to engage in illicit sex. Have you ever heard of pornographic material showing a husband and wife enjoying normal, marital love-making? No, it's **intent** is to make us *lust*. Lusting is not the simple acknowledgment, "God really made a beautiful body when He made that one." It's not even the biological changes that are involuntarily triggered by pictures of nude bodies. It is allowing your mind to **dwell** on the pictures and **nurture** the arousal. Jesus did not condemn lust because He wanted to spoil our pleasure. He, our Creator, knows how devastatingly **dangerous and destructive** it is when we allow it to get a hold on us.

Because pornography depicts sex devoid of love, commitment, mutuality or responsibility, when we watch it, it imprints on our minds those same values, as well as permanent mental pictures. Even Christian couples who think they use pornography to *enhance* their sex lives, will eventually begin to **use** their partners and focus on **self gratification** instead of focusing on **shared pleasure** and the joy of **mutual love**. Pornography is also **addictive**. People who use it, find they need more and more of it, and eventually believe they cannot function sexually without it. If you have allowed pornography into your life, you have welcomed in a powerful enemy. But it is an enemy that **can be defeated** by the power of the Holy Spirit. It'll take more than prayer, it will take your consistent obedience to the Word of God. Read Chapter 2 for instructions and Scriptures on how to take control over your thoughts (as 2 Corinthians 10:5 puts it, *take captive every thought to make it obedient to Christ).* Use those thought-stopping techniques, decisively replace them with positive memories of mutual love-making with your spouse, and depend on the Holy Spirit to **renew** your mind.

2. What about fantasizing?

This question was partially answered in the previous response. Fantasizing about having sex with someone other than your mate is lust, and, therefore, sin. However, fantasizing about making love with your **mate** is perfectly permissible. In fact, we encourage it. Throughout Song of Solomon (which, remember, was inspired by the Holy Spirit), Shulamith and Solomon spent a great deal of time thinking erotic thoughts about each other. Fantasizing about an especially wonderful memory of sexual intimacy, or a fanciful dream of one, with your **mate** before and during love-making can enhance your mutual pleasure and fulfillment.

3. If my wife needs manual stimulation of her clitoris during foreplay every time we make love, is this abnormal? Shouldn't normal intercourse arouse her enough?

Most women need clitoral stimulation in addition to vaginal intercourse in order to reach orgasm. In fact, according to THE HITE REPORT: A NATIONWIDE STUDY OF FEMALE SEXUALITY (by Shere Hite, published by Macmillan), only 30% of all women can regularly have orgasm with intercourse alone. But remember, husbands, your wife is not a gadget you can turn on with the flick of her "clitoral switch." There still must be foreplay: that close, tender, intimate time of caressing, kissing and stroking one another's bodies. As foreplay continues, you can begin to gently manipulate your wife's clitoris.

Since not all women need or desire clitoral stimulation, communication is essential in this matter. Wives, we urge you to be honest about your needs with your husband. Only by being honest about your needs, will they be met. Do you need and enjoy clitoral stimulation — all the time, or just some of the time? Do you need more foreplay before clitoral stimulation? Talk about this as a couple — lovingly, with the desire to meet each other's needs, and a goal of mutual fulfillment.

4. Should we generally try to have orgasm together?

Having simultaneous orgasm is great when it happens, but very few couples can experience it on a regular basis. This means, if most of us make simultaneous orgasm the goal of our lovemaking, we will be disappointed **most** of the time. Feeling unsuccessful so often will certainly take its toll on our sex life. But our goal for love-making is not to get the timing right; it is mutual satisfaction, fulfillment and expression of love and closeness. So, don't concentrate on getting the timing right, concentrate on loving each other and meeting one another's needs.

5. You mentioned that if one partner is overly aggressive about wanting sex, the other one will retreat even more. Well, what if the aggressive partner backs off and the passive partner still isn't interested?

Since we don't know the particulars of this situation, we need to ask some questions of both the overly aggressive and overly passive mate. First, some questions for the overly aggressive partner: How often do you give your partner signals that you want sex? Is your desire frequency overwhelming to your mate? How do you treat your mate during the day? Are you disrespectful and rude, or loving and tender? Have you studied the art of love-making, and do you spend enough time in foreplay, lovingly trying to meet your mate's needs? Do you try to make your mate feel guilty when she/he does not respond sexually? Is there unresolved resentment and anger between you? Do you help your mate, without being asked, with burdensome chores that make her/him too tired to make love? Any of these things, and many more we don't have room to mention, can adversely affect your mate's sexual response. But **you do have control** over every possibility we asked about? You need to examine yourself and your motives, honestly admit what you need to change, and then do something about it.

Now, some questions for the overly passive mate: Were you taught sex is dirty and "nice girls" or "nice boys" don't do "things like that"? Were you taught women aren't supposed to like sex? Do you immediately shut down erotic thoughts? Do you feel God made women to be sexually passive — that's just the way it is? Are you harboring resentment toward your mate? Do you see withholding sex as a means to gain control in one area of your relationship? Is sexual intimacy a priority to you? How often do you ever have orgasm when you and your mate make love? So many questions to take into account; so many possibilities that can affect the way you view sex. Please note: some of these questions were directed to wives, but some were directed to **both**. Although sexual passivity affects more women than men, it is not exclusively a female problem.

God intended sex for pleasure. It is His gift to both husbands and wives. It's not a "dirty" gift — it is a **beautiful gift**. The trouble is that the world has distorted God's gift and tried to make it look ugly. Perhaps some of that distortion has affected you. Whatever your particular situation, if as a couple, you cannot find mutual, workable solutions for an unsatisfactory sex life, we urge you not to be content with status quo. Seek help. There are many books available with detailed solutions for specific sexual problems: books like INTENDED FOR PLEASURE by Ed and Gaye Wheat, THE GIFT OF SEX by Clifford and Joyce Penner and THE INTIMATE MARRIAGE by Howard and Charlotte Clinebell. If you need more help than books can give, then we encourage you to seek Christian sexual counseling, which has an extremely high success rate. Your sexual happiness is very important to the One who made you a sexual being. Don't snub His gift.

6. How can you include God in your sex life?

God does not shut His eyes in embarrassment when married couples make love. He's right there; and He approves. He declares in Hebrews 13:4 that *the marriage bed is pure* or *undefiled*. If you are following His principles of real love, you don't need to be ashamed to make love in His presence. As Christians, we need to be more aware and acknowledge His place in our marriage...even in our bedrooms. Have you ever prayed together during afterglow? It's a wonderful time to pray, a time of intense feelings of closeness. It's a good time to express your thanks to the Lord for one another, for the precious gift of your mate and for the intimacy you can share.

7. What is the most loving and effective way to tell your mate, who is presently trying to seduce you, that you are not feeling like making love tonight?

Gently...very gently. You could say something like, "I'm too tired to get much out of sex tonight, but if you will wait 'til tomorrow, I can promise you a good time!" Then follow through with your promise and plan toward a romantic encounter. Just make sure "Not tonight, Dear" does not become a habit nor an excuse for not wanting to make the effort. Catch a nap, turn the TV off earlier, change your schedule — do whatever you have to do to make love-making a priority in your marriage.

8. How important should spontaneity be in love-making?

Spontaneity is highly overrated! Some of the best lovemaking encounters are those which are planned for and anticipated by both mates. Usually, women are not quick igniters sexually. A woman needs time to think erotically about her husband, time to reflect upon that sweet word he whispered in her ear at breakfast. (Husbands, take note.) Sexually, most women are like a tea kettle. If a tea kettle sits on a shelf all day, it will take a lot of heat to bring the water to boil. But if the tea kettle has been simmering on a back burner all day, it doesn't take long at all for the water to boil. Often a woman needs time to "simmer," and planning toward a romantic, sexual encounter allows that to happen. The saying that "SEX BEGINS IN THE KITCHEN" is true. (You may want to read the book by the same title — see our reading list in **Appendix D**.)

Some couples think that after they get married, only the "spontaneous" times really count. That is simply not true! Planning for romantic encounters enhances enjoyment. And besides, with some of the hectic schedules that many couples have today, planning for those special encounters may be the **only** way they are able to occur.

9. Is masturbation OK under any circumstances? When? Does the Bible say anything about it?

This is a very controversial subject, which makes us wonder why God never said anything about it in Scripture. But He didn't; so we have to be careful with being authoritative concerning something God is silent about. The Catholic church for many years used the story in Genesis 38:6-10 — known as "the sin of Onan" — to prove God's condemnation of masturbation. The problem with this, however, is that Onan's sin was not masturbation, it was his unwillingness to fulfill the Law and give his deceased brother's wife, Tamar, offspring. You see, Onan didn't want his older brother's child (as the law would consider Tamar's baby) to inherit all the good stuff his own son stood to receive. So he acted deceitfully with Tamar. He had the fun of sex, but escaped the responsibility of it by interrupting the sex act and "spilling his seed on the ground" (*coitus interruptus*). God condemned his selfishness and deceit and took his life. For many years, using this as a proof-text of the evils of masturbation, young people were warned that it caused mental illness, blindness and even death.

Since God chose not to mention it specifically in His Word, we must see what general principals apply to the act of masturbation. Remember the guidelines listed on pages 137-138? Let's take a look at masturbation in light of those principals.

(1) Is it loving? Masturbation is basically a self-centered act. You can gratify your own urges without depending on anyone else. You can actually reach orgasm more quickly than with vaginal intercourse, and you don't have to bother with all the fuss and trouble of fulfilling your mate. So, we'd have to say that if you use masturbation as a substitute for responsible sexual intimacy with your mate, it is definitely wrong. It is not loving.

(2) Do we feel peace or guilt after we have finished? Most people feel guilt. Some feel overwhelming guilt. Romans 14:23 clearly teaches that if we act against our conscience, it is sin. We must qualify some of the felt guilt, however, because at least part of it is probably due to the false teaching mentioned earlier.

(3) Is it mutually agreed upon without pressure of any kind? People who masturbate on a regular basis usually do so in solitude and secret. Though we can see that an occasional act of masturbation might be mutually agreed upon in cases of extreme illness or extended separations.

(4) Are we being gentle with each other? Actually, married couples who regularly practice masturbation, are **excluding** each other. To deny your partner regular, loving sexual intimacy because you are substituting self-gratification, is certainly not being gentle with them. In such cases, masturbation is being used as a weapon against the spouse.

(5) Is it constructive? Will it add to your oneness or take away from it? Remember what Paul said in 1 Corinthians 10:23: *...not everything is beneficial.* When one or both partners use masturbation to avoid true intimacy with one another, it certainly will tear down their oneness, and will not be beneficial.

(6) Will it enslave me? If masturbation is used regularly for some of the negative reasons we have mentioned, then it has the power to enslave.

If for some reason, you are faced with situations in which sexual intercourse is not the loving, or perhaps practical, choice, may we suggest a better way than masturbation? We recommend that one partner manually stimulate the other to orgasm. While in one sense, the stimulating partner is not being actively sexual, the couple is still experiencing loving sexual intimacy. You see, sex is not a way of **performing**, it is a way of **loving**.

10. What about oral or anal sex?

We need to talk about these one at a time. The Bible is silent about oral sex. Some say the Song of Solomon alludes to it, but we're not so sure. Again, we should handle this subject by applying the guidelines in III. A. Is it loving? Do we feel peace or guilt after we have finished? Is it mutually agreed upon without pressure of any kind? And are we being gentle with each other? Each couple must decide for themselves if oral sex should be part of their love-making. If these guidelines are met, then how a married couple chooses to mutually express their love behind their closed bedroom door is up to them. We do have one word of caution: don't allow oral sex to replace intercourse. There is a feeling of closeness in vaginal intercourse that oral sex cannot duplicate.

Anal sex is not specifically discussed in Scripture, however, we know it is involved when homosexuality is spoken of. Unlike oral sex, there are medical objections to anal sex. Small fissures can open in rectal tissue and cause bleeding and infections. We do not recommend it, but neither do we have real Biblical grounds to condemn it. So again, we point you to the guidelines stated above.

11. Will it still be fun when we're old and gray?

The factor which determines continued sexual intimacy as we grow older, is our consistency of sexual intimacy all along. Couples naturally slow down sexually as they age. Let's face it — everything about us slows down! But even though older couples may not be able to have intercourse as often as they used to, they still can have a full, satisfying, enjoyable sex-life. As long as we live, we continue to be sexual creatures...even at 80 years old and beyond.

This reminds us of a funny story we heard a few years ago. A local newspaper reports it to be a true story. It happened in a small town in southern California well known for its abundant Senior Citizen Population and mobile home parks. One summer evening, in a Senior Retirement park, some men were standing around talking about the good old days, when they heard a faint cry for help. "It sounds like it's coming from Ed and Gracie's. What could be wrong?" The men grabbed their golf clubs and cautiously approached Ed and Gracie's mobile home. Again, they heard Gracie's cry, "Help! Help!" Finding the front door unlocked, they slowly and vigilantly crept inside. "Sounds like it's coming from the bedroom," one whispered. With golf clubs raised, they tiptoed to the bedroom, determined to surprise the culprit. When they flung open the bedroom door, there was Gracie, naked as a jay bird lying on the bed with her wrists tied to the headboard with pink ribbons. "Ed! Help Ed!" she pleaded. There in a heap beside the bed was Ed, wearing only a Bat Man cape and mask. It seems he had knocked himself out on the ceiling while jumping from the dresser to the bed. Ed and Gracie moved to Florida shortly after this incident.

12. Should you be submissive to your spouse even when you don't want to make love and they do?

Making love is all about **loving**. And that means that sometimes you defer to your mate out of love and **have** sex because he/she desires it, even though you don't feel particularly passionate. It also means that you will sometimes defer to your mate and **not have** sex because he/she doesn't desire it, even though you do. 1 Corinthians 7:3-4 teaches that *The husband should fulfill his marital duty to his wife, and likewise the wife to her husband. The wife's body does not belong to her alone but also to her husband. In the same way, the husband's body does not belong to him alone but also to his wife.* Paul teaches a **mutual giving** in these verses. Not one partner demanding or refusing sex, but a mutual giving of themselves to their partners for the benefit of their oneness.

We must confess that when we first started teaching GTO marriage enrichment retreats, we believed, practiced and taught the philosophy that anytime one mate wanted sex, the other should give it. But after a time, we noticed something negative happening in our relationship. Bette's sex drive was lowering dramatically. After talking at length about this, we concluded that if one partner simply **gives** in a majority of their sexual encounters, after a while sex is not going to be very exciting to that mate. On the contrary, negative memories of unfulfilled sex build over time to cause that mate's sex drive to lower. We were actually sabotaging our own sexual relationship. Also, we weren't taking into consideration the whole context of the 1 Corinthian passage. Both partners are urged to give themselves to each other. And sometimes that means to **have** sex, and sometimes that means to **not** have sex. In the answer to the question about masturbation, we suggested that one mate can lovingly bring the other to orgasm by manual stimulation. This kind of loving, sexually intimate response can also be used by couples when one partner is passionately desiring sex and the other is not, or when one mate is physically unable because of health problems.

13. What is "improper" when sexually relating to your mate, in terms of "Let the marriage bed be undefiled"?

There are definitely certain sexual behaviors that are strictly forbidden by Scripture: adultery, fornication, incest, prostitution, bestiality, lust (i.e. use of pornography, etc.) and homosexuality and lesbianism. If any of these are brought into a marriage, the "marriage bed" will be defiled — become impure. Besides these obvious sins, however, we must also take into consideration unloving, selfish behavior. Do we bring self-gratifying demands into our marriage bed? Do we lay guilt on our mates when they don't meet our sexual expectations? Are we rough, rude or unkind with our partners? We must be careful to not allow selfishness to defile our marriage bed, as well as obviously deviant behaviors.

14. What about making love during menstruation? Is the woman "clean" during that period and should we abstain from sex during that time?

There is no medical reason why sex during menstruation is harmful. However, it usually isn't comfortable for the wife because of swollen, tender breasts and sex organs; and can be downright painful for some women, especially during the first three days of menstrual flow. It also isn't very esthetic. But the ceremonial law concerning it was given before showers made cleanliness so easy to maintain. This is one of those areas you will have to decide about as a couple. Talk about it without putting pressure on one another, and decide for yourselves.

For some women, the time of menstruation is their most sexually desirous time. If this is your dilemma, because it still is not esthetic to you or your husband because of blood-flow, you might speak with your doctor about using a diaphragm birth control device.

15. What do you do to adjust to differing sex drives? And are men's sex drives always higher than women's?

Differences in sexual desire is the primary sexual problem of the nineties. To discuss it properly would take an entire chapter, so please understand, we are barely scratching the surface. If sexual desire differences are causing serious difficulty in your relationship, we encourage you to talk further with your pastor or a counselor. Sexual desire differences improve greatly with proven programs of counseling and behavioral exercises. So, don't sit back and **wish** things were different — things **can** be different, but you must take the proper steps.

First, we must make one thing clear. Men often have higher sex drives than women, but not always. There are many cases in which the wife has the greater sex drive. It is a myth we have lived under for many years that men are always ready, no matter what. They aren't; neither do they have to be.

The low sex desire therapy program we mentioned has basically four steps. The **first** one simply helps a person become aware of, and verbalize, how he or she feels about sex and about being sexual. The **second** step is to help the person discover why he or she feels that way — finding out where those feelings come from. The **third** involves changing Thot-Talk — confronting distorted ideas and replacing them with positive ideas and true assumptions. The **final** step is a process of reintroducing sexual arousal. Many people who have low sexual desire, have somewhere along the way, turned off their sexual awareness. They have shutdown their sexual feelings for so long, they have to be reintroduced to them.

One exercise is to have them privately **examine themselves** in a mirror. Psalm 139 reminds us that we are "fearfully and wonderfully made." We don't need to be ashamed of our bodies; God does good work, and we can honestly thank Him for the way He made us — genitals and all. Another practice is **Kegel exercises**. These increase a woman's sexual sensations. They also have several other benefits: they prevent bladder and uterus prolapse, and help women with loss of bladder control. You can identify the muscle wall being strengthened with these exercises by cutting off flow of urine while urinating. After you learn how, you should Kegel around 50 times a day. And you can Kegel anywhere, anytime, no one will ever know. One woman told us everytime she comes to a red light, she Kegels until the light turns green. Another exercise is called **sensate focus**. The third Couple Sharing option for this session is a **sensate focus** exercise, which you will hear more about before being dismissed. The good news is that low sexual desire is curable. Both the husband and wife must work toward **solutions**, but they **are** reachable.

16. One is a morning person — the other a night person. The "owl" wants to make love at night when the "dove" is bushed. The "dove" wants to make love in the morning when the "owl" can hardly get their eyes open. How can sex and intimacy work itself into such an environment?

What do you think about afternoons? Seriously, I can remember being given a few quarters to go to movies as a child. The point is, sexual intimacy must be made a priority in our marriages. We need to **make** time for it and for one another, even if we must go to great lengths to do so. It's more important than Monday night football or movie of the week, so turn the TV off early and make love before the dove is bushed. A nice back rub can go a long way to revitalize that sweet bird. Sexual intimacy is also more important than forty more winks, so splash some water on your face or take a shower to wake up a little earlier. Our sleeping patterns are habits — habits we can vary a little bit if it's important enough to do so. Sex and intimacy **can not work itself** into our relationship. **We** have to work it in.

17. Is it really true that women are more romantic than men, or do men really need and desire romance as well?

Women **feel** the need for romance more, but one doesn't have to feel a need to actually have it. Our western society has to accept a lot of the blame for squashing men's realization of their need for romance. The media perpetuates the nonsense by glorifying self-reliant, strong, silent types like Rambo and Superman. The truth is, men have been desensitized to many of their own feelings. Women have been confused by this whole "male image" thing, too. And in turn heap more confusion on their husbands, expecting them to be always strong and have the answers to life's problems one minute, and then be intuitively sensitive to their needs the next.

Solomon certainly didn't seem to have any problem expressing his romantic feelings. Both he and Shulamith were passionately romantic. The Song of Solomon leaves no doubts as to the answer to this question. Solomon was a very romantic guy. And God gave us a whole book, intimately describing Solomon and Shulamith's romantic, married love. With this in mind, we believe God must think it's O.K. for men to feel romantic, don't you?

18. What is "normal" in terms of how often a couple should have sex?

"Normal" frequency is how often making love is **mutually pleasurable** for each couple. According to Dr. Ed Wheat, two to three times per week is "average," but normal and average are two different things. Also, "normal" doesn't necessarily stay static throughout your married life. Lots of factors — outside stresses, children, aging — can change your normal frequency in different periods of your life. However, your "normal" in each of these periods, remains what is mutually satisfying and pleasurable to you as a couple.

The number of times you and your mate have sex will even change from week to week. As you are already aware, women have hormone cycles. Female hormones do more than cause menstruation once a month; they also cause changes in desire. The simplest way to explain a woman's monthly hormone cycle is to describe it in terms of seasons: Spring, Summer, Fall and Winter. If hormones are cooperating, this is also the weekly sequence of a woman's passion. Spring: passion begins to blossom after menstruation. Summer: passion is hot. Fall: passion begins to slow down. And winter: menstruation puts passion on hold. Each week to ten days is another season. Not all women follow the same sequence of seasons each month, so we recommend, Wives, that you carefully note your seasons on a calendar for several months. It's extremely freeing for couples to know what season the wife is in. As we get to know ourselves and our mates better, it gives us more understanding and acceptance of one another.

19. How much sex is too much sex?

Too much sex is when the frequency desires of one partner become more than the other partner can handle — that is, when it becomes unpleasant and burdensome for the less desirous mate. How much sex is that? Only you as a couple can answer that. For some couples, fourteen times per week might be too much, while for other couples, two times per week is too much. Other factors, some of them mentioned in the answers regarding differing sex drives and sexual aggressiveness, should also be taken into consideration here.

20. Is the use of massage type items acceptable?

We have a genuine concern about vibrators, because they can become a fetish. A fetish is the "misdirected association of sexual excitement with an object" (A CHRISTIAN GUIDE TO SEXUAL COUNSELING, by Mary Ann Mayo, published by Zondervan). In other words, you can become so dependent on a vibrator or any other "sex toy," that eventually you can't enjoy sex without them. That's why fetishes are dangerous.

21. Should sexually intimate matters be held confidential and not discussed outside the bedroom unless mutually agreed upon?

Absolutely. You need to feel completely safe with one another, both physically and emotionally. This means being able to trust that your sexual intimacy remains private. The only exception to this rule is in the case of counseling. Sexual matters may need to be brought to light in order for therapy to be effective. However, even in such cases, we hope that the other spouse would agree to that invasion of privacy.

22. How do you suggest working a sexual life with intimacy around children?

It is imperative to a healthy marriage that you consider your sexual intimacy a **priority**. It isn't easy to maintain a passionate love-life when you have active, nosy children, but it is possible. In fact, if you really want to be a good parent, the best thing you can do for your children is to maintain a solid husband-wife relationship. This is how you give them real **security**. They need to know that Mommy and Daddy truly love each other. They also need to know that your marriage relationship is **primary**. This means except for emergencies, your children should not sleep in your bed. If they are ill and come into your room during the night, comfort them then put them to sleep back in their own bed. If they need further attention, go to them — even sleeping in their bed if necessary.

You should also put a good lock on your bedroom door. And teach your children that Mommy and Daddy's room is your special room and that sometimes you need private time together without them. This is not harmful at all for your children. On the contrary, it is very healthy for them.

23. How do I overcome my shyness of my naked body? I feel that I have too many physical flaws and I feel self-conscious. Do other people feel this way?

Just about everybody feels this way to some extent. It's why men get hair transplants and women get breast implants. It's why plastic surgeons make hundreds of thousands of dollars a year — because people want to perfect their body's imperfections. There are a few questions you should ask yourself, however, the main one being, "Why do I feel this way; where did these feelings come from?" Did your parents instill a feeling of shame connected with nakedness? Did they convey the concept, verbally or non-verbally, that your body was somehow dirty or ugly? Parents don't always realize they give such impressions by their embarrassment over their child's or their own nudity. Instead of teaching that our bodies are private, they often end up conveying the impression that our bodies are shameful. Regardless of such early training, your concept of your body can change — with work. One suggestion is to take time weekly to examine your nude body, in private, in front of a full-length mirror. As we mentioned in the answer to the sex drive question, read Psalm 139 while you're standing in front of the mirror. Thank God for making your body so wonderfully — even with it's faults. He won't be a bit embarrassed to see you pray nude. Repeat this exercise at least once a week until you no longer feel overly sensitive about your anatomy; and follow up with a once-a-month "viewing" until you feel comfortable with yourself.

24. How can I as an "ever ready" person, down shift to allow for foreplay or stimulate my spouse through the foreplay process more quickly?

Let's see if we have this question straight. You want to know how to hurry your wife through foreplay, so you can get to the good stuff, right? Someone, it seems, has misled you about foreplay...you see, it **is** part of the good stuff! Foreplay is part of making love, not the preamble to it. An extended time of foreplay can be intensely enjoyable for both you and your wife, for it is during this time of stroking and caressing that closeness and trust grow. Many women are non-orgasmic because their husbands do not take the time to be sensitive and skillful lovers. Usually, it simply takes a little re-education. May we recommend you read INTENDED FOR PLEASURE by Ed and Gaye Wheat? If you don't like to read, Dr. Wheat also has an INTIMACY TAPE SERIES. Sexual intimacy is about loving, not just about orgasm. And *loving* means taking the time and trouble to learn what pleases our mates, and then expressing our love in the enjoyment of mutual pleasure.

While we're at it, we need to mention "afterglow," for it is also a part of making love. The loving isn't finished after intercourse. You need time to bask together in the glow of your love. As you lie nude in each other's arms, inhibitions are probably lower than at any other time. Talk about intimate things: desires, dreams, fears.... And pray together; thank God for your love and His gift of one another.

25. When your sex life has been dead for an extended period of time, how do you do CPR? Does it almost require a counselor or third party to help with the rescue?

This is a complicated question, because it involves so many possible factors. The biggest question in our minds is "why?" Why has your sex life been dead for so long? Whatever dragged you into this severe situation, **you do need help** with the rescue.

In our response to the question about sex drives, we asked some pointed, searching questions of our own. These questions are ones you need to investigate for yourselves, especially concerning anger. If there has been a great deal of anger and conflict in your relationship, that may be translating itself into your sex life. The other questions about why you feel the way you do about sex are also applicable.

Without knowing the specifics of your particular situation, we can only address what we believe are the two most prevalent problems that afflict many married couples: non-orgasmic response in women and premature ejaculation or impotency in men. There are many factors which interact to cause non-orgasmic problems for women, some being the same problems that hinder desire. Trust is a primary factor in both desire and orgasmic problems. But there is help; these problems are solvable. There are proven programs of treatment which have been successful in many cases. A pastor or Christian therapist who is skillful in sexual therapy (Yes, there are such people!) can help non-orgasmic women learn to become joyfully orgasmic. There are also highly successful treatment programs for husbands with premature ejaculation or impotency problems. But in order for you to receive help, you must be **willing to seek it**. Ask the Lord to lead you to the right counselor — one who can offer you the best help. Our Lord is extremely interested in your sex life. You, as a couple, are not alone on your journey to wholeness. Jesus has promised to be your partner.

26. What, if anything, is the Christian teaching on having a vasectomy?

The only Biblical guideline for birth control that we have found is that the method must not abort a fetus, as some techniques do. With that restriction in mind, the decision is between you, your mate and God.

We have heard men say, "If I get a vasectomy, I won't be a real man anymore." A vasectomy does **not** lower a man's sex drive or make him any less a man than he was before he had the vasectomy. The procedure simply disconnects the passage for sperm to flow into the seman, and so prevents pregnancy. If a couple decides together, for whatever reason, that they do not want any more children, a vasectomy is a much easier sterilization procedure than a woman must have to get the same results. A vasectomy is an out patient procedure, often performed in the surgeon's office; whereas, a tubal ligation is major surgery.

27. What is the best way/time to teach your kids about sex?

The best time is when they are interested — little by little. The best way is to give them only as much information as they are ready to handle — little by little. We recommend you read the following books for more detailed instructions: SEX IS A PARENT AFFAIR by Letha Scanzoni, SEX EDUCATION IS FOR THE FAMILY by Tim LaHaye, and PREPARING FOR ADOLESCENCE by James Dobson.

27. How can a spouse communicate to their partner that certain things that they do during foreplay really turns them off and makes them feel uncomfortable?

We're glad you asked this question, because it shows you have a desire to communicate about this important area of your relationship. Many couples do not communicate about their sexuality, and some communicate in code — both lead to frustration. What if you communicated your desires about what you want to eat for dinner the way you communicate what you want in bed? Would you ever get your favorite meal? We encourage every married couple to com-municate about their sex life, because your mate is not a mind reader — and probably can't decipher code well either.

To talk with your mate about what you'd like them to do during foreplay (or during any other part of making love), you must approach them in gentleness and love.

(1) Ask God to help you talk about your concern with honesty and kindness.

(2) Schedule a time when you will not be interrupted or rushed.

(3) Don't talk about it in bed.

(4) Assure them of your love and desire to please them and affirm their love and desire to please you.

(5) Talk in "I messages." ("I feel this...." "I would be aroused if ...." **not** "You do this... or that.")

(6) Ask your mate if there is something he/she would like you to do differently that would give him/her more sexual pleasure.

God intends for our marriages to be a safe place in which to grow and change — sexually, as well as every other way. We need to be creating the kind of accepting environment which says, "O.K. That didn't work. Let's try something else."

RELATIONSHIP SKILLS
Chapter 8

Day 1

According to Martin Luther, "There is no more lovely, friendly and charming relationship, communion or company than a good marriage." This was not only a man of **fire**, but also a man of **family**. A man who knew the importance of relationship. Many of us get so busy with the realities of living, we neglect what we desire most — a close, loving, secure relationship with our mate and family. But relationships **don't just happen** any more than a garden just happens. Both must be **cultivated**. You've heard the term, "relationship skills"? They are called skills because that's exactly what they are — **skills**. Skills we can **learn and practice** in our relationships — or **ignore**. But remember, if you ignore a garden, you can't expect much fruit from it. If, however, you will take the time and effort to cultivate the following relationship principles, you **can** be a better mate, a better parent and a better friend. These relationship guidelines apply to all close relationships. We, of course, will be applying them especially to marriage.

Guidelines for Cultivating Relationships

1. **Give TOP PRIORITY to relationships.** Proverbs 18:24b — *...there is a friend who sticks closer than a brother.* John 15:15 — *I no longer call you servants, because a servant does not know his master's business. Instead, I have called you friends, for everything that I learned from my Father I have made known to you.*

Proverbs 18:24b — *...there is a friend who sticks closer than a brother.*
John 15:15 — *I no longer call you servants, because a servant does not know his master'*
Instead, I have called you friends, for everything that I learned from my Father I have made known to you.

Jesus recognized the importance of relationships. In fact, He gave relationships top priority. He spent almost every day with his 12 closest friends. He listened to them, edified them, encouraged them, corrected them, affirmed them, directed them and led them to God. His friends were more important to Him than a home, a well-manicured lawn, food and clothing, a good job, time, money and possessions. They were more important than what people thought of Him. They were even more important than what **they** thought of Him. Jesus was the very best **Friend,** because He treated friendship as significantly valuable. Do you?

Here's a friendship test. Answer these questions out loud. Do you have at least one person nearby whom you can call on in times of personal distress? Do you have several people whom you can visit with little advance warning without apology? Do you have several people with whom you can share recreational activities? Do you have people who will lend you money or those who will care for you in practical ways if the need arises?

If you answered "Yes" to **at least** three of these questions, then you have some good friends. You probably perceive friendship as being extremely important. Most of these relationship guidelines should be a snap for you.

If you answered "Yes" to **less** than three of these questions, don't get discouraged. If you practice the following guidelines, your "No's" will turn to "Yes's" within a few months.

Love relationships do not just HAPPEN — we have to devote ourselves to them. Let's return to the "garden" we mentioned earlier. How do you produce a fruitful garden? By paying proper attention to it: hoeing, raking, digging, weeding, sowing and watering. If you want to reap lots of good tasting fruit from your garden, then you have to devote yourself to it. In the same way, if you want friends with whom you can have warm relationships, then you have to devote yourself to them.

Give top priority to friendship with your MATE. Of all earthly friendships, the one with your mate should be the best. God has given you to your mate as his or her **best friend**. Don't wait for your mate to treat you like **their** best friend; begin treating **them** that way. It shouldn't take long for them to respond to you in like manner.

Do you give top priority to relationships? Rate yourself on a scale of 1 to 10.

Wife: 1   2   3   4   5   6   7   8   9   10 (circle one)

Husband: 1   2   3   4   5   6   7   8   9   10 (circle one)

What can you do to give more priority to relationships?

Wife: _____

Husband: _____

2.   **Dare to TALK FREELY about your feelings.** 1 Samuel 20:17 — *And Jonathan had David reaffirm his oath out of love for him, because he loved him as he loved himself.*

Appearing strong undermines sharing emotions. Who said, "Real men don't cry"? John Wayne? Well, if he didn't say it, he certainly could have. He was the epitome of the "strong, silent type." But Jesus was never ashamed to show His feelings. When He was at His friend Lazarus' funeral, He wept openly (John 11).

He didn't try to hide His tears. He didn't say, "Oh, I'm so embarrassed for you to see me cry!" He didn't even try to tough it out. Was Jesus a wimp? Certainly not! And **He** was **NOT** the "strong, silent type".

Three magic words — "I need you." Don't be ashamed to share your feelings. Put aside your embarrassment and say to your mate, "I need you in my life." Everyone **needs to feel needed.** Let your mate know **how much** you need them.

Don't expect people to read your mind. We often hear husbands repeat that old joke: "I told you I loved you when I married you. I'll let you know if I ever change my mind." You can laugh at it, just don't ever say it to your partner. Express your love. Don't risk living with regret. We've never heard a surviving mate say, "My only regret is that I told him/her 'I love you' too often."

Do you talk freely about your feelings? Rate yourself on a scale of 1 to 10.

1 Samuel 20:17 — *And Jonathan had David reaffirm his oath out of love for him, because he loved him as he loved himself.*

Notes

Wife: 1 2 3 4 5 6 7 8 9 10 (circle one)

Husband: 1 2 3 4 5 6 7 8 9 10 (circle one)

What do you need to do in order to talk more freely about your feelings?

Wife: _____

Husband: _____

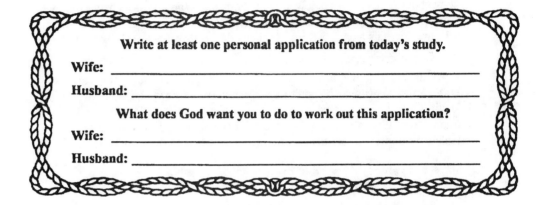

Write at least one personal application from today's study.

Wife: _____

Husband: _____

What does God want you to do to work out this application?

Wife: _____

Husband: _____

REFLECT TOGETHER: Read John 15:9-17. How far did Jesus go for His friends?

PRAY TOGETHER: Dear God, help us be true friends. Give us grace to talk freely with each other about our feelings.

Day 2

1 Samuel 18:1 — *After David had finished talking with Saul, Jonathan became one in spirit with David, and he loved him as himself.*

3.   **Develop TRANSPARENCY.** 1 Samuel 18:1 — *After David had finished talking with Saul, Jonathan became one in spirit with David, and he loved him as himself.*

HONESTY promotes deep friendships. We need relationships in which we can be ourselves. We need someone (or a few) with whom we can be completely honest, and know that he/she will be honest and accepting in return. This is the kind of relationship that satisfies and lasts throughout our lives.

Transparency was discussed in detail in Chapter 1 (Communication). It continues to be of primary importance to a deep relationship — especially your marriage relationship.

It is necessary to remove MASKS. We leave them on because we fear rejection. We are afraid that if others saw the *real* us, they would be repelled. So we construct facades, showing only what we think others want to see. We slip our masks on as we walk up the steps to church or work. We keep them securely locked in place as we discuss pertinent subjects in Sunday School and business meetings. Unfortunately, some of us can't seem to remember to take them off once we're home again.

We need to take off our masks, both inside our homes and out. We don't need to be afraid that others will reject us. Some might, it is true. That's O.K., because there will be others brave enough to love us as we are, and honest enough to allow us to love them as they are. It is especially essential to cultivate an honest relationship with your mate.

Removal of our masks helps us know and accept ourselves. If we leave our masks on all the time, eventually we will forget what we really look like...how we really feel. And if we don't know who we really are, how can others relate to us and meet our needs? Fortunately, there is Someone Who knows us better than we know ourselves. God knows and accepts each of us *as we are*. He sees beyond our masks and loves us anyway. Dare to believe this truth, and you will begin to know and accept yourself.

We are drawn to transparent people. Real people are refreshing to be around. We are drawn to people who don't wear masks. We have trouble, however, believing this same phenomena could be true of us. But it can! Others will be attracted to us if we allow ourselves the privilege of being real. Our mates especially will draw closer to us as we reveal ourselves to them.

Are you developing transparency? Rate yourself on a scale of 1 to 10.

Wife: 1   2   3   4   5   6   7   8   9   10 (circle one)

Husband: 1   2   3   4   5   6   7   8   9   10 (circle one)

What specific things can you do to develop more transparency?

Wife: _____

Husband: _____

4. **Learn the GESTURES of love.** John 12:3 — *Then Mary took about a pint of pure nard, an expensive perfume; she poured it on Jesus' feet and wiped his feet with her hair. And the house was filled with the fragrance of the perfume.*

   Minister acts of love even when EMOTIONS WANE. You don't have to **feel loving to be loving.** You can perform acts of love when you are tired. You can perform acts of love when you are grouchy. Anyone can give a back rub, a hug or a smile when they feel "lovey-dovey." But to give these acts of love when you **don't feel** like it...now **that** takes **love!**

   Recognize the significance of RITUALS. Giving a kiss when your partner comes home, reading to your children at bed time, singing a "love you" song to your children when they first awaken, kissing goodnight, holding each other close before falling asleep: repeated daily, these simple actions become rituals. You can tell when a behavior pattern has become a ritual, because you will miss it when it's not there. Rituals are extremely important to the bonding process. They are the mortar between the bricks.

John 12:3 — Then Mary took about a pint of pure nard, an expensive perfume; she poured it on Jesus' feet and wiped his feet with her hair. And the house was filled with the fragrance of the perfume.

Notes

Give GIFTS — not big, expensive gifts — **thoughtful** gifts. Thoughtful gifts can cost little or no money. We can give an inexpensive item we've noticed our mate needs, or something free, like a back rub or a break from kitchen duties. Thoughtful gifts are **tangible evidence** of our love. We need to give them often.

Are you learning the gestures of love? Rate yourself on a scale of 1 to 10.

Wife: 1   2   3   4   5   6   7   8   9   10 (circle one)

Husband: 1   2   3   4   5   6   7   8   9   10 (circle one)

What gestures of love can you do even when you don't feel like it?

Wife: _____

Husband: _____

Write at least one personal application from today's study.

Wife: _____

Husband: _____

What does God want you to do to work out this application?

Wife: _____

Husband: _____

REFLECT TOGETHER: Read John 12:1-3. Do you think Mary gave top priority to relationships?

PRAY TOGETHER: Lord, we want to be real with each other. Teach us to be transparent. And Lord, help us love in deed even when we don't feel loving.

Day 3

5.   Don't let **NEGATIVES** control your life.

- **CRITICISM.** Hebrews 12:15 — *See to it that no one misses the grace of God and that no **bitter root** grows up to cause trouble and defile many.*
  Philippians 2:14 — *Do everything without complaining or arguing.*

Notes

Reasons to avoid criticism. We have discussed criticism quite a bit, so you are already aware of how destructive it is. If it has gained a foothold in your life, ask the Lord to rip it out. You don't want it to control your life, because (1) It leads to and results from a negative mind-set. It makes us, and everyone around us, miserable. And (2) We are directed to fill our minds with positive things. Have you ever found a command in God's Word to "think of all the things your family and friends need to correct, and improve them with diligence"? We'd all be great at obeying that one, wouldn't we?

Hebrews 12:15 — *See to it that no one misses the grace of God and that no bitter root grows up to cause trouble and defile many.* Philippians 2:14 — *Do everything without complaining or arguing.*

How to respond to criticism — using the "PLAN" method.

1. **P — Pray** — rather than defend. Our natural reaction is to defend ourselves. Bite your tongue, grit your teeth, cross your eyes — do whatever your have to do, but don't allow yourself to **react**. Instead **respond — pray.** Exodus 15:23-25 — Moses and the Israelites at Marah: *When they came to Marah, they could not drink its water because it was bitter....So the people grumbled against Moses, saying, "What are we to drink?"* **Then Moses cried out to the Lord....**

Exodus 15:23-25 — *When they came to Marah, they could not drink its water because it was bitter....So the people grumbled against Moses, saying, "What are we to drink?"* **Then Moses cried out to the Lord....**

2. **L — Listen and Learn.** You won't want to listen. None of us likes to hear criticism. But we need to listen before we answer. Proverbs 18:13 — *He who answers before listening — that is his folly and his shame.*

Proverbs 18:13 — *He who answers before listening — that is his folly and his shame.*

3. **A — Answer Positively:** Calmly and quietly as directed in Proverbs 15:1 — *A gentle answer turns away wrath.* Understand what your critic is saying. If you don't, ask questions. Try to find truth (even a little) in what is said and immediately agree with all you possibly can. And ask for your critic's help in finding a solution.

Proverbs 15:1 — *A gentle answer turns away wrath.*

4. **N — Note your critic's need.** The criticism may actually stem from a problem within the critic himself. Don't try to "turn the tables" with such an accusation, but keep it in mind. Your critic may desperately need your understanding and prayer. Numbers 16:41-48 — (Moses, Aaron and the Israelites after Korah's rebellion) *The next day the whole Israelite community grumbled against Moses and Aaron....the Lord said to Moses, "Get away from this assembly so I can put an end to them at once....The plague had already started among the people, but Aaron* **offered the incense and made atonement for them.** *He* **stood between** *the living and dead, and the plague stopped.*

Numbers 16:41-48 — *The next day the whole Israelite community grumbled against Moses and Aaron....the Lord said to Moses, "Get away from this assembly so I can put an end to them at once....The plague had already started among the people, but Aaron offered the incense and made atonement for them. He stood between the living and dead, and the plague stopped.*

I use criticism...

Wife: Never Seldom   Sometimes Often   Too Much (Circle one)

Husband: Never Seldom   Sometimes Often   Too Much (Circle one)

What specifically can you do to get criticism out of your life?

Wife: _____

Husband: _____

Notes

In Romans 1:18 — *the wrath of God is being revealed from heaven against all the godlessness and wickedness of men.*

- **GOSSIP.** In Romans 1:18, Paul declares that the *wrath of God is being revealed from heaven against all the godlessness and wickedness of men.* In the next fourteen verses, he describes these godless, wicked people, listing their horrible sins. Tucked in between murder and ruthlessness, is listed "gossip" and "slander." God wants to be sure we know exactly what He thinks about this **negative which can control our lives.** It is sin — plain and simple. Gossip is defined as *idle talk and rumors,* especially about *the private affairs of others.*

Some husbands and wives bad-mouth their mate and tell tales of their private lives to anyone who will listen — especially extended family. It can destroy that mate's ability to form relationships with those who've heard the "gossip." And if what was said ever gets back to the slandered mate...! It also destroys the relationship between spouses, as the one gossiping tells and re-tells the negative stories. This type of gossip can be harder to acknowledge because it often takes the form of seeking help and comfort due to a "problem" spouse.

It also occurs in idle banter and casual conversation, when a spouse tells about a "funny" incident ("You should have seen what my wife/husband did....") No wonder "gossip" is listed with murder, for it just as surely **destroys** lives and relationships, and perhaps does so more painfully than a knife or gun.

Proverbs 16:28b — *...a gossip separates close friends.*

Proverbs 25:23b — *...a sly tongue brings angry looks.*

Proverbs 26:20 — *Without wood a fire goes out; without gossip a quarrel dies down.*

Consequences of gossip: (1) It separates friends, even intimate ones. Proverbs 16:28b — *...a gossip separates close friends.* **(2)** It wounds people and even destroys them. **(3)** It instigates anger. Proverbs 25:23b — *...a sly tongue brings angry looks.* **(4)** It causes contention and strife. Proverbs 26:20 — *Without wood a fire goes out; without gossip a quarrel dies down.*

Cures for gossip:

Deal with others directly. Don't discuss the matter with others; go directly to the person involved. If a sin or personal offense is involved, use the confrontation process described in Matthew 18:15-17: first confront the Christian brother alone, then take 2 or 3 witnesses, and finally, if he still will not listen, bring him before the church.

Proverbs 20:19 — *A gossip betrays a confidence; so avoid a man who talks too much.*

Refuse to listen to gossip. Proverbs 20:19 — *A gossip betrays a confidence; so avoid a man who talks too much.* Simply refusing to listen may help others stop. If one person consistently attempts to draw you into gossip, consider confronting them.

Be more open about your own weaknesses. Be vulnerable.

Proverbs 10:12 — *Hatred stirs up dissension, but love covers all wrongs.*

Psalm 141:3 — *Set a guard over my mouth, O Lord; keep watch over the door of my lips.*

Learn to love. Proverbs 10:12 — *Hatred stirs up dissension, but love covers all wrongs.*

Ask the Lord to help you guard your tongue. Psalm 141:3 — *Set a guard over my mouth, O Lord; keep watch over the door of my lips.*

I gossip...

Wife: **Never Seldom   Sometimes Often   Too Much** (Circle one)

Husband: Never Seldom   Sometimes Often   Too Much (Circle one)

What can you specifically do to root gossip out of your life?

Wife: _____

Husband: _____

- MANIPULATION. Philippians 2:3 — *Do nothing out of selfish ambition or vain conceit, but in humility consider others better than yourselves.*

Philippians 2:3 — *Do nothing out of selfish ambition or vain conceit, but in humility consider others better than yourselves.*

Our demands and expectations lead to manipulation. Our DEMANDS of others carry with them the specter of retribution, punishment or revenge when not fulfilled. Another name for unspoken threats is **manipulation**. Of course, we would never admit there was a threat hidden behind our demands, but if our mate or family does not measure up, we punish them with silence, sharp words or denials of pleasure.

Our EXPECTATIONS of others result in frustration and disappointment when not fulfilled. Our mate, family and friends will never be able to meet all our expectations. We stubbornly hang on to them, though, manipulating others to meet as many as possible.

Our demands and expectations are SELF-CENTERED and hurt **us** as well as others. When we place our demands and expectations on others, we make ourselves a target for defeat. Manipulation **does not work**. The people we try to manipulate catch on eventually. They resent and resist our control. In turn, we feel frustrated because we don't get the results we wanted, and try even harder to manipulate others to meet our expectations and demands. It's a vicious and counter-productive cycle.

Types of Manipulators: Check out these three categories of manipulators. Do you see yourself in any of them?

The Take-Charge Manipulator — These people think and act like they are in control. How would you answer the following questions? Do we usually go to the restaurant or movie I prefer? Do I enjoy correcting factual errors in other people's conversation? Do I use humor to put down my mate or friends? Do I have to know more about a topic than others to feel comfortable discussing it? Do I flare-up in anger at those who don't do as I expect? If you answered "Yes" to even two of these questions, you are a Take-charge manipulator. The Take-charger's weapon of choice is **fear**. Their sub-conscious line of thinking is, "Do what I want! If you don't, you'll **be** sorry."

The Poor-Me Manipulator — These are the sneaky manipulators...the martyrs. Do you ever say, "Never mind, I'll do it myself." "Go ahead, take the last one. Don't bother about me." "I was looking forward to it, but, that's O.K., we'll do what you want. (sigh)" If these statements sound like you, you are a Poor-me manipulator. The Poor-me's weapon of choice is **guilt**. Their sub-conscious line of thinking is, "You really should do what I want. If you don't, you'll **feel** sorry."

The Need-to-be-needed Manipulator — These folks make others dependent on them. They're doers, bustling over their loved ones, making themselves indispensable. Do you feel that others **owe** you their gratitude? Are you hurt when you don't get the recognition you feel you deserve? Do you need to know your husband or wife and children can not do without you? If these reflect your feelings, then you are a Need-to-be-needed manipulator. The Need-to-be-needed's weapon of choice is **obligation**. Their sub-conscious line of thinking is, "Look what I do for you. You should do what I want because you **owe me**."

Notes

Manipulation is **deceit**. Instead of honestly saying what we want, we try to slip our expectations through the back door. We don't have time to go into all the ramifications of manipulation here. But we must make this clear: we are **all** guilty of manipulation. We must see it for the deceit that it is, and, with God's power, rid our lives of it.

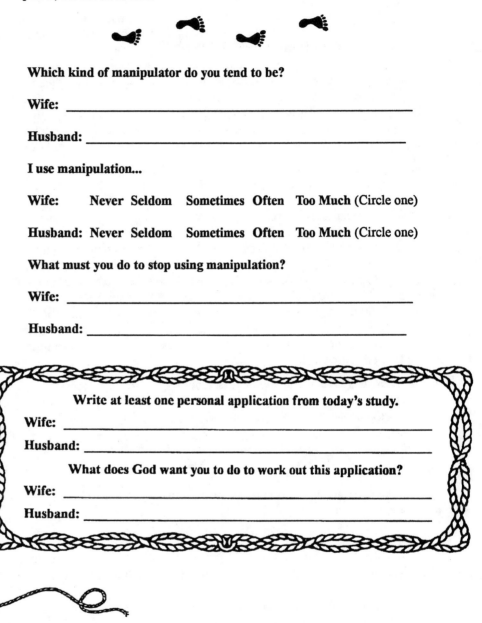

Which kind of manipulator do you tend to be?

Wife: _____

Husband: _____

I use manipulation...

Wife: Never Seldom   Sometimes Often Too Much (Circle one)

Husband: Never Seldom   Sometimes Often Too Much (Circle one)

What must you do to stop using manipulation?

Wife: _____

Husband: _____

Write at least one personal application from today's study.

Wife: _____

Husband: _____

What does God want you to do to work out this application?

Wife: _____

Husband: _____

REFLECT TOGETHER: Read James 3:1-12. What little bodily organ gets us into big trouble?

PRAY TOGETHER: Dear Father, don't let us allow negatives to control us. Please root all criticism, gossip and manipulation out of our lives.

6. **Use your body to DEMONSTRATE warmth.** Luke 18:15 — *People were also bringing babies to Jesus to have him touch them.*

We all long to be touched. Cats purr for it, dogs quiver and whine for it, but most of us humans just crave it in silence. The largest organ of the body is our skin, with millions of tiny touch sensors . **God designed us for touch.** We all need **"vitamin T"** (Touch). There have been many studies done on how babies respond to touch. One study, detailed in *Science News* (1985), revealed that "massaged babies gain weight much faster than unmassaged babies. They're more active, alert and responsive, better able to tolerate noise and emotionally more in control....eight months later, the massaged preemies were bigger in general, with fewer physical problems." (Diane Ackerman, *Parade Magazine,* March 25, 1990) Just because we get older, doesn't mean we need touch any less.

Many parents stop touching their children at around age five or six. An interesting phenomena then takes place: children stop touching each other. And, as adults, we consider **not touching** to be **normal.** Suppose you were watching several American men standing on a street corner talking. Say they conversed for one hour, how many times do you think they would have touched during their conversation? You might be surprised to know they would have touched fewer than three times in a whole hour. Now suppose you are watching Italian or French men conversing for one hour. Can you believe it? They would have touched around 100 times. We, in this country, have strangled touch, choking it out of our conscious sense of need. But our bodies haven't forgotten how much we need to touch and be touched. Like all those babies in the studies, we are healthier when we touch and are touched.

Touching is a form of communication that says, "I care about you. I'm listening. I'm interested." A touch is stronger than verbal communication. It expresses comfort, acceptance, encouragement and love. Touch the people you love.

Do you use your body to demonstrate warmth? Rate yourself on a scale of 1 to 10.

Wife: 1   2   3   4   5   6   7   8   9   10 (circle one)

Husband: 1   2   3   4   5   6   7   8   9   10 (circle one)

What can you do to remember to touch your loved ones more?

Wife: _____

Husband: _____

7. **Schedule time for CONVERSATION and LEISURE.** Proverbs 27:17 — *As iron sharpens iron, so one man sharpens another.* Mark 6:31-32 — *Then, because so many people were coming and going that they did not even have a chance to eat, he [Jesus] said to them, "Come with me by yourselves to a quiet place and get some rest."*

Day 4

Luke 18:15 — *People were also bringing babies to Jesus to have him touch them.*

Proverbs 27:17 — *As iron sharpens iron, so one man sharpens another.*

Mark 6:31-32 — *Then, because so many people were coming and going that they did not even have a chance to eat, he [Jesus] said to them, "Come with me by yourselves to a quiet place and get some rest."*

Notes

Emotional intimacy takes time — time shared with one another in transparent communication. Our conversation should sharpen each other, like *iron sharpens iron*. Remember how you talked and talked while courting? You talked about everything, and excitedly informed your friends about the **interesting** person you had found.

No matter what it takes, keep making time to talk with one another. Even if your house sounds like the description in Mark 6 — *people coming and going...no chance to eat* — take time to get away and rest and talk.

Our prescription for bonding: Once per week—a date together. Once per month—a long (over 4 hours) date. Once per quarter—an overnight away together. Once every 6 months— a weekend away together. Emotional intimacy takes **time**. Bonding takes **time**. You can not cheat yourselves out of time and still achieve oneness.

Do you schedule time for conversation and leisure? Rate yourself on a scale of 1 to 10.

Wife: 1   2   3   4   5   6   7   8   9   10 (circle one)

Husband: 1   2   3   4   5   6   7   8   9   10 (circle one)

What can you do to invest more time in leisure and conversation with your mate?

Wife: _____

Husband: _____

James 1:19 — My dear brothers, take note of this: Everyone should be quick to listen, slow to speak and slow to become angry.

8.   **Learn to LISTEN.** James 1:19 — *My dear brothers, take note of this: Everyone should be quick to listen, slow to speak and slow to become angry.* "Listen," as it is used here, means "to hear the **meaning** or **message** of the thing perceived" (Vine's *Expository Dictionary of New Testament Words*). We are exhorted to listen attentively to what our loved one's say and what they mean. Someone once said, "God gave us **two** ears and **one** mouth, and we should use them in the same proportion."

- **Listen with your ears, eyes and body**...Lean toward the one speaking.

- **Dispense advice sparingly.**

- **Don't break confidences shared.**

- **Give engaging responses.** "Uh-huh" and "Huh-uh" don't count.

- **Show gratitude when loved ones confide in you.**

- **Be patient with slow talkers.** Resist the urge to provide a word or finish a sentence.

How well do you listen? Rate yourself on a scale of 1 to 10.

Wife: 1   2   3   4   5   6   7   8   9   10 (circle one)

Husband: 1   2   3   4   5   6   7   8   9   10 (circle one)

What can you do to improve your listening skills?

Wife: _____

Husband: _____

Notes

Write at least one personal application from today's study.

Wife: _____

Husband: _____

What does God want you to do to work out this application?

Wife: _____

Husband: _____

REFLECT TOGETHER: Read Deuteronomy 24:5. Does God think it's important for husbands and wives to spend time together?

PRAY TOGETHER: Dear Lord, warm our marriage with Your principles of relationship. Teach us to touch each other more, talk and listen more, and take more time to enjoy being together.

Day 5

Ephesians 4:29 — *Do not let any unwholesome talk come out of your mouths, but only what is helpful for building others up according to their needs, that it may benefit those who listen.*

Proverbs 12:18 — *Reckless words pierce like a sword.*

Proverbs 27:15 — *A quarrelsome wife [or husband] is like a constant dripping on a rainy day.*

9. **Be liberal with PRAISE.** Ephesians 4:29 — *Do not let any unwholesome talk come out of your mouths, but only what is helpful for building others up according to their needs, that it may benefit those who listen.*

Avoid DESTRUCTIVE words: There are obvious words to avoid, such as lies (Eph 4:25), and bitter, angry, and malicious words (v 31). But there are other types of words that destroy, such as:

CUTTING words: Proverbs 12:18 — *Reckless words pierce like a sword.* Razor sharp, sarcastic words might be spoken with a hint of humor, but they still stab, and the wounds are deep. Do you ever say anything like, "Oh, yeah, you work hard all day watching TV while the kids run around." Or do you use a harsh tone when speaking to your mate or children? Remember, your tone of voice says more than your words.

NAGGING words: Proverbs 27:15 — *A quarrelsome wife [or husband] is like a constant dripping on a rainy day.* There is a difference between nagging and giving a reminder. A reminder is friendly and free from impatience or irritation, while nagging is **critical** and marked by exasperation and anger. Women have not cornered the market on nagging. In fact, we've heard it said that women nag and men badger. They both boil down to the same thing, don't they? It's like being nibbled to death by a duck!

EXAGGERATED words: Exaggerated generalizations that take the form of absolute statements are emotional clubs. Statements like, "You **always** say stupid

stuff like that!" "You're just like your mother!" "You **never** listen to me!" We can leave each other bruised and bleeding with unwholesome word-clubs like these.

VENGEFUL words: 1 Peter 3:9 — *Do not repay evil with evil or insult with insult, but with blessing, because to this you were called so that you may inherit a blessing.* If you insult your mate because they insult you, if you hurt your children because they hurt you, if you neglect your friends because they neglect you, where will it end? God wants you to break the cycle. And the only way to do that is to give a blessing for insult, a blessing for hurt and a blessing for neglect.

1 Peter 3:9 — *Do not repay evil with evil or insult with insult, but with blessing, because to this you were called so that you may inherit a blessing.*

I use destructive words...

Wife: Never Seldom   Sometimes Often   Too Much (Circle one)

Husband: Never Seldom   Sometimes Often   Too Much (Circle one)

Practice CONSTRUCTIVE words:

GENTLE words: Proverbs 15:1 — *A gentle answer turns away wrath.* Gentle words are "fair, forbearing and considerate" words. Does this describe the way you talk?

Proverbs 15:1 — *A gentle answer turns away wrath.*

UNDERSTANDING words: Proverbs 15:28 — *The heart of the righteous weighs its answers.* Do you think before you speak? Do you consider how you should answer **before** you open your mouth?

Proverbs 15:28 — *The heart of the righteous weighs its answers.*

APPRECIATIVE words: Philippians 1:3-5 — *I thank my God every time I remember you. In all my prayers for all of you, I always pray with joy because of your partnership in the gospel from the first day until now.* Paul wrote to his friends in the city of Philippi, expressing his appreciation to them. Do you tell your loved ones how much they mean to you...not just on their birthday, but on a regular basis?

Philippians 1:3-5 — *I thank my God every time I remember you. In all my prayers for all of you, I always pray with joy because of your partnership in the gospel from the first day until now.*

ENCOURAGING words: Hebrews 10:25 — *Let us not give up meeting together, as some are in the habit of doing, but let us encourage one another — and all the more as you see the Day approaching.* Encouraging words are full of "comfort and support," words that "spur us on to goodness." Encouraging words are an excellent way to start the day off right.

Hebrews 10:25 — *Let us not give up meeting together, as some are in the habit of doing, but let us encourage one another — and all the more as you see the Day approaching.*

COMPLIMENTARY words: Philemon 7 — *Your love has given me great joy*

Notes

Philemon 7 — Your love has given me great joy and encouragement, because you, brother, have refreshed the hearts of the saints.

2 Timothy 1:5 — I have been reminded of your sincere faith, which first lived in your grandmother Lois and in your mother Eunice and, I am persuaded, now lives in you also.

Luke 7:12-15 — As he approached the town gate, a dead person was being carried out — the only son of his mother, and she was a widow....When the Lord saw her, his heart went out to her and he said, "Don't cry." Then he went up and touched the coffin....He said, "Young man, I say to you, get up!"...Jesus gave him back to his mother.

and encouragement, because you, brother, have refreshed the hearts of the saints. Paul wrote to his friend, Philemon, praising him for his loving and giving heart. Give your spouse and children a compliment every day, and watch them blossom. Everyone thirsts for compliments. Are the people in your house dying of thirst?

AFFIRMING words: 2 Timothy 1:5 — *I have been reminded of your sincere faith, which first lived in your grandmother Lois and in your mother Eunice and, I am persuaded, now lives in you also.* Paul affirms Timothy in his faith and value. To affirm means "to confirm the value of and declare as true." Do you often tell the people you love how valuable they are to you?

EMPATHETIC words: Luke 7:12-15 — *As he approached the town gate, a dead person was being carried out — the only son of his mother, and she was a widow....When the Lord saw her, his heart went out to her and he said, "Don't cry." Then he went up and touched the coffin....He said, "Young man, I say to you, get up!"...Jesus gave him back to his mother.* You don't have to have experienced the same problem or hurt to empathize with someone. You must simply imagine how you would feel in the same situation, allowing their hurt to touch you. Empathetic words say, "I feel with you. I understand your pain." The widow in Luke 7 **knew** Jesus understood her pain. Jesus can **fix** other's pain, you **can not**. But you **can** empathize.

I am liberal with praise. (Rate yourself on a scale of 1 to 10)

Wife: 1   2   3   4   5   6   7   8   9   10 (circle one)

Husband: 1   2   3   4   5   6   7   8   9   10 (circle one)

What can you do to be more liberal with praise?

Wife: _____

Husband: _____

Write at least one personal application from today's study.

Wife: _____

Husband: _____

What does God want you to do to work out this application?

Wife: _____

Husband: _____

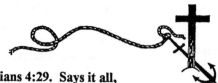

REFLECT TOGETHER: Re-read Ephesians 4:29. Says it all, doesn't it?

PRAY TOGETHER: Oh, God, help us be aware of destructive words before they come out of our mouths. Help us build each other up with constructive words.

10. **Allow people to FAIL.** Allow the people you love to make mistakes. Proverbs 17:17 — *A friend loves **at all times**, and a brother is born for adversity.*

Anatomy of failure:

Fear of failure: Are you open to change? Are you willing to take risks? Are you confident in decision making? Are you open to constructive criticism by others? If you answered "no" to any of these, **you are afraid to fail.** You are not alone. We are **all** afraid to fail.

Effects of failure: We either accelerate our performance. We say to ourselves, "I'll show him. He'll never call me a failure again.!" "No one will ever see me fail again." **Or we quit.** We think, "What's the use? Why try, if I'm never going to get it right?"

Both reactions sabotage us. They both dump guilt, fear and low self-esteem on us. If you react to failure in these ways, call a halt, turn around, fix your mind on how

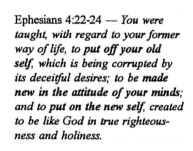

much God loves and values you. And take to heart these instructions: Ephesians 4:22-24 — *You were taught, with regard to your former way of life, to **put off your old self**, which is being corrupted by its deceitful desires; to be **made new in the attitude of your minds**; and to **put on the new self**, created to be like God in true righteousness and holiness.*

Freedom to fail. Because you know how hard it is to overcome feelings of failure, you need to stop encumbering your family and friends with your judgment and condemnation of their mistakes. The following are **positive responses to failure** you can use to give others the freedom to fail.

Give COMPASSION — Many believe that rejection is the natural consequence of failure. "If I fail, I'll be rejected." Isn't that the way it usually is? But that's **not**

Day 6

Proverbs 17:17 — *A friend loves **at all times**, and a brother is born for adversity.*

Ephesians 4:22-24 — *You were taught, with regard to your former way of life, to **put off your old self**, which is being corrupted by its deceitful desires; to be **made new in the attitude of your minds**; and to **put on the new self**, created to be like God in true righteousness and holiness.*

Notes

the way it should be! When your loved ones fail, you need to give them compassion. Compassion says: "I'm not like those who have rejected you. I feel with you. My commitment to you is **unconditional**."

Give AFFIRMATION — You never need affirmation more than when you fail. And you never need to **give** it more than when your loved ones fail. Affirmation says: "You are not a dummy if you make a mistake. You are still worthy." There was a young boy who, after attending school only three months, was labeled "addled" by his schoolmaster. This boy's mother marched directly to his teacher and told him her son "had more sense in his little finger" than the schoolmaster had in his whole body. She snatched the child from that negative environment and taught him at home. She affirmed him often, assuring him he was no dummy. As the boy grew into manhood, he faced failure often; and just as often, his mother reminded him how smart and valuable he was. This man continued to make many mistakes. In fact, he worked day and night for two years on one task, failing thousands of times. But one day, the light bulb worked. Thomas Edison was no failure! He had a mother who believed in him and affirmed him.

Romans 8:28 — *And we know that in all things God works for the good of those who love him, who have been called according to his purpose.*

Give PERSPECTIVE — Failure steals our perspective. We become so overwhelmed, all we can see is our mistakes. You need to help your loved ones view their failures with perspective. Perspective says: "This failure isn't pleasant, but it is not monumental. It is solvable. God doesn't waste anything — and He will somehow use this for good." (Romans 8:28)

Give DISASSOCIATION — When we fail, we tend to **define** ourselves by that failure. Instead of saying, "That was a failure." We say, "**I** am a failure." You need to help your loved ones separate themselves from their mistakes. Disassociation says: "What you **did** failed, but **you** are not a failure."

Give ENCOURAGEMENT in Decision Making — Failure makes us afraid to make decisions, because we might make a mistake again. You need to let your loved ones know you trust their choices. Encouragement says: "What do you think? I trust your opinion. And I'll back you, whatever you decide."

Give FORGIVENESS — We all need forgiveness when we fail. You must be careful not to give **denial of failure** to your loved ones by saying things like, "It will be O.K. No one will notice." Instead, you must give them forgiveness. Forgiveness says: "I won't reject you for your failure. I choose to forgive and accept you fully, just as you are; and I won't throw this back at you in the future."

Ecclesiastes 4:9-10 — *Two are better than one, because they have a good return for their work: If one falls down, his friend can help him up. But pity the man who falls and has no one to help him up!*

Your loved ones make mistakes. They spill the coffee. They forget important things. They lock their keys in the car. They track mud in the house. They lose their jobs. They wreck the car. How are you going to respond to them? Will you heap guilt and recrimination on them? Or will you give them freedom to fail? Ecclesiastes 4:9-10 — *Two are better than one, because they have a good return for their work: If one falls down, his friend can help him up. But pity the man who falls and has no one to help him up!*

Do you allow people to fail? (Rate yourself on a scale of 1 to 10)

Wife: 1   2   3   4   5   6   7   8   9   10 (circle one)

Husband: 1   2   3   4   5   6   7   8   9   10 (circle one)

Which of the 6 positive responses to failure do you have the most difficulty with?

Wife: _____

Husband: _____

Which response does your mate most need from you?

Wife: _____

Husband: _____

Talk about this together.

Write at least one personal application from today's study.

Wife: _____

Husband: _____

What does God want you to do to work out this application?

Wife: _____

Husband: _____

REFLECT TOGETHER: Re-read Ecclesiastes 4:9-10. Notice who "can help him up."

PRAY TOGETHER: Thank You, Lord, that You have shown us mercy. We want to pass Your mercy on to each other and our children by allowing them to fail.

WRAP UP: Read the following story to one another, then answer the questions at the end.

Day 7

Once upon a time, there was a beautiful Princess who married her Prince Charming. They were so much in love, they spent every possible minute together. They talked for hours about their hopes and dreams for the future. They grew to know each other so well, they could almost tell what the other was thinking. Their love was marked by kind deeds and thoughtful gestures, and never was there a critical or demanding word spoken between them, but only words of praise. As they walked hand in hand through the village streets, the villagers would exclaim, "What a perfect couple!" But they were so intent on their own conversation, they hardly noticed when

Notes

others interrupted. The Prince never fussed when the Princess forgot to press his royal robes, and she would simply smile and shrug when he tracked mud on the royal carpets.

The Prince worked very hard as he climbed the royal ladder of success, and spent more and more time on his many duties. With the Prince away so much, the Princess lavished her time on the little prince and princesses, especially as they became active in the royal Little League and Archery Club. Whenever the Prince returned home from his princely work, exceedingly tired and tense, he would proclaim, in his princely way, that he wished not to be disturbed. Then he would prop his feet on his footstool and read the Royal Gazette. The Princess, when she wasn't transporting the little prince and princesses hither and yon in the royal carriage, threw herself into her royal duties of charity.

How does your garden grow?

The Prince and Princess did not spend much time together any more. By the time they entered their royal bed chamber, they were too tired to talk and listen to one another about hopes and dreams. After a while, they no longer held hands as they walked. But, since they took walks together so seldom, the lack of touch went almost unnoticed. Their kind deeds and thoughtful gestures were forgotten, replaced by words of criticism and sarcasm. The Prince now demands his royal robes be pressed and ready every morning by 7:00. And the Princess frets greatly over the prince's thoughtless messes. How sad! What has happened to the Prince and Princess' "happy ever after"?

They so carefully cultivated their relationship garden when they were first married. It was thriving, healthy and fruitful. But when they began to neglect it, weeds crept in and choked out the plants they had nurtured. Now, instead of harvesting fruit from their garden, they reap only weeds.

How does your garden grow? Are you harvesting fruit...or reaping weeds? If you consistently use the ten "gardening tools" we have described, you will have fruitful, fulfilling relationships. Please, don't neglect **your** garden!

1. Write a list of 10 qualities you like about your mate.

Wife: _____ _____

_____ _____

_____ _____

_____ _____

_____ _____

Husband: _____ _____

_____ _____

_____ _____

_____ _____

_____ _____

Review all of these together as a couple. Keep your list as a guide from which to compliment your mate.

2. Which of the relationship guidelines do you most want to apply?

Wife: _____

Husband: _____

Why?

Wife: _____

Husband: _____

REFLECT TOGETHER: Re-read John 15:12-17. Jesus certainly knows how to be a friend, doesn't He?

PRAY TOGETHER: Father God, our relationship garden is more valuable than gold. Help us tend to it with diligence and care.

Group Discussion:
If you are using this study in a group setting, the following may be used as group discussion questions.

1. Praise:

    (1) List some situations where destructive words are commonly used.

    (2) How could constructive words work in these same situations?

2. Manipulation:

    (1) What are some situations where you have seen or used a manipulative technique? Try to think of a situation to illustrate each of the 3 categories: Take-Charge, Poor-Me, and Need-to-be-needed.

    (2) Using the same situations, discuss how the truth could be spoken in love and manipulative techniques not used.

3. Allowing Your Mate to Fail: Relate a time when you were given the needed compassion, affirmation etc. by your mate or someone else when you failed.

Have a frank discussion

Effective Financial Planning
Chapter 9
by Stephen R. Bolt, CFP

Biblical Principles

Day 1

Proverbs 29:18 — *Where there is no vision, the people perish.*

Where there is no vision, the people perish (Proverbs 29:18). The title of this chapter could as easily be "Making Sure You Have Sufficient Resources To Fund Your Vision," for without the necessary resources, whatever vision you and your life partner share will be destined for failure.

There are some Christians who try to shift their responsibility for providing their required financial resources off on God. Their feeling is that all they need to do is ask God for whatever financial help they need and He will provide. Certainly, **He does provide**, but not the way these mistaken Christians assume. The laws of economics are as natural as the laws of physics. **We don't ask God to suspend the law of gravity** in order to allow us to move about with less effort. Therefore, we should not expect God to suspend the laws of economics so we don't have to apply ourselves in an intelligent, disciplined manner in the area of personal financial planning. Martin Luther had some harsh words for those who would choose a more lazy approach to life, misappropriating God's grace. "All this is said against those who tempt God, who want to do nothing, and who imagine that God should give and do whatever they desire, without their labor and industry. To them this proverb is proper advice: 'Rely on God's help, and do not bake;' again: 'Wait until a fried chicken flies into your mouth.' You see, God wants no lazy idlers; but we should work faithfully and diligently, everyone of us, according to his calling and office; He then will bless and prosper our efforts." (What Luther Says, by Ewald Plass, Concordia Publishing House, pg 1494)

1 Thessalonians 1:9 — *...we worked night and day, that we might not burden any of you, while we preached to you the Gospel of God.*

2 Thessalonians 3:10 — *...we laid down the rule; the man who will not work, shall not eat.*

This correlation between a healthy Christian life and applying our best efforts in order to provide for ourselves was such a concern for the Apostle Paul that even while he was being pursued and persecuted, and while investing virtually all his energy in teaching the Gospel and starting the first churches, he made it known that his welfare was not anyone else's responsibility. We know while in Thessalonica, Paul once again took up tent-making in order to earn a living. In his first letter to the Thessalonians he writes, *...we worked night and day, that we might not burden any of you, while we preached to you the Gospel of God* (1 Thessalonians 1:9). And again, *...we laid down the rule; the man who will not work, shall not eat* (2 Thessalonians 3:10).

Mark 12:30 — *Love the Lord your God with all your heart, and with all your soul, and with all your mind, and with all your strength.*

Life is work. To make a marriage a fulfilling, happy and God pleasing partnership takes effort. It requires establishing goals, prioritizing objectives, open, meaningful and constant communication, as well as learning. To know God more fully and be in a continually maturing relationship with Him requires effort, as well. In Mark 12:30, we read Jesus' admonition, *Love the Lord your God with all your heart, and with all your soul, and with all your mind, and with all your strength*. Certainly to do all of that requires even more than effort - it will take vigilance. And so it should not be surprising that **to make the most of what financial resources you are blessed with will also require effort.**

One of the most dramatic parables in Scripture refers specifically to this effort being applied toward multiplying financial resources. In Luke chapter 19, Jesus tells the story of a nobleman and those he charged with multiplying his financial resources.

"A man of noble birth went to a distant country to have himself appointed king and then to return. So he called ten of his servants and gave them ten minas (1 mina=3 month's wages). 'Put this money to work,' he said, 'until I come back.' But his subjects hated him and sent a delegation after him to say, 'We don't want this man to be our king.' He was made king, however, and returned home. Then he sent for the servants to whom he had given the money, in order to find out what they had gained with it. The first one came and said, 'Sir, your mina has earned ten more.' 'Well done, my good servant!' his master replied. 'Because you have been trustworthy in a very small matter, take charge of ten cities.'

"The second came and said, 'Sir, your mina has earned five more.' His master answered, 'You take charge of five cities.' Then another servant came and said, 'Sir, here is your mina; I have kept it laid away in a piece of cloth. I was afraid of you, because you are a hard man. You take out what you did not put in and reap what you did not sow.' His master replied, 'I will judge you by your own words, you wicked servant! You knew, did you, that I am a hard man, taking out what I did not put in, and reaping what I did not sow? Why then didn't you put my money on deposit, so that when I came back, I could have collected it with interest?' Then he said to those standing by, 'Take his mina away from him and give it to the one who has ten minas.'
(Luke 19:12-24)

'Put this money to work,' he said, 'until I come back.'

'Because you have been trustworthy in a very small matter, take charge of ten cities.'

If we as Christians are not diligent in multiplying our financial resources, how will the Great Commission be carried forward? The early church needed the benefits of the financial resources it received from new believers to allow Paul, and Timothy, and Silas and others to preach the Gospel, and to help the poor and needy as the churches were planted and grew. Such financial sustenance is no less critical in our world today. Because the Church relies exclusively on the gifts it receives from today's believers in order to teach the new believer, to witness to the unbeliever, and to give to those in need, any diminished effort we apply at multiplying our financial resources ultimately reduces the amount of financial sustenance through which the Lord's work can be carried out.

We don't expect God to suspend the natural law of gravity, so we should not expect Him to suspend the laws of _____.

Paul's life was an example of the principle that "Life is _____."

What does the parable in Luke 19 teach about multiplying financial resources?

_____

_____

_____

In what way do we limit the Church's ability to carry out the Great Commission when we fail to multiply our financial resources?

_____

_____

_____

Notes

John 10:10 — *I came that they may have life, and have it more abundantly.*

Many Christians actually believe they are not called to live an abundant life, but rather a life which is normal, routine, fits in and doesn't call attention.

Matthew 28:19-20 — *...Go therefore and make disciples of all nations, baptizing them in the name of the Father, and of the Son, and of the Holy Spirit, teaching them to observe all that I have commanded you.*

One final dimension to the Biblical principles for financial planning should be mentioned. Up to this point we have concentrated on the need for applying ourselves in the area of financial planning as part of our walk with Christ. There is another blessing which will inevitably result from our effort and that might be best conveyed in Jesus' words in John's Gospel, *I came that they may have life, and have it more abundantly* (John 10:10). Too often Christians mistakenly believe we please God by having less, being less, and living in relative obscurity. The Apostle Paul held no place for this kind of Christian life. He told the Thessalonians that "...their way of life should be a rebuke to foulness and a spur to their neighbors to seek for themselves this new, extraordinary existence; Christians must outlove, outjoy, outthink, and always welcome those who oppose them." (The Apostle - A Life Of Paul, by John Pollock, Victor Books). We are to live life with passion, applying ourselves to all that we do with all of our effort, and 'rejoicing always, and in everything giving thanks.'

Evangelist John Maxwell preached a sermon to his staff entitled "Passion." In it he lists several reasons why most Christians seemingly choose to live life without passion. My summary of most of those reasons is that **many Christians actually believe they are not called to live an abundant life, but rather a life which is normal, routine, fits in and doesn't call attention.** Can you think of a better way for Satan to attack the Great Commission than by attempting to convince Christians that they should not be too happy, too optimistic, too wealthy? If Satan's attack works, Christians will move from the abundance to which God has called us, to a life of mediocrity, a lukewarm existence where the idol is the status quo. Where then will the energy and zeal come from to witness, to teach, to help? Where then shall the missionaries find sufficient money to go to 'the nations,' to witness and baptize? And the churches to teach and comfort? And the outreach ministries to help the suffering?

We have been charged with the greatest privilege and responsibility in the history of the universe; the call to *...Go therefore and make disciples of all nations, baptizing them in the name of the Father, and of the Son, and of the Holy Spirit, teaching them to observe all that I have commanded you* (Matthew 28:19-20). We are to respond to this call in a physical universe of God's own design; one that is governed by natural laws of physics, of climate, of chemistry, of physiology, **and of economics.** In this environment, our God tells us He wants us to live 'abundantly,' and to apply ourselves diligently to living the life He has given to us.

Along the way you will make mistakes. So did Peter whom Jesus called the rock of His church. So did Paul who did more to spread the Gospel than any other apostle. But they did *something* - and they did it with their all. Don't be anxious about the results. Just as it is our responsibility to *witness*, but the Holy Spirit's to *save*, so too **God asks us to apply ourselves and yet not be anxious.** As a dynamic evangelist friend of mine, Maury Davis, exclaims, "You do what you can; let God do what you can't."

In Day 2's study, we will move toward understanding what we *can* do.

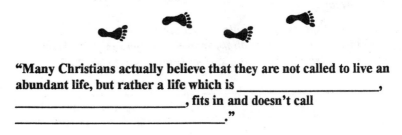

"**Many Christians actually believe that they are not called to live an abundant life, but rather a life which is _____, _____, fits in and doesn't call _____."**

"You do what you_____; let God do what you
_____."

**What life goals have you not yet attained because you have not
developed an adequate financial plan?**

Wife: _____

Husband: _____

**Choose one or two life goals and discuss how much money would be
required to achieve them.**

Write at least one personal application from today's study.

Wife: _____

Husband: _____

What does God want you to do to work out this application?

Wife: _____

Husband: _____

REFLECT TOGETHER: Re-read Luke 19:12-24.

PRAY TOGETHER: "Lord, we ask that You help us develop and
sustain the passion for achieving all that You would have us do in life.
And help us see that our effort toward developing a financial plan
will enable us to have the resources we will need."

Financial Planning: The Process

*Wisdom cries aloud in the street; in the markets she raises her voice; on the top of the
walls she cries out; at the entrance of the city gates she speaks: 'How long, oh simple
ones, will you love being simple? How long will scoffers delight in their scoffing and
fools hate knowledge?*

*Because they hated knowledge and did not choose the fear of the Lord, would have
none of my counsel, and despised all my reproof, therefore they shall eat the fruit of
their way and be sated with their own devices (Proverbs 1:20-22, 29-31).*

Proverbs 1:20-22, 29-31 —
*Wisdom cries aloud in the street;
in the markets she raises her
voice; on the top of the walls she
cries out; at the entrance of the
city gates she speaks: 'How long,
oh simple ones, will you love being
simple? How long will scoffers
delight in their scoffing and fools
hate knowledge?*

There are five primary dimensions to the financial planning process:

1. Determining which professional will assist you

2. Taking a snapshot of where you are right now

3. Establishing financial goals

4. Implementing your financial plan

5. Integrating your financial plan with your real life

1. Finding Professional Assistance

There are two reasons why everyone should take advantage of a financial professional. First, our world today has become so specialized, there is literally no way a consumer can even approach being able to know what financial instruments are available, let alone be able to distinguish the benefits and disadvantages of each, or exactly which ones to use and in what proportion - and when. Certainly, it is possible for someone to develop a do-it-yourself financial plan, but it will necessarily be 'dumbed down' to the level of expertise and accessibility of the individual. It is similarly possible for a person to be his/her own doctor, or dentist, or veterinarian, or legal counsel, but - again - the results most often will not approach those of the professional.

The second reason professional assistance is required is that most of us, being human, lack sufficient discipline to 'stay the course.' Instead, we meet a financial crisis with a newly developed conviction to "develop a financial plan." Then, as the crisis subsides and the kids' soccer season begins, the muffler on the car needs replacing, the house needs painting, and the grandparents come for summer vacation, that financial plan begins to lose its sense of urgency. A Canadian Planner I know has a saying that fits here; "If you have a problem, turn it into a procedure and you won't have that problem anymore." **The problem** is the lack of a systematic plan to meet our financial wants and needs. **The procedure** is the professionally managed financial planning process.

Before we move to a further explanation of that process, **let's take a brief look at the world of financial professionals** and provide some definition. There is only one independent academic institution established for the purpose of certifying financial planners, and that is the College for Financial Planning in Denver, Colorado. Operated by the National Endowment for Financial Education (NEFE), the College has established a rigorous curriculum which tests for competency in each of the following areas: insurance and risk management, investment planning, income taxes, retirement planning, and estate planning. At the end of each quarter of study, a test is administered. Then, after the candidate has successfully tested in each area of study, a two day - ten hour - comprehensive exam is administered. The certification of the candidate is granted only after the successful completion of these exams, a personal background check by the College, and a level of vocational experience attained. Only then does the candidate attain the status of Certified Financial Planner (CFP). Because of the rigorous educational curriculum, as well as the academic integrity of the entire program, I am of the opinion that the best place to start looking for professional assistance is with a CFP. Of course there are other designations - such as ChFC (Chartered Financial Consultant), or CLU (Chartered Life Underwriter), but, in my opinion, the course of study which these designations represent are not nearly as comprehensive, or intellectually demanding. Additionally, they tend to be weighted toward life insurance. Other designations such as LUTCF or FIC are simply training programs for the insurance industry.

Regardless of whether you utilize the services of a CFP, be certain you follow three principles when searching for professional assistance: (1) academic integrity, (2) product neutrality, and (3) plan management.

Academic Integrity

Sometimes it is easier to define what financial planning is not, than it is to define what it is. It is **not** simply a budget. It is **not** the purchase of an insurance policy, or annuity. It is **not** an account with your father's favorite broker. Rather, financial planning is the systematic management of your financial resources in the most prudent manner in order to maximize financial benefit and assist you in reaching your financial goals. From that definition, two things should jump out: financial planning is dynamic, in other words, it is alive; it is a plan which is forever changing and evolving. The second thing you should notice from that definition is that financial planning is multidimensional. In other words, every aspect of your financial consideration should be included, from cash flow to retirement, from income taxes to estate transfer, and so on. Consequently, it is imperative that whoever the professional you choose to work with might be, that person must have the academic knowledge required to perform some very complex considerations. He must be constantly engaged in the field of study, and hopefully, be associated with a firm of other professionals whom he can call on for additional assistance where necessary.

It is imperative that your financial planner has the academic knowledge required to perform some very complex considerations.

It is also important to point out that bankers, attorneys, and CPA's are not financial planners. Although these professions are very important to the financial planning process they are not specifically equipped to help you meet your financial goals. Most bankers have virtually no formal education in financial planning. Attorneys are required to take only a few hours of education in estate planning in order to be able to sit for the bar exam. And CPA's are accountants, not financial planners. The fact that they perform audits, or tax returns, or business planning does not provide them the requisite academic base to help you develop a financial plan. Similarly, do not confuse intelligence with competency. A nuclear engineer is most likely very intelligent, but because he lacks the formal academic training in financial planning, he will be a terribly incompetent financial advisor (whether he admits it or not!). Finally, do not misconstrue trust and love for competency. Your father may love you dearly, so when you ask him for financial planning advice, he may be inclined to offer what he can. Unfortunately, his lack of competency in the field will eventually manifest itself in your poor performing financial plan. I'll bet if you asked him to perform brain surgery on you, he would recognize his incompetency in that field (unless, of course, he was a brain surgeon), and out of love for you, refer you to a good surgeon!

Product Neutrality

If you were looking to buy a new car, and drove into a Ford dealership to get advice, what kind of car do you think the salesman would recommend? A Toyota? A Chrysler? I don't think so. Yet, many people get their 'financial advice' from a salesperson who is associated with a company which sells only its products. In many cases, the highly regulated securities industry strictly prohibits representatives of one company (broker-dealer) from recommending any product *not* offered through the broker-dealer he is registered with. Therefore, what typically happens is the majority

Many people get their 'financial adivice' from a salesperson....

Notes

of salespeople in the financial services industry don't even *know* any other financial strategy other than the ones they can offer through their own broker-dealer! Which leads me to a very important statement: a salesperson doesn't really have to know very much, he only needs to know slightly more than the buyer!

My advice is to find a professional who is associated with an independent broker-dealer which offers multiple options in all the mainstream financial product categories. This way you will have the benefit of his firm's research into all the competing products that are available in the marketplace.

Plan Management

Believe it or not, life will deal you change. So, you want to be sure the plan you worked diligently to develop continues to be congruent with your financial needs and wants. At a minimum, you should meet with your Planner once each year. Prior to that meeting, the Planner should update all your financial records and rerun all the analyses, so that at your meeting you can best determine whether any changes need to be made.

Your should meet with your Planner once each year.

Let me make a quick comment about how financial planners are compensated. If you have diligently followed the above advice, don't worry too much about making a mistake in this area. Fee-only planners charge a fee for their time and proclaim that their advantage is neutrality (in other words, they won't be guilty of recommending a high commission strategy). Their strength is also their weakness. If you research any category of financial instruments (life insurance, annuities, tax credit programs, portfolio managers, etc.), you will find anywhere from dozens to thousands of available options. If the Planner is 'out-of-the-loop' after he has made certain recommendations, then later you are left without continuing competent assistance to help you actually implement your plan. On the other side of the equation is the commission-only planner whose advantage is that he will work for free — sort of. He actually can't get paid until you buy something, which naturally gives him the incentive to sell you something.

My suggestion is to find a CFP who works with an independent broker-dealer, whose fees are low and who will help implement your plan, whose values are similar to yours, who has a team of professionals he can refer to for help, and with whom you enjoy working.

The best possible professional assistance you can get is with a CFP
(_____ _____ _____)
because: _____
_____

When searching for professional assistance, the three principles you should follow are:
(1)_____
(2) _____
(3) _____

2. A Current Snapshot

Before you can begin developing a financial plan, you must first know where you are in relation to where you want to go. We refer to this part of the process as *taking a current snapshot.* This critically important step places side by side (A) what your current situation truly is, with (B) your life and financial goals.

This analysis should be comprehensive and unbiased. Comprehensive, because in order to really assess any situation, you must first be able to see the whole picture. It should also be unbiased — not be a part of any salesperson's marketing system. Keep in mind that any analysis used by a salesperson who specifically markets life insurance, or annuities, or stocks, might have a bias toward that product built into the analysis.

Your comprehensive financial analysis should include:

- cash flow report
- net worth statement
- insurance analysis
- income tax projection
- investment portfolio analysis
- retirement income projection
- education funding report
- estate transfer report

Establish clear direction for each of the areas which are important to you.

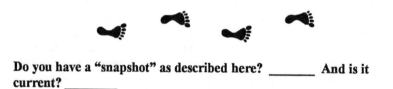

Do you have a "snapshot" as described here? _____ And is it current? _____

Note: See page 208 for further information or help in obtaining a "current snapshot" of your financial situation.

3. Establishing Financial Goals

One of my favorite sayings is, "Some people like to tip toe through life, so they can arrive at death safely". All too often Christians take this same approach toward their financial planning. If you don't have clear, specific financial goals, you will continually find yourself lost. And many times the natural reaction to that uncomfortable feeling is to simply try not to make any mistakes.

God placed each one of us in this place, at this time for His purpose. And it is up to each of us to constantly evaluate what that purpose is, giving it specificity, structure, and resources. There is no correct standard for when to retire, or how much to help with college education, or whether to save for a leave of absence in order to perform missionary work. There is only *what is right for you* in your relationship with God. In this way, living life *correctly* is a function of *who you are* as a child of God, *what you believe He is leading you to do*, and whether *you actually do it*!

As you attempt to determine what goals in your life will require financial resources, I encourage you to not become too hung up on the finer specifics; they'll change over time, anyway. Rather, establish clear direction to the <u>what you want to have happen and when</u> part of the puzzle. Then do the math to determine <u>how much</u> will be required. Your fully developed financial plan will then provide the structure — the <u>how it will be accomplished</u> part.

4. Implementing Your Plan

If the first step is locating the appropriate financial professional who will guide you in your planning process, and the second step is comparing where you are right now with where you want to go, then the third step is actually making some decisions about what you need to change about your current financial situation in order to reach those goals. This part of the process should be highly interactive, with your planner pointing out areas of deficiency or risk, and then making suggestions about how to mitigate those problems. Through this dialogue, you will have an opportunity to become more aware of both the problems and solutions, and begin to develop a sense of creating a strategy for developing a plan. Typically, this session will last about two hours. At the end you will probably feel like the Gary Larson cartoon character who is a student sitting in a classroom, raising his hand and saying, "Teacher, may I be excused? My brain is full."

> Don't allow yourself to get caught up in 'analysis paralysis.'

Hopefully, your Planner will summarize the discussion and recommend a course of action. This course of action is what we refer to as 'plan implementation'. There may be paperwork to do, as well as a series of details for you to take back home to allow further thought. One caution at this point: don't allow yourself to get caught up in 'analysis paralysis.' Such a state of mind finds itself totally immobilized for fear of making a mistake. Remember the adage from the book *In Search Of Excellence*: "disorganized action is always preferable to organized inaction". **Do something!**

5. Integrating Your Plan With Real Life

Unfortunately, life is much too complicated to be able to do a financial plan 'once and for all.' **You won't be able to make 30 year rigid decisions.** You'll be fortunate to stay most of the course for five years! On the other hand, keep in mind that a good plan, well thought through, with competent professional assistance, will be sufficiently elastic to enable the ups and downs of real life to be easily accommodated.

> Your goals will change!

Remember that life is dynamic — always changing, always moving, always evolving. And **that is the way your financial plan should be developed.** Your goals will change, you might change careers, get married, have children, watch them leave home, receive an inheritance, take time out for missionary work, or decide to start your own business.

Summary

Establish goals! Find a professional financial planer to help you develop a plan. Start the process by comparing where you are now with where you want to go. Implement your plan (beware of 'analysis paralysis'). Review your plan to be sure it reflects your real life as it evolves.

Discuss and agree on three financial goals. List them here.

(1) _____

(2) _____

(3) _____

Discuss how confident you are that your present course of action will achieve them.

> Write at least one personal application from today's study.
>
> Wife: _____
>
> Husband: _____
>
> What does God want you to do to work out this application?
>
> Wife: _____
>
> Husband: _____

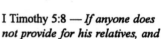

REFLECT TOGETHER: Read Deuteronomy 8:10-18.

PRAY TOGETHER: As we begin thinking about establishing life and financial goals, Lord, help us apply wisdom and intelligence. We want the plan we implement to glorify You."

Deuteronomy 8:18 — *But remember the Lord your God, for it is he who gives you the ability to produce wealth....*

Insurance Review

If anyone does not provide for his relatives, and especially for his own family, he has disowned the faith and is worse than an unbeliever (I Timothy 5:8).

Before you can afford to invest a dollar, you must first have that dollar protected. **Insurance is a wonderful financial instrument** which allows us to exchange what could be profound and unlimited personal risk for a reasonable cost (i.e., the premium). By transferring this unlimited liability to an insuring "company," we are able to go about our lives with the confidence of knowing that if something tragic were to occur, we at least would be financially protected.

Insurance is also a much maligned and confusing financial tool. How much do we need? What type should we purchase? For how long should we hold it? What benefits should we include? In the following information, we'll consider these questions and more. For the sake of simplicity, I've divided this section into the following components:

1. Liability insurance
2. Homeowners Insurance
3. Automobile Insurance
4. Disability insurance
5. Long Term Care Insurance
6. Medicare Supplement Insurance
7. Health Insurance
8. Life Insurance

Day 3

I Timothy 5:8 — *If anyone does not provide for his relatives, and especially for his own family, he has disowned the faith and is worse than an unbeliever.*

Before you can afford to invest a dollar, you must first have that dollar protected.

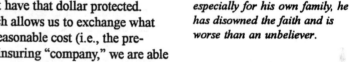

Notes

One admonition before we delve into the specific types of insurance: THE reason why our country is on the verge of bankruptcy today is that we as individual citizens failed to take the responsibility for accumulating sufficient assets to cover our retirement (social security), and failed to protect ourselves from the high cost of health care with adequate insurance protection (Medicare and Medicaid). If you eliminate these "entitlement" programs from the budget of the United States, our country would not only be able to significantly reduce taxes, but run a continual surplus, as well. Fully FORTY NINE PERCENT (49%) of the fiscal 1995 budget was earmarked for social welfare programs. And with projected increases for 1996 and beyond, our annual 200 billion dollar deficit (shortfall) keeps on growing. So, as you consider today's study on insurance (and the later ones on investing and retirement), remember that in a free society, it is each of our individual responsibility to appropriately manage our own insurance and accumulation plans — *not the government's*. And to the extent that we fail to take that responsibility, we contribute to the fiscal (and therefore social) decay of our nation.

So, there are two points to remember: **first**, be responsible! Buy the insurance that you need. **Second**, remember that insurance must be purchased before the risk that it is insuring actually occurs! You can't wait until you have an auto accident to buy insurance to cover that claim, any more than you should expect to wait to purchase appropriate health insurance until your health deteriorates to the point where no insurance company will accept you. Apply for the insurance *before you need it — and while you are healthy!*

Do you agree that we as individuals are responsible for providing for our own retirement and health care needs? Why or why not?

Wife: _____

Husband: _____

1. Liability Insurance

We don't need to spend much time on the subject of lawsuits and subsequent personal liability. Unfortunately, in this age of law suits, we know all too well how quickly a simple mishap can turn into a nightmare. All you have to do is turn on your television and you'll see attorneys advertising their legal prowess. It is certainly a sad state of affairs, but at least for the interim, the best we can do is protect ourselves. That means being certain we have a minimum personal liability policy. As the book *The ABC's of Managing Your Money* points out, a "Personal liability umbrella policy will protect you and your family from claims arising out of nonprofessional activities." The author, Jonathan Pond, CPA, goes on to say, "A good umbrella policy will protect you, family members living in your home, children attending school away from home, and even pets. In addition, the policy should cover legal defense costs, critically important since even the successful defense of a lawsuit can be very costly. The best protection against the threat of a lawsuit is to purchase a personal liability umbrella insurance policy."

This policy can be purchased at a very reasonable cost, given the amount of exposure you'll be covered for. It should give you a lot of peace of mind when you watch those video blooper shows which replay a neighbor's car rolling down the sidewalk without a driver — headed toward the swimming pool across the street!

Be certain you have a minimum personal liability policy.

2. Renter and Homeowners Insurance

Just as in the case of the liability policy, your property insurance should cover unexpected loss to your property. Most policy holders tend to be under-insured. **Some suggested coverage guidelines would include:**

$ Homeowners/renters insurance should cover at least 80% of the replacement value of your home, allowing for annual inflation. This will add additional cost to the policy, but it represents a necessary value.

Most policy holders tend to be under-insured.

$ You should also add replacement cost coverage for household contents, to avoid having to haggle with the insurer over the actual cash value of any losses.

$ If you have a special collection such as jewelry, guns, paintings, etc., you'll want to add a floater policy to your basic contract to cover the value of the collection over the minimum allowed in the basic plan.

$ Be aware that computer equipment and other material used to operate any business inside the home will necessitate additional coverage.

Liability Insurance: Wife _____ Husband _____

Homeowner/Renter Insurance: Wife _____ Husband _____

If you already have adequate coverage, place a check mark (✓) on the lines above.

If you need to add coverage, place a plus sign (+) on the lines above.

If you feel you can presently do without coverage, place a minus sign (-) on the lines above.

Discuss those which require change or further evaluation.

3. Automobile Insurance

Most automobile insurance policies today cover a standard which meets the minimum needs of most motorists. Following is a list of **five coverages you want to be sure are contained in your policy:**

$ Bodily injury and property liability: This insurance covers injury to pedestrians and occupants of other vehicles and damage done by you to the property of others. Discuss with your insurance agent the proper amount of coverage, being aware that the more assets you have accumulated, the higher the amounts of insurance you should purchase.

$ Medical payments insurance: This insurance will cover medical payments on behalf of the policyholder and family members, as well as other passengers in the vehicle. Ask your agent to compare the need for this insurance with what your health insurance policy will cover.

$ Uninsured motorist coverage: Although most states require a minimum amount of liability insurance for any vehicle, unfortunately some motorists disobey this law. Additionally, the minimum required may be under what is needed to compensate for actual loss. By purchasing this insurance, the policyholder will be covered for both uninsured and under-insured risks from other drivers.

$ Collision insurance: This insurance is usually required on any vehicle with a mortgage, or lease. It covers damage to the vehicle regardless of who actually caused the loss. If your vehicle is not financed, you may find it more economical to reduce or eliminate this coverage, particularly if your vehicle has little monetary value.

$ Comprehensive coverage: This insurance covers your vehicle from virtually all risks including theft, vandalism, collision with animals, etc.

4. Disability Insurance

Probably the greatest exposure that most working people face is loss of income from a disability. Yet, unless a good policy is provided by the employer, most people do not own nearly sufficient amounts of disability insurance to protect against such a loss.

Most people do not own nearly sufficient amounts of disability insurance to protect against such a loss.

Disability insurance is designed to replace your lost future wages in the event of an illness, or injury. For example, if you are currently earning $40,000 a year and expect to work for another 20 years, adjusting for inflation at 4%, even without any real increase in your salary, you will earn $1,191,123 over that time period. In other words, you and your family will expect at least 1.1 million dollars from your wages over the next 20 years in order to accomplish your dreams. So, if you suddenly became disabled and could not work any longer, your and the family's dreams would evaporate. Additionally, because along with a disability you can typically expect an increase in expenses, those dreams can become nightmares for the entire family.

Disability insurance protects wage earners from having to add financial tragedy on top of personal tragedy. Following are guidelines to look for when shopping for this insurance:

Disability insurance protects wage earners from having to add financial tragedy on top of personal tragedy.

$ Cover at least 65% of your earnings. If the policy is purchased by you, any benefits you receive will be tax free.

$ Extend the period of time between when the disability begins and when you start receiving benefits as long as your assets will provide. This will result in reduced premium rates.

$ Be sure to add some kind of inflation protection, and update your coverage annually.

$ If you are in a specialized field, you may want to add your "own occupation" to the definition of disability. This will add expense to the policy, but will allow you to collect benefits if you cannot perform the primary duties of the job you are working.

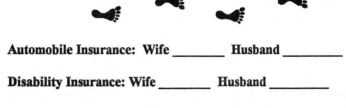

Automobile Insurance: Wife _____ Husband _____

Disability Insurance: Wife _____ Husband _____

If you already have adequate coverage, place a check mark (✓) on the lines above.
If you need to add coverage, place a plus sign (+) on the lines above.
If you feel you can presently do without coverage, place a minus sign (-) on the lines above.

Discuss those which require change or further evaluation.

5. Long Term Care Insurance

This type of insurance is quite similar to disability income insurance in that **it is designed to protect assets.** As our population grows more senior, we will increasingly find need for long term care (LTC) insurance. Understand, too, that Medicare is not intended to cover the costs associated with long term convalescent care. So, unless you intend to pay upwards of $40,000 a year for that care from your own assets, you'll need a well thought through LTC insurance policy.

Until the late 1980's, there was scant actuarial information available to insurance companies which could be used to establish baselines for benefits and premiums. Today, however, all of that has changed. There are a number of excellent plans available from reputable and established insurance companies. In fact, the way a long term insurance plan should be purchased today is through a "building process". There are numerous benefits which can be "built into" a plan in order to develop just the right package for any insured. For example, some individuals are quite adamant about their refusal to ever be interned at a convalescent home. For those individuals, a LTC plan with the primary benefits weighted toward home health care will not only allow them to remain in their home while receiving care, but also give them peace of mind as they face their twilight years.

There are so many types of benefits which can be customized into a LTC insurance plan, that there is insufficient space in this text for me to address each. Instead, I'll suggest the following **guidelines for you to use when considering LTC insurance:**

$ The primary need is for people approaching retirement who have a net worth of between $200,000 and $1,000,000. Below $200,000, the premiums might be prohibitively expensive when compared with income. Above $1,000,000, it might make more sense to pocket the premium and self-insure.

$ Remember that you are in the driver's seat. There are almost limitless ways you can arrange benefits to fit your need. Don't mistakenly buy a policy that a salesperson suggests. Rather, contact your state insurance commissioner's office and ask for information about LTC insurance. They will provide you with a pamphlet which details what to look for in a policy.

Remember you are in the driver's seat.

$ Don't be "penny wise and pound foolish." Add the benefits you need in the proportion which will provide you with what you are looking for. For example, let's say you want your insurance to cover the cost of any extended convalescent care you might need. If the average cost for that care in your area is running at $90 per day, don't buy a policy that covers only $65 a day. Additionally, make sure you add an inflation adjustment feature.

6. Medicare Supplement Insurance

Medicare supplement insurance is designed to cover the "gap" between what Medicare will pay in medical care expenses versus what you'll actually be charged. Instead of fully explaining the details of this type of insurance, because it will vary by state, and also because of its political component which causes it to change frequently, I suggest that you contact the state insurance commissioner's office and ask for their information pamphlet on Medicare supplement insurance. It will explain why this coverage is necessary for anyone who is a participant in the Medicare insurance program (age 65 and over), what types of standard policies can be obtained, and how to compare when shopping for this insurance.

Contact the state insurance commissioner's office and ask for their information pamphlet on Medicare supplement insurance.

Be aware that there is a six month "open enrollment" period surrounding your 65th birthday when you will be able to apply for this insurance without having to be

You **cannot be denied** this insurance *if you apply during this period.*

approved medically. In other words, you cannot be denied this insurance *if you apply during this period.* Beyond that six month period, you will have to go through an underwriting process, and it is quite possible your application will be turned down due to medical history.

Long Term Care Insurance: Wife _____ Husband _____

Medical Supplement Insurance: Wife _____ Husband _____

If you already have adequate coverage, place a check mark (✓) on the lines above.
If you need to add coverage, place a plus sign (+) on the lines above.
If you feel you can presently do without coverage, place a minus sign (-) on the lines above.

Discuss those which require change or further evaluation.

7. Health Insurance

Most people in America today have health insurance through their employer. Self employed workers and those not covered by a group plan will need to buy an individual policy. There are three types of plans on the market today: HMO's (health maintenance organizations), PPO's (preferred provider organizations), and traditional health plans. HMO's and PPO's will be less expensive than a traditional plan, but the policy will not usually be as flexible or portable as a traditional plan.

Following are some features you should make sure are part of your health insurance plan:

$ Comprehensive coverage which will cover you wherever you need treatment, and for "whatever ails you." Stay away from the cheaper policies which cover only certain types of illnesses, or injuries.

$ Acceptable and definite maximum out-of-pocket cost. Know what *your* maximum portion of any catastrophic claim would be.

$ Only purchase a health insurance policy which is *guaranteed renewable*. Comprehensive policies sold by reputable insurers which have a long history in the industry will almost always include this provision as part of the contract.

Never buy premium!

$ *Never buy premium!* Health insurance is like everything else in a free market — you get what you pay for. Don't shop for the lowest premium until you first (1) have the policy provisions you want, (2) know you are dealing with a financially secure insurer which has been in the health insurance business for many years, and (3) know that you can be approved medically for the policy.

8. Life Insurance

This is the type of insurance which people get tied to most emotionally.

OK, here we go. This is the one type of insurance which people get tied to most emotionally. They'll say things like, "I don't believe in whole life insurance," or "You should always buy term insurance and invest the difference" (between what your reduced cost is versus what you'd pay for the same amount of insurance purchased as a whole life policy). First of all, understand that life insurance has no place in your "belief" system; I *believe* in God the Father, but I don't ascribe that same level of value to a simple financial instrument! **Life insurance is an exceedingly important instrument in most people's financial planning** — that's all. Deal with it on an *intellectual level - not an emotional one.* Unfortunately, if you talk with a life insurance salesperson, you'll probably find yourself being taken down an emotional path. Recognize what is happening and redirect the discussion back to the intellectual level.

Most people are substantially under-insured. There are two reasons for this: first, they don't know how to calculate what their true need really is; and second, they think that even if they did know what their need was, they couldn't afford to purchase that amount of insurance. You can solve these problems by simply calculating what your need is and then shopping for the least expensive way to solve that need. A good rule of thumb is to have between five and ten times your annual earnings in life insurance coverage. To solve this need, start out by considering annual renewable term insurance. You will be amazed how inexpensively you can provide the amount of financial security your family deserves!

There are two additional points to consider before you actually make a purchase decision. The first one has to do with love, and the second one with taxes:

Life insurance might be considered **the greatest love letter you could ever write to your family.** If the most traumatic event did occur — a wage earning spouse/parent was to die — the emotional toll on the family would be incalculable. There is no way in our earthly world to mitigate that loss. However, we can substantially eliminate the accompanying financial loss. In fact, I will say that Christians have a responsibility to see to it they provide for their family whether they are alive, or dead! I bring this into this material because I have so often heard spouses say things like, "Oh, she'd get remarried," or "He could get a better job," when confronted with decisions regarding life insurance. So, here is my rule about the decision making process: before you decide on how much insurance to purchase, first assume you are already dead and looking down at your family left on earth — and you can now posthumously write a check to replace your lost income. How much do you want that check to be made out for?

The second point to consider is income taxes. Life insurance enjoys very special tax treatment. First, to the extent that your life insurance has a cash value (savings) portion to it such as whole life, or universal life, that savings element of the contract will grow tax deferred. In other words, you won't have to pay income tax on the gain until you pull out more than you have invested (the actual tax effects will vary). Second, life insurance death benefits are received by beneficiaries income tax free (except in rare instances where it is being used in a sophisticated plan). This is the first reason that attracts me, as a financial planner. Let me illustrate how powerful these benefits can be.

Let's say you are going to save $300 each month for the next 20 years. Investment A is currently taxable, but investment B is tax deferred. We'll assume the same hypothetical rate of return for both — say 12% annually. If you are in a 28% tax bracket, at the end of 20 years investment A would be worth $191,443 — but investment B would be worth $296,777! That's a difference of $105,334! Deferring the income tax on your investment gain can make a tremendous difference in the ending net value. So, if cash value life insurance offers a tax deferral advantage, we should certainly consider it for planning purposes. The actual decision whether to use cash value insurance instead of term, or which type of cash value insurance to use, and how much to invest will be contingent upon many additional factors beyond the scope of this chapter. **But I strongly suggest you and your Planner consider this special tax treatment** before you decide on how to solve your insurance need, as well as the most appropriate method for addressing your long term savings program.

If after you die you could write your family a check, for how much would it be?

Notes

I would recommend some form of straight term insurance or universal life.

Finally, in order to add some degree of counsel to the area of life insurance, I'll also state my opinion that **whole life insurance is an expensive, inflexible and obsolete type of life insurance.** I would recommend some form of straight term insurance or universal life, especially if you are considering an investment plan or if you are in a higher tax bracket,. To really give you some insight into what you can do with life insurance as a financial planning tool, I'll give you a peek at what I personally own. I have a variable universal life policy which offers as investment choices 12 non-proprietary mutual funds. These represent multiple asset classes which I have managed by a portfolio management process based on Modern Portfolio Theory. They offer a contractually guaranteed 'wash-loan' provision which allows me to access the profit from my investment without ever having to pay any income tax. **Now, that's a life insurance policy!** (However, certain situations could occur which might cause these tax benefits to be lost. That is why it is so important to rely on professional assistance.)

Health Insurance: Wife _____ Husband _____

Life Insurance: Wife _____ Husband _____

If you already have adequate coverage, place a check mark (✓) on the lines above.

If you need to add coverage, place a plus sign (+) on the lines above.

If you feel you can presently do without coverage, place a minus sign (-) on the lines above.

Discuss those which require change or further evaluation.

Write at least one personal application from today's study.

Wife: _____

Husband: _____

What does God want you to do to work out this application?

Wife: _____

Husband: _____

I Timothy 5:7, 8 — *Give the people these instructions, too, so that no one may be open to blame. If anyone does not provide for his relatives, and especially for his immediate family, he has denied the faith and is worse than an unbeliever.*

REFLECT TOGETHER: Read I Timothy 5:7, 8.

PRAY TOGETHER: Lord, the responsibility of providing all the needed insurance is overwhelming. Please give the wisdom and the determination to do all that you desire of us in this area.

Cash Flow, Budgeting, and Emergency Reserves

Solomon also had twelve district governors over all Israel, who supplied provisions for the king and the royal household. Each one had to provide supplies for one month in the year (I Kings 4:7).

We all know Solomon was wise. In fact, even the secular world refers to the *wisdom of Solomon*. In chapter 4 of I Kings, we not only learn that Solomon had considerable organizational structure to ensure provision, we even learn the names of the individuals who were responsible for providing those resources.

Knowing *where* your money comes from, *how much* money to expect, *when* to expect it, and *where* it will be allocated is probably the most fundamental dimension to the financial planning process.

Establishing A Budget

Most people look at budgeting as a necessary restraint. However, a properly thought out and workable budget actually produces a certain freedom that cannot be obtained any other way. A budget is a tool of financial discipline, much like God's Word is a tool of spiritual discipline. God's yoke is easy (Matthew 11:30). It assures our salvation and is our defense against the ravages of a sinful world. A budget, similarly, can be an easy way to avoid the tremendous pain and devastation brought on by unbridled spending — especially in a world swimming in consumer credit.

One aspect of the budget process that must not be overlooked has to do with balancing our needs and wants against *our actual* resources instead of our *available* resources. Too often people find themselves in terrible financial difficulty simply because they did not pay adequate attention to this profound difference. Your income and net worth represent a true reflection of your *actual resources*. Your *available resources* consist of your *credit* — which is, in reality, only a mirage. It tempts the less discerning with the promise of instant gratification. First, the mirage takes the shape of credit cards. Once those are expended, its shape becomes that of a home equity line of credit. Soon, that too, is exhausted and the resulting chronic pressure and frustration seeps into every aspect of life, especially the marriage!

A very appropriate admonition which fits here was spoken by General Robert E. Lee. The very prominent and popular icon of Virginia was seen walking through the city shortly after the Mexican War. Recognized by a lady walking with her young son, she asked the General what one thing she should teach her child which would have the greatest impact on his life. Gen. Lee paused and then responded, "Teach him to deny himself." When your *actual resources* — as documented in your budget — preclude additional purchases regardless of their attraction, and you begin to feel the temptation of spending beyond your means through credit, remember General Lee's "Deny yourself." There are few exceptions to this rule, and they would fall into the category of life emergencies, or business development. **Live within your means and you'll enjoy all of life's possibilities**; <u>live beyond your means, and you'll find that your life will be lived for the **benefit of your creditors**</u>!

Your budget should be a realistic reflection of both your goals and your financial resources. Remember, since God did not call all of us to teach, or to build, or to farm, or to program computers, to a large extent *your* budget will be quite different from that of your Christian brothers and sisters. On the other hand, every budget should reflect our common values by making provision for gifts, taxes and the basics of food,

Day 4

I Kings 4:7 — *Solomon also had twelve district governors over all Israel, who supplied provisions for the king and the royal household. Each one had to provide supplies for one month in the year.*

Matthew 11:30 — *"For my yoke is easy and my burden is light."*

Your income and net worth represent a true reflection of your *actual resources*.

Live beyond your means, and you'll find that your life will be lived for the **benefit of your creditors!**

Notes

clothing and shelter. Beyond these essentials, there are future responsibilities such as retirement. Finally, every budget must also include allocation for all the necessary insurances.

There are many excellent budget programs available. Whichever one you choose, remember these two points: **First**, any budget program's effectiveness is a function of 80% will, and 20% program. In other words, the budget program is only the mechanical part; it will be your commitment and discipline which will ultimately determine its value. **Second**, look for a budget program that fits your personality. The reason so many attempts at using time management programs fail, is that the program (the mechanical part) does not fit the personality. Do you think there might be legitimate personality differences between an engineer and an entertainer? Obviously, if a time management program - or a budget program - are to be effective, they will need to be **consistent with the user's personality.**

Have you done a working budget <u>together</u> for your family? Yes ___ No ___ Is it current? Yes ___ No ___

Any budget program will require that you identify monthly income and expenses. If you answered "No" to the last question, complete the following:

Monthly Income:

Include items with their corresponding amounts.

Monthly Expenses:

Total Monthly Income = _____   Total Monthly Expenses = _____

One final point before we consider emergency reserves. As we move toward the next century, we are being propelled into an entirely new world which offers unprecedented opportunity. There are two primary reasons for this: knowledge and technology. The body of all knowledge such as the hard sciences, humanities, politics, economics, etc. is growing at a geometric rate. This phenomenon is obvious in everything from the demise of the Soviet Union, to Modern Portfolio Theory, to the mass production of microchips. Technology will present humanity with previously unimaginable new opportunities. In Alvin Tofler's excellent work on this subject titled <u>Power Shift</u>, the author offers his readers a glimpse of one such evolving opportunity in the world of personal finance which will allow us to control every aspect of our financial affairs with a card the size of a credit card. With this one little instrument, you will be able to use the equity in your home (or car, or collection, or anything else) to purchase everything from mutual funds to groceries. In fact, we will soon become a virtually currency-less world, where financial transactions are accomplished by electronic means instead of cash.

What makes this evolution important for us as we consider choosing the most appropriate budget program, is that we must begin to see our financial resources as a **continuous part of a whole**, instead of distinctly separate and exclusive categories. For example, a budget program which suggests using a series of letter envelopes as a system for saving weekly for items such as food, clothing, entertainment, etc. might inadvertently teach the user to view his or her financial planning one dimensionally. I have often heard people refer to certain parts of their financial portfolio as "insurance dollars," or "college education dollars" in a way that excludes any opportunity for coordination. This **one-dimensional thinking** can keep us from taking advantage of certain "combinations," which could prove more efficient. An example of this might be comparing the value of a separate life insurance policy (insurance dollars) and separate college savings investment (college education dollars). In certain situations, it might be more efficient to **combine the two** into a cash value life insurance program, since any college savings investment will then enjoy added income tax benefits.

If we limit our budget planning to one-dimensional thinking, we will be completely unprepared for the new technology to which Alvin Tofler refers. Instead, just as the Apostle Paul admonished the new Corinthian believers to grow in their spiritual wisdom so as to be able to eat spiritual meat instead of only milk, we too must not allow the mechanics of a budget to hinder our **learning** and **growing**.

Discuss the advantages of seeing your financial resources as a "continuous part of a whole" versus the limiting, one dimensional view which separates your budget into exclusive categories.

Emergency Reserves

You should be sure you maintain a minimum of three to six months' expenses in "ready reserve." This money should be liquid; that is, it should be immediately accessible (able to be withdrawn within one week), have no penalties for withdrawal, and not be subject to additional taxes. Typically, these reserves should be placed in a **money market account** which offers free and unlimited check writing privileges.

Some people prefer to maintain high balances in these accounts. If you are one of these, keep in mind that money market accounts, checking accounts, and savings accounts are not designed as long term growth investments. Over time, you will probably be forfeiting considerable gain which you might have otherwise obtained by using a different financial instrument.

Remember; **the primary consideration** in establishing a ready reserve fund is **liquidity**.

The primary consideration in establishing a ready reserve fund is **liquidity**.

Summary

Research your local office supply store, or computer vendor for a budget program which *fits* your personality, your life-style, and your personal situation. Then consider your goals and your resources. Be realistic in establishing your budget. Allow for some "fun" in your life! Remember that making a budget work is 80% your will and 20% the program.

Making a budget work is 80% your will and 20% the program.

Your weekly and monthly budget will become part of your annual cash flow report. This vital information allows you to project into the future in order to determine whether you are making progress toward your long term goals.

Notes

Don't allow the mechanics of your budget program to instill one-dimensional thinking. Our world is changing dramatically, and we need to **grow with the changes** if we are to effectively manage our finances. And be sure your budget produces and maintains a liquid emergency *ready reserve* fund equal to three to six months' expenses.

The primary consideration in establishing a ready reserve fund of 3 to 6 months expenses is _____.

Making a budget work is ____% your will and ____% your budget program.

Write at least one personal application from today's study.

Wife: _____

Husband: _____

What does God want you to do to work out this application?

Wife: _____

Husband: _____

REFLECT TOGETHER: Read Luke 16:1-13. Who can be "trusted with much?" (v. 10)

PRAY TOGETHER: Lord, we want to be found faithful in managing the resources You have given us. Help us persevere in keeping a budget that meets Your standards.

Luke 16:10 — *"Whoever can be trusted with very little can also be trusted with much, and whoever is dishonest with very little will also be dishonest with much."*

Day 5

Proverbs 10:15 — *The wealth of the rich is their fortified city, but poverty is the ruin of the poor.*

Investment Planning And Retirement

The wealth of the rich is their fortified city, but poverty is the ruin of the poor (Proverbs 10:15).

Investments — stocks, bonds, and mutual funds, individual Retirement Accounts, 401(k)'s, Tax Sheltered Annuities, limited partnerships, oil and gas programs, tax credits, gold and precious metals — Where do we begin? It is easy to become confused when considering the proper investment program. Therefore, in order to gain the proper perspective, let's take a step backwards — to the right fundamentals. The scripture we quoted above is taken from a book in the Bible which is devoted to *wisdom.* Let's approach our study about investing in a *wise* manner. The American Heritage Dictionary defines wisdom as the "...understanding of what is true, right, or lasting. Common sense, good judgment." So, let's proceed based on what is true, right, lasting and of common sense and good judgment.

First, we must recognize that each of the investments listed above is neither right nor wrong. Rather, each is only *appropriate, or inappropriate.* For example, an investment in a natural gas program, which is considered speculative, where the investor has no liquidity and little net worth, would be an *inappropriate* investment. However, that same investment, used as part of a strategy to reduce taxable income by an investor who has ample liquidity, a strong net worth, and suffering from the effects of a sale of taxable, appreciated stock might be a very *appropriate* use of that investment. Each investment has its own unique characteristics, advantages, and disadvantages. Whether a particular investment should be included in your financial plan should be dictated by your **individual situation**, not the characteristics of the **investment**. Developing an appropriate investment plan requires a systematic and logical process. This is especially important to remember, because too often Christians invest emotionally instead of logically.

An investor should not purchase a certificate of deposit (CD) simply because it is FDIC insured. Similarly, one should not refrain from investing in mutual funds on the basis that their value will fluctuate. Rather, the question *whether* to invest in either a CD, or mutual funds, as well as *when* and in *what amounts* and for *what duration* should be approached solely on the basis of the **objectives of your plan**! How much money do you need? When do you need it? Will you need it in a lump sum or over a period of time? Should anyone else's needs be considered? How will this investment be funded — as a single deposit, or monthly installments? What are the income tax considerations?

When

What amounts

What duration

Objectives of your plan

Whether a particular investment should be included in your financial plan should be dictated by your _____ _____, not the characteristics of the _____.

Do You Have A Financial Junk Drawer?

Most people's investment portfolio looks something like a **junk drawer**. At home, your junk drawer probably has various items in it which have no **coordination** or **organization**: a ruler, flashlight, tape, rubber band, pencil. You never know what you are going to find when you open it, because there's really no commonality among the various items. Similarly, your investment portfolio might have in it a savings account, an IRA, a mutual fund, some stock, and an annuity. You bought each item somewhere along the way for various reasons which might have seemed good at the time, or because your friend went into the insurance business, or your father recommended the mutual fund, or your boss suggested a certain stock. But now you wonder if your emerging investment "program" really makes any sense. **Good question!**

Does your investment portfolio look like a junk drawer?

The Retirement Income Equation

"The best way to predict the future is to create it." *Wisdom.* Let's go back to our fundamentals and use them to help us approach the investment issue of planning a retirement income. As a context for the following, please keep in mind that all our numbers are hypothetical and that each individual investor needs to consider various

A postage stamp cost 3¢ in 1954.

risk factors before deciding to invest in any program. What follows is intended to present relative comparisons on a hypothetical and conceptual level. There is no assurance you would actually achieve similar results. Additionally, in the interest of simplifying the equation, income taxes have not been factored into the formulas.

We'll say that your objective is $4,000 a month beginning in 20 years and which will need to continue for the balance of your life — say, 30 years. Your **first task** is to consider *inflation*. $4,000 a month in 1996 is something quite different from an equal amount of dollars in 20 years. In fact, after adjusting for an inflation rate of 4%, you will need $8,890 the first month of your retirement if you want the same *purchasing power* as $4,000 today! And, because of inflation, that $8,890 is likely to continue to go up! (When I present this scenario before a live audience, I usually encounter some degree of disbelief regarding the numbers. So don't take my word for it, just take a look back in time to 1954. In that year a US first class postage stamp cost three cents, the average family car could be purchased for just over $2,700, and a loaf of bread cost 17 cents! The difference between the prices in 1954 and the cost of the same items today is the effect of *inflation*.)

The **next step** involves **adding up all the potential income sources** which will be available to help make up your retirement income. These sources might include a company sponsored retirement plan such as a 401(k), or an individual program such as an IRA. There may also be a pension or annuity benefit. Finally, you may or may not want to include social security benefits. I am of the opinion that the social security system as it exists in 1996 will be dramatically altered within a few years. Based on current funding and benefit projections, it will literally be impossible for social security to pay benefits to me that have been promised (I was born in 1955). Therefore, if you were born in 1950 or later, you might want to eliminate consideration of social security benefits from your available retirement income sources. After you have all of these projected values, you can then subtract this amount from your desired retirement income ($8,890 per month).

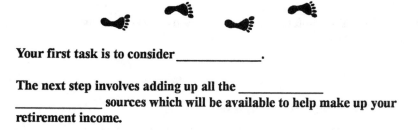

Your first task is to consider _____.

The next step involves adding up all the _____
_____ **sources which will be available to help make up your**
retirement income.

The **final step** in this process involves **accounting for the difference** between *your desired retirement income* and your *available retirement income*. For a simple example, let's assume your available retirement income will be $5,700 a month. Since your desired monthly income is $8,890, you will need to find a solution for the difference, which is $3,190 per month.

What a tremendous difference the rate of return on your investment makes!

Now comes the interesting part. How much money must you accumulate in the next 20 years in order to produce $3,190 a month for the rest of your life? (To simplify this example, we are not adjusting for inflation.) We'll assume a 30 year post-retirement life (in other words, the moment you use up all your money will be the moment you leave this earth). The answer to this question will be entirely contingent upon the rate of return your savings will be earning. For example, if you are able to achieve a 6% rate of return, you will need to have $534,726 on deposit the day you retire. However, if you are able to achieve an 8% return, you would only need $437,643. And a rate of return of 12% would require that you have $313,228 on deposit on the day you retire. You can see what a tremendous difference the rate of return on your investment makes! And that impact is even more noticeable if we carry this scenario to the present and consider how much you will need to invest each month between now and your retirement in order to reach your goal.

Once again, <u>the answer to this question is a function of the rate of return you will be earning on your investment</u>. A goal of $534,726 in 20 years (6%) will require a monthly investment of $1,157. If you are able to achieve an 8% return on your investment and have a goal of $437,643, your monthly investment will need to be $743. And at 12% with a goal of $313,228, you need only invest $317.

The operable question each of us must consider is, **"Are we being wise about our investment planning?"** This question has profound implications, because ultimately, a properly devised investment program (returning 12% on your investment) would require $840 a month less than one which is not as well thought through (at a rate of return of 6%). That $840 per month difference represents additional funds which could have been used to help fund a new addition to your church, assist a missionary family, or print and distribute Bibles. How big a difference might this sum turn out to be? <u>One $840 difference per month for 20 years totals a whopping $830,947 if the rate of return were 12%</u>. Just think, if there were 200 families in a church who would have given that money in 20 years had it been available, the amount they would have given would be $16,619,490. And if a city had 50 churches with 200 of such families in each church, the amount of money that could have been used to further Christian ministry in that city in 20 years would be an incredible $830,974,507! Do you think Christianity would have a greater impact in this world if a sum just under a billion dollars were invested in mission work, church growth, staff and personnel?

It is important we keep in mind that alternative sources of funding are simply not available. Corporations are not in the habit of underwriting Christian outreach and missions, and the federal and state governments certainly don't issue grants for such programs. Consequently, to the extent that we are not wise in our investment planning, **we literally *waste* tremendous sums of potential funding of God's work!** And all because we as a Church have not applied ourselves to learning the fundamentals of investing, to seeking professional counsel, and to following through on an appropriate investment strategy.

The final step in this process involves accounting for the difference between your _____ retirement income and your _____ retirement income.

Summary

As you approach the issue of developing an investment program, remember that the <u>first step is to do the math</u>. First determine *how much you will need, when you will need it, and for how long*. Then subtract your available income sources and determine your shortage. At this point you can begin finding solutions for that need, considering different rates of return. Once this math is accomplished, you can then begin the task of selecting appropriate investments which will best help you achieve your goal. Remember, rather than *emotionally* determining in advance whether you *like* a particular investment or not, instead search *logically* for those investments which may best *help you solve your investment goal*.

Although we considered only the hypothetical investment goal of retirement income, the process described above should be used for *any* investment goal: college education funding, a down payment on a home, or the dream of your own cabin in the woods.

Search logically for those investments which may best help you solve your investment goal.

Matthew 25:14 — *"Again, it will be like a man going on a journey, who called his servants and entrusted his property to them."*

Notes

Write at least one personal application from today's study.

Wife: _____

Husband: _____

What does God want you to do to work out this application?

Wife: _____

Husband: _____

REFLECT TOGETHER: Read Matthew 25:14-30. What did the man entrust to his servants? (v.14)

PRAY TOGETHER: Father, we know You have entrusted Your property to us. We want to be wise in the investment of Your resources. Give us discernment in the choices we face.

Day 6

Ecclesiastes 9:11 — *I have seen something else under the sun: the race is not to the swift, or the battle to the strong, nor does food come to the wise, or wealth to the brilliant, or favor to the learned; but time and chance happen to them all.*

Don't allow the fear of risk to control you!

Investment Risk

I have seen something else under the sun: the race is not to the swift, or the battle to the strong, nor does food come to the wise, or wealth to the brilliant, or favor to the learned; but time and chance happen to them all (Ecclesiastes 9:11).

Before we conclude our review of investment planning, a brief overview of the issue of investment risk might be helpful. The *concern* for risk many times paralyzes Christians. It is the fear of making a mistake. As our scripture points out, **life is full of chance, of risk.** Many times it seems the better course is to try to eliminate as much risk as possible and thereby reduce our pain and suffering. But as Larry Wilson points out in his corporate seminars: you can choose to live your life in an effort to *not lose*, or you can live your life *to win*. In that decision lies the difference between a purposeful life which God will use, and simply existing. Risk, whether in life, or investing, is inevitable. Approach it with care, prudence, and awareness, but **don't allow the fear of it to control you.**

As you consider various investments, you will be confronted with many different types of risk, all of which need to be investigated. Everyone is familiar with **market risk.** Market risk is that which you would accept if you invested in a variable investment, that is, one which will fluctuate in value, such as a mutual fund. **Purchasing power risk** is that which would be assumed by someone who invested all their money in something which held little prospect for growth, such as a savings account, or money market fund. **Financial risk** and **business risk** are associated with investments in specific and singular investments, such as one company, or one industry. This risk is easily eliminated almost entirely through diversification. Finally, **liquidity risk** refers to an investment which is not easily redeemable at a reasonable price.

All investments hold some form of risk. It is impossible to eliminate all risk. However, it is both possible and prudent to *manage your risk* through a properly developed and well managed investment program. Don't let the concern for risk paralyze you. It is possible to make some mistakes along the way and still come out better than if you chose what appeared to be the *safe* alternative. Consider the following hypothetical comparison between Gary, the more aggressive investor, and Thomas who is more concerned with *safety* than with results. They both plan to retire in 20 years, and each needs to accumulate $500,000 within that time in order to retire comfortably. In our comparison, we'll say they each start with $100,000 in cash.

Gary decided to split his $100,000 equally — $25,000 into four different investments, each with varying types and degrees of risk. After 20 years, those investments achieved the following results: one investment failed completely and he lost all his money ($0); one achieved a 3% average annual return ($45,153), one achieved an 8% return ($116,524), and the other achieved 15% ($409,163) — for a total of $570,840.

Gary's friend Thomas was skeptical and decided to put all his money into a safe investment where he would not be exposed to market risk, business risk, liquidity risk, or financial risk. Thomas chose a CD because it offered guarantees. Over the 20 years it returned an average of 6.5%. At the end of that time, his total was only $352,365!

Intuition might suggest that since Gary actually lost *all* of one of his investments and saw only a minimal return on one other, that the more prudent path would have been the one which Thomas chose. However, when it comes to investment planning, a *logical strategy* will **almost always produce better results** than one which is simple, offers guarantees, and only makes us *feel* safe.

A logical strategy will almost always produce better results than one which is simple, offers guarantees, and only makes us feel safe.

Discuss why a logical strategy will almost always produce better results than one which is simple, offers guarantees, and only makes us feel safe.

Income Taxes

Tell us then, what is your opinion? Is it right to pay taxes to Caesar, or not? ... Then he said to them, 'Give to Caesar what is Caesar's, and to God what is God's' (Matthew 22:17, 21).

The United States Tax Code places the burden for determining how much is "Caesar's" on each individual citizen. It distresses me to hear a well intentioned, but naïve Christian proclaim they *gladly* pay their taxes. Sometimes this kind of attitude camouflages the fact that *too much tax* is being paid unnecessarily. The philosophical issue of just how much is enough came before the courts in 1947 in *Commissioner v. Newman* when justice Learned Hand wrote, " Over and over again courts have said that there is nothing sinister in so arranging one's affairs as to keep taxes as low as possible. Everybody does so, rich or poor, and all do right, for nobody owes any public duty to pay more than the law demands: taxes are enforced exactions, not voluntary contributions. To demand more in the name of morals is mere cant." So, from both our Scripture in Matthew 22 *and* the tax court, we can proceed to review the US income tax system with the philosophical premise that while we should pay our taxes, we *should not* pay any more tax than that which is required.

Matthew 22:17, 21 — *Tell us then, what is your opinion? Is it right to pay taxes to Caesar, or not? ...Then he said to them, 'Give to Caesar what is Caesar's, and to God what is God's'.*

Notes

Discuss your opinion about the philosophical premise that while we should pay our taxes, we *should not* pay any more tax than that which is required.

Investing And Income Tax

Never make an investment exclusively on the basis of tax implications.

There are few absolutes in the world of investment planning. However, one which comes close is that you should **never make an investment exclusively on the basis of tax implications.** There are few exceptions to this. One exception might be IRC section 42 (affordable housing program) and the tax credits it offers. Other possible exceptions might be certain types of qualified energy programs. However, as an operating rule of thumb, investments should be made for their *economic potential*, with income tax considerations an auxiliary part of the decision process.

Investments should be made for their economic potential.

One more general rule might be helpful to point out. Usually, there is a corollary between *tax benefit and loss of liquidity*. For example, an investment in an annuity enjoys tax deferred status on any subsequent gain. However, any distribution from that annuity prior to age 59 ½ will be treated as income-out-first (LIFO), and the gain will be subject to a 10% tax penalty. So much for liquidity.

There are numerous investments which offer enticing income tax advantages. When properly arranged, for example, annuities and life insurance encounter no income tax on the gain in the contract cash value until there is a distribution. This tax advantage is referred to as **tax deferral**. Municipal bonds are generally free of federal income tax, and may also be free of state income tax. The dividends on these investments are then said to be **tax exempt**. As pointed out earlier, an investment in a properly managed section 42 affordable housing program may offer tax credits. **Tax credits are the most powerful tax advantage**, since *each dollar of credit* reduces by *one dollar your tax liability*.

Tax credits are the most powerful tax advantage.

One of the most common mistakes people make is to equate a tax benefit with the underlying investment. For example, I have heard people say they would not invest in an IRA again, because it had a poor rate of return. In fact, the portion of the tax code which authorizes Individual Retirement Accounts (IRA's) distinctly lists the types of investments which may qualify for special tax advantage. A mutual fund might be categorized as **tax-exposed** (meaning any dividends, interest, or capital gains would be taxable in the year they are earned), or **tax deferred** in the case of an IRA. It might even be offered as a "separate account" in a variable annuity or variable universal life contract, and qualify as tax deferred as a result. So, be careful you don't mistakenly assume that any special tax advantage an investment is qualified to receive is synonymous with the underlying investment itself.

It is almost always preferable to defer income taxes on investments.

Finally, although our philosophical premise which states we should not pay any more tax than what we truly owe suggests that we use all tax advantages we are provided, this may not always be true. For example, there is a continuing debate over whether a participant in a qualified retirement plan — such as a 401(k) — is best served by investing the maximum allowed, thereby reducing his taxable income. Part of the answer to this apparent dilemma lies in the determination of what our net after-tax result will be. It is almost always preferable to defer income taxes on investments, but the investor must also compare what an expected rate of return on the tax deductible 401(k) investment would be versus a nondeductible tax deferred alternative, such as a variable annuity. The 401(k) might offer few investment choices and no professional management, while the alternative variable annuity may offer 30 different investment options and a choice of professional portfolio management styles. If this is the case, it is quite possible that even though the 401(k) is tax deductible, it will show poorer investment performance over time. I must quickly point out that I am referring to that portion of the participant's contribution to the 401(k) which would otherwise not be eligible for a company match. It is almost always preferable to invest enough to qualify for the maximum company match.

Considering all the details of investing, tax credits and benefits, loss of liquidity, employer matching portions of 401(k)'s, etc., how qualified do you feel to make appropriate financial decisions on your own?

Discuss whether you currently need competent financial counsel in these areas, and where you will seek it.

Write at least one personal application from today's study.

Wife: _____

Husband: _____

What does God want you to do to work out this application?

Wife: _____

Husband: _____

REFLECT TOGETHER: Read Matthew 22:15-22.

PRAY TOGETHER: Lord, we want to be more than merely "safe" investors, we want to be "wise" investors. Grant us discernment to give Ceasar only what is his, not what is Yours.

Matthew 22:21 — *"Give to Ceasar what is Ceasar's, and to God what is God's."*

A good man leaves an inheritance for his children's children... (Proverbs 13:22).

In Strong's <u>Concordance Of The Bible</u> there are a total of 237 verses of Scripture listed which contain the word *inheritance*. Did you know there are only 96 verses with the word *forgive or forgiven* in them? This comparison helps us understand with proper perspective how important the concept of *inheritance* is in God's eyes.

The material worth we accumulate on this earth can be used to glorify God in the next generation only if we protect it through developing an appropriate estate transfer program. There are almost countless ways your estate may be eroded after your death. Most often, however, the primary reason has more to do with the lack of an effective transfer process being in place *prior* to death.

The most popular means of transferring our possessions to others as an inheritance is

Day 7

Proverbs 13:22 — *A good man leaves an inheritance for his children'*

Notes

If you die without a will, the state then dictates by statute how your possessions will be distributed.

Will

Living Trust

Living Will

through the use of a will. The will is, in its most basic form, a **letter of instructions** which is usually administered through the state probate court system. Although many states have improved on this process by making it less time-consuming and expensive, still those two dimensions to the process can add a great deal to the survivors' stress and frustration. However, the worst situations develop when the deceased failed to leave a will at all! In these situations the probate court administers what are referred to as the laws of intestacy. In fact, <u>if you die without a will, the state then dictates by statute how your possessions will be distributed</u>. This causes tremendous grief and frustration among sometimes competing family interests, all of which could have been avoided through proper planning.

One way people are addressing the concerns of cost, time and lack of privacy in the management and transfer of an estate is through the use of a **living trust**. This process begins the estate management process while the parties are still alive by transferring all assets to the trust. There may be some additional effort, time and expense involved in setting up a living trust when compared with a simple will; but there will be considerably less hassle, cost and frustration at the time of death, or cognitive disability, because **a trust would not be subject to the probate court process**. My suggestion is to consult with a financial planner and attorney to determine whether a will or a living trust would be most appropriate in your particular situation.

Another item you will need to address is that of a **living will**. This document sets forth your wishes regarding life support systems. You will want to consult family and your pastor for proper counsel before signing such a document.

Estate Taxes

A thorough review of the Unified Transfer Tax (estate and gift tax) is well beyond the scope of this chapter. However, be aware that unless you have a properly constructed will which includes a **Credit Shelter trust**, you may be positioning your family for a severe estate tax bite at a later date. Each citizen is allowed to use tax credits which equal an equivalent exemption of $600,000. In other words, every person may pass up to $600,000 in possessions on to others. The problem arises when a couple decides to use the Unlimited Marital Deduction and one spouse passes the entire value of their portion of the estate to their surviving spouse. When the transfer is made this way, it effectively eliminates the opportunity to apply the otherwise available tax credits to the decedent's portion of the combined estate. Over time, it may be that the real estate, savings, retirement account, business, stock and other property in the decedent's estate combined with the survivor's portion will exceed $600,000. At this point, there may be federal estate tax liability on any portion exceeding that $600,000. Keep in mind the minimum tax rate begins at 37% and goes all the way up to 55%! When combined with state inheritance tax, income tax, and any excess accumulation tax, or excise tax, it is possible the ultimate beneficiaries may receive well below 50 cents on each dollar.

The obvious approach is to plan!

The obvious approach to this problem is **to plan**. Plan your investments so you won't trigger excise, or excess accumulation taxes. Use financial strategies which reduce the ultimate impact of income taxes. And above all, <u>be sure you are positioned through proper planning to take full advantage of any tax credits you might be able to use</u>.

He is not finished when we are!

Maybe the emphasis placed on inheritance in Scripture is there because an apathetic attitude about the issue would tend to suggest ultimate selfishness. A "since we can't take it with us, we really don't care what happens to it" attitude. But according to God, we should care. **He is not finished when we are.** His purpose, His truth, His ministry lives on. Our selfishness and callousness is exposed when we don't glorify the Lord by preserving the material wealth He gave us during our life, so that future generations and His church on earth might carry on.

Discuss how important leaving an inheritance is to you and your family.

Do you have a current and adequate will in place? Yes _____ No _____

Does consideration of a living trust or estate and gift tax effects
warrant getting additional financial counsel at this time?
Yes _____ No _____

Effective Financial Planning Review

As Christians, we know our life here on earth is not simply a random event. We know
that God placed us here to live life according to His purpose. We are to continually
grow in our understanding of all things, so that we might be better stewards of our
potential, our resources, and His grace and love. <u>The more we learn, the more we can
apply.</u>

Financial planning is a tremendously important part of our life with Christ. Through
the laws of economics we can arrange our financial resources in such a way that we
maximize their value. Our specialized world now offers professionally trained
financial planners who can help us develop and manage an appropriate plan for our
unique situation and needs. Through proper insurance planning we can live life
without the threat of financial catastrophe. The technological and political develop-
ments of the late twentieth century present countless investment opportunities for us to
select from and construct an investment plan which can best help us reach our
financial goals. Our tax code, fleecing as it is, still makes it possible for us to pay only
those taxes which are necessarily due "Uncle Caesar." And through a properly
devised estate transfer program, we can look forward to leaving behind a material
legacy which will benefit our families and our church.

The more we learn, the more
we can apply

<u>Whether we effectively manage our financial resources or not is entirely up to each of
us.</u> There is both an earthly accounting and a heavenly accounting. *That servant who
knows his master's will and who does not get ready, or does not do what his master
wants, will be beaten with many blows. But the one who does not know and does
things deserving punishment will be beaten with few blows. From everyone who has
been given much, much will be demanded; and from the one who has been entrusted
with much, much more will be asked* (Luke 12:47,48).

There is both an earthly
accounting and a heavenly
accounting.

In the United States of the late twentieth century, truly we have been given much.

With respect to what you have learned about effective financial
planning, how would you evaluate your current status? (with 10
being perfect)

Wife: 1   2   3   4   5   6   7   8   9   10 (circle one)

Husband: 1   2   3   4   5   6   7   8   9   10 (circle one)

Of the wealth of information in this chapter, identify 3 areas which
need more attention.

Wife: _____ _____ _____

Husband: _____ _____ _____

Notes

Determine together which of the above areas are top priority. Formulate your strategy for becoming effective financial planners in these areas.

> **Write at least one personal application from today's study.**
>
> Wife: _____
>
> Husband: _____
>
> **What does God want you to do to work out this application?**
>
> Wife: _____
>
> Husband: _____

I Chronicles 29:19 — *And give my son Solomon the wholehearted devotion to keep your commands, requirements and decrees and to do everything to build the palatial structure for which I have provided.*

REFLECT TOGETHER: Read I Chronicles 29:14-20. What inheritance did David leave Solomon?

PRAY TOGETHER: Father, thank You for the inheritance You have provided for us. Help us be diligent to provide a worthy inheritance for our family, both materially and spiritually.

GROUP DISCUSSION: If this study is being used in a group setting,

discuss the following questions with your group.

1. Why do you think many Christians want to live a life which is "normal, routine, fits in and doesn't call attention," rather than a life of "passion."

2. Look at the five primary dimensions to the financial planning process (p. 181), and discuss each.

3. Of the 8 insurances discussed in Day 3, identify the most important one you do not have. Why is it important?

4. Why is it important to have a workable budget and an emergency reserve? (see Day 4)

5. Of all the information presented in Days 5-7 about investments, retirement planning and leaving an inheritance, what do you feel is the most valuable? Why?

6. Discuss the Christian's financial responsibility for carrying out the Great Commission, including the example discussed on pages 199-200. (see also pages 177 and 179)

Have a frank discussion

Stephen R. Bolt, CFP and author of Chapter 9, "Effective Financial Planning."

Stephen graduated from the University of Alabama in 1978, and later earned his Certified Financial Planner designation from the College for Financial Planning, Denver, Colorado. He began his career in the financial services industry in 1981.

He is now president of

(1) **Shepherd Financial Group**, a financial planning firm which focuses primarily on the Christian Community;

(2) **Synergy Asset Management System, Inc.**, an advanced portfolio management program based on Modern Portfolio Theory;

(3) **Shepherd Corporate Consulting Services**, which designs and manages Corporate qualified retirement plans;

(4) and **Shepherd Socially Responsible Investing**, the first portfolio management system which attempts to screen out investments which might be offensive to Christian values. He is also host of a daily radio program — "Financial Point." Stephen Bolt can be contacted at Shepherd Financial Group, 112 Long Hollow Pike, Suite 208, Goodlettsville, TN 37072 — (615)859-6942.

Stephen R. Bolt, CFP

Stephen R. Bolt is a Registered Representative offering Securities through FFP Securities Inc., Member NASD/SIPC and a Registered Investment Advisor-Agent offering services through FFP Advisory Services Inc., a Registered Investment Advisor with the Securities and Exchange Commission.

Note: If you would like an individual comprehensive financial analysis prepared for you, you may contact Shepherd Financial Group (Nashville, TN) at 800-632-6363. You will be provided the necessary paperwork and instructions, as well as a planner with whom you may discuss the report. (There is a fee for this service.)

If you would like help in finding a qualified financial planner in your area who shares a Christian perspective and Christian values, we would be happy to assist you.

Recommended Financial Planning Reading List

The ABC's of Managing Your Money, by Jonathon D. Pond, National Endowment for Financial Education, 1993

How to Win the Losers Game in Investment Management, by Charles D. Ellis, Irwin Professional Publishing, 1985

Power Shift, by Alvin Tofler, New York Bantam Books, 1990

COUPLE GOAL SETTING
Chapter 10

Day 1

This chapter will be different from all the others. It will be somewhat like a workshop, without your actually being in a workshop. Goals are extremely important in our lives. If we **don't** have goals, we **can not** reach them. (Profound, huh?) Most people think of goals in a business context, but they are essential in our personal lives as well.

GOALS — What Are They?

Purposes, Objectives and Goals: Purpose is the over-all general direction we want to take. We say, "Our purpose in life is...." It's very broad and far-reaching. God is clear about His purpose in our lives. Romans 8:28-29 declares, *And we know that in all things God works for the good of those who love him, who have been called according to his purpose. For those God foreknew he also predestined to be conformed to the likeness of his Son, that he might be the firstborn among many brothers.*

An objective is still rather general, but is more narrow than "purpose." Within one purpose, we might have three or four objectives. Within our life's purpose of wanting God to "conform [us] to the likeness of his Son," we can have the objective of reading God's Word on a regular basis to find out about His plan for our lives. We might also have the objective to obey what He says and another objective to pray daily about our walk with Him.

When we speak of goals, however, we are being **specific**. That's what we want to be in this chapter — specific. So let's talk specifically about what elements a goal needs to have.

Elements of a good goal: Goals must be...

Realistic

REALISTIC: If my goal is to lose fifty pounds by next Wednesday, would that meet the criteria of a good goal? No, it's not realistic. But if my goal is to lose fifty pounds in eight months, that would be realistic. We must keep our goals realistic or they won't mean anything, and we will feel like failures.

Specific

SPECIFIC enough to be measurable: If my goal is stated, "I want to lose a lot of weight in eight months or so," is that a good goal? No, it's not specific and can not be measured. How will I know if I've lost enough weight? Let's restate the goal to read, "I want to lose 50 pounds by August 30 of this year (eight months away)." Stated this way, the goal is specific enough to be **measurable**.

Time Limited

TIME LIMITED: What if my goal is, "I want to lose 50 pounds as soon as possible." Does that do it? No, there is no time boundary. When is "as soon as possible"? But if I say, "I want to lose 50 pounds in eight months, which would be by August 30 of this year," that is a well stated goal. It's realistic, specific enough to be measurable and limited by time.

The 3 elements of a good goal are:

1. _____

2. _____

3. _____

Romans 8:28-29 — *And we know that in all things God works for the good of those who love him, who have been called according to his purpose. For those God foreknew he also predestined to be conformed to the likeness of his Son, that he might be the firstborn among many brothers.*

Is Goal Setting Scriptural?

We are to "count the cost" of projects and involvements: Luke 14:28:30 — *Suppose one of you wants to build a tower. Will he not first sit down and estimate the cost to see if he has enough money to complete it? For if he lays the foundation and is not able to finish it, everyone who sees it will ridicule him, saying, 'This fellow began to build and was not able to finish.'*

We are advised to sit down and plan, to think things through before we proceed with them. Otherwise, we might end up with a lot of unfinished towers in our lives. Can you think of a few unfinished towers in your life?

Our goals must please the Lord. 2 Corinthians 5:9 — *So we make it our goal to please him, whether we are at home in the body or away from it.*

We must consult God's Word to ensure that our goals are in line with biblical principles. His Word reveals many things about how we should conduct our lives. Setting goals that change our life style and behavior to reflect His ideals will naturally please Him. We also need to submit our goals to the Lord. Sometimes, we might choose a worthy goal, but He has other plans. For instance, we may set a goal to save a certain amount of money, but He may want us to offer the money for His service. As we search His Word and submit our goals to Him, He will guide us.

"So we make it our _____ to _____ him, whether we are at home in the body or away from it" (2 Corinthians 5:9).

We are to "care for our own." 1 Timothy 5:8 — *If anyone does not provide for his relatives, and especially for his immediate family, he has denied the faith and is worse than an unbeliever.*

This verse gives us a specific objective: to provide for our family. To fullfill this responsibility, we need to have specific goals. We must determine many things, such as how much we need to earn, where we want to live, and what we can afford to buy. As you can see, this one accomplishment — providing for our family — requires several goals.

Luke 14:28:30 — *Suppose one of you wants to build a tower. Will he not first sit down and estimate the cost to see if he has enough money to complete it? For if he lays the foundation and is not able to finish it, everyone who sees it will ridicule him, saying, 'This fellow began to build and was not able to finish.'*

2 Corinthians 5:9 — *So we make it our goal to please him, whether we are at home in the body or away from it.*

1 Timothy 5:8 — *If anyone does not provide for his relatives, and especially for his immediate family, he has denied the faith and is worse than an unbeliever.*

> **Write at least one personal application from today's study.**
>
> Wife: _____
>
> Husband: _____
>
> **What does God want you to do to work out this application?**
>
> Wife: _____
>
> Husband: _____

Notes

REFLECT TOGETHER: Read 2 Corinthians 5:6-10. Do goals reflect the way we live our lives and visa versa?

PRAY TOGETHER: Lord, we want our goals to please You. As we plan for the future, we commit every goal to You.

Day 2

Goal-Setting in Nine Areas of Life

Definition - Sample - Writing of Goal: We have identified nine areas of life in which we all need to set goals. They are: (1) Marriage, (2) Spiritual life, (3) Parenting/family, (4) Vocation, (5) Physical life, (6) Finances, (7) Recreation, (8), Emotional life, (9) and Social life. Before going any farther, find your goal sheets at the end of this chapter. You each have one on the front and back of the last page. If you find it more convenient to tear them out for ease of use with the following exercises, feel free to do so.

As we go through each area, we will first define the goal, then give you a sample of what we're talking about. Finally, we will ask you to write out your own goal in each area on your goal sheets. As you write your goals, keep in mind that each goal you make impacts your marriage relationship and your coupleness. Try for goals which will enhance your coupleness, not tear it down. **Don't give each other suggestions or look at one another's goals.** You'll have plenty of time to discuss your goals on day 6.

Marriage Goal

1. **Marriage goal definition** — Goals that affect the husband-wife relationship.

   Sample — "Plan a date for the entire day for our anniversary at least three weeks ahead of the day."

   Write a Marriage goal on your goal sheet, making sure it is realistic, specific and time limited.

Spiritual Goal

2. **Spiritual goal definition** — Goals that affect our relationship with God and church.

   Sample — "Have devotions with my spouse at least four times per week for 15-20 minutes each time."

   Write a Spiritual goal on your goal sheet, making sure it is realistic, specific and time limited.

Parenting/Family Goal

3. **Parenting/Family goal definition** — Goals that affect our relationships with our children or relatives.

   Sample — "Plan a date with each of my children for 2 hours apiece within the next 2 months."

Write a Parenting/Family goal on your goal sheet, making sure it is realistic, specific and time limited.

Write at least one personal application from today's study.

Wife: _____

Husband: _____

What does God want you to do to work out this application?

Wife: _____

Husband: _____

REFLECT TOGETHER: Read Ephesians 2:6-10. Did you know God has goals for you?

PRAY TOGETHER: Dear Father, we submit our goals to You. Guide us in making them, and show us if we need to change them.

4. **Vocational goal definition** — Goals that affect our career pursuits.

   Sample — "Start classes for my Master's Degree by September of this year."

   Day 3

   Vocational Goal

   Write a Vocational goal on your goal sheet, making sure it is realistic, specific and time limited.

5. **Physical goal definition** — Goals that affect our bodies.

   Physical Goal

   Sample — "Take a 30 minute walk at least 4 times per week after dinner, starting this week."

   Write a Physical goal on your goal sheet, making sure it is realistic, specific and time limited.

Notes

Financial Goal

6. **Financial goal definition** — Goals that affect our monetary welfare.

   Sample — "Collect a savings account of $2000 for emergencies by November of this year."

Write a Financial goal on your goal sheet, making sure it is realistic, specific and time limited.

Wife: _____

Husband: _____

Write at least one personal application from today's study.

Wife: _____

Husband: _____

What does God want you to do to work out this application?

Wife: _____

Husband: _____

REFLECT TOGETHER: Read 2 Corinthians 9:6-8. Sounds like God wants us to keep our goals about giving, doesn't it?

PRAY TOGETHER: Dear God, we know that fulfilling our goals is very important to You. Help us take our goals seriously and keep them diligently.

Day 4

Recreational Goal

7. **Recreational goal definition** — Goals that affect our fun and relaxation pursuits.

   Sample — "Plan a two week summer vacation for this summer. Have planning done and reservations made by June 1."

Write a Recreational goal on your goal sheet, making sure it is realistic, specific and time limited.

8. **Emotional goal definition** — Goals that the affect the well-being of our mind, heart and souls.

Sample — "Read one book strictly for pleasure each month."

Write an Emotional goal on your goal sheet, making sure it is realistic, specific and time limited.

9. **Social goal definition** — Goals that affect interpersonal relationships or civic welfare.

Social Goal

Sample — "Have one couple in our home for a social time at least once per month, starting next month."

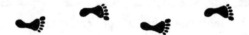

Write a Social goal on your goal sheet, making sure it is realistic, specific and time limited.

Write at least one personal application from today's study.

Wife: _____

Husband: _____

What does God want you to do to work out this application?

Wife: _____

Husband: _____

REFLECT TOGETHER: Read Proverbs 20:24 and James 4:13-17. Do we have enough wisdom to set goals on our own?

PRAY TOGETHER: We know the goals we set, Lord, are important to You, because they influence our daily walk. So again we submit our plans to You, since You alone understand our way.

Notes

Day 5

Working With Your Goal Worksheets.

You will be working with your goal sheets to complete this exercise. It is our hope that this exercise will help you think through your goals: why they are important to you, where they come from, whether they are viable or not, etc. Again, **do this without looking at your mate's worksheet!**

Place a star (*) beside the **4 goals** you feel are most important to your marriage. Then number them in order of importance — 1 through 4.

Place a zero (0) beside the **two goals** you would be willing to live without if it were absolutely necessary. These, of course, should be chosen from the remaining five goals. This does not eliminate these two goals. It is simply a tool to help you decide which are the least and which are the most important.

Place a dollar sign ($) beside each goal that costs money.

Place a "P" beside those influenced by your parents, from either a negative or positive point of view. Positive: "I want to have family devotions just like my parents had with me." Or negative: "I want to have family devotions because my parents never had them, and I don't want our children to miss out."

Which are the most important?

Knowing what you're aiming at isn't enough. You must take the steps needed to "reach the target."

Place an "S" beside those you think your spouse has written down. No peeking!

Which goals does God think are important?

Place a cross (+) beside the goals you feel God considers important. You might mark only a few or all of them. Think carefully and answer honestly.

Write a few sentences about one of your goals. Choose whichever one you wish and write two or three sentences explaining the importance of that goal to your marriage.

Wife:

_____

_____

_____

_____

_____

_____

The importance of the goal to your marriage.

Husband:

_____

_____

_____

_____

_____

_____

Write at least one personal application from today's study.

Wife: _____

Husband: _____

What does God want you to do to work out this application?

Wife: _____

Husband: _____

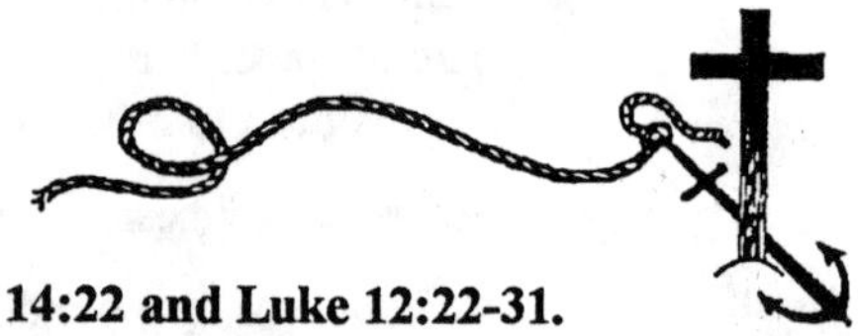

REFLECT TOGETHER: Read Proverbs 14:22 and Luke 12:22-31. If you seek God's will and kingdom first, what will you receive?

PRAY TOGETHER: Dear God, we want to plan good plans, ones You consider important. May our goals bring glory to You.

Notes

Day 6

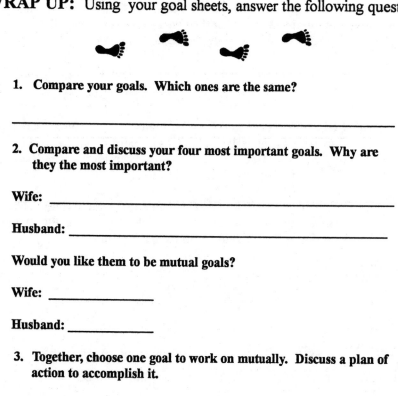

WRAP UP: Using your goal sheets, answer the following questions.

1. Compare your goals. Which ones are the same?

_____

2. Compare and discuss your four most important goals. Why are they the most important?

Wife: _____

Husband: _____

Would you like them to be mutual goals?

Wife: _____

Husband: _____

3. Together, choose one goal to work on mutually. Discuss a plan of action to accomplish it.

Write that mutual goal here:

_____

REFLECT TOGETHER: Re-read Luke 14:28-30.

PRAY TOGETHER: Father God, help us keep our goals and promises so we won't have any more unfinished towers in our lives and relationship. Don't let us forget the plans we have made this week.

Pray over your goal sheets, asking God to help you keep your goals and promises. Then tape them both to the front of your refrigerator or bathroom mirror. Don't stick them in a drawer and forget about them. Keep your goals (and your goal sheets) in sight.

REFLECT TOGETHER: Read Daniel 1:8-16. What goal had Daniel set for himself? (v. 8) Was it realistic, specific and time limited? (vv. 11-14) Was it a goal God considered important? Did God honor Daniel's goal? (vv. 15-16)

PRAY TOGETHER: Oh, God, we want to "be resolved" like Daniel to follow through on our goals. Thank You that we, like Daniel, can experience the rewards of fulfilling our goals.

Group Discussion: If you are using this study in a group of couples, the following questions should be used as group discussion:

1. Read Luke 14:28-30 and discuss some examples of "unfinished towers."

2. Read James 4:13-17 and discuss what it means and how it can be applied.

3. Have each share one goal they wrote during this study, and have the group determine how well they meet the three criteria for good goals (see Day 1).

4. Have each couple share the mutual goal they wrote in Day 6 and how they plan to achieve it.

Have a frank discussion

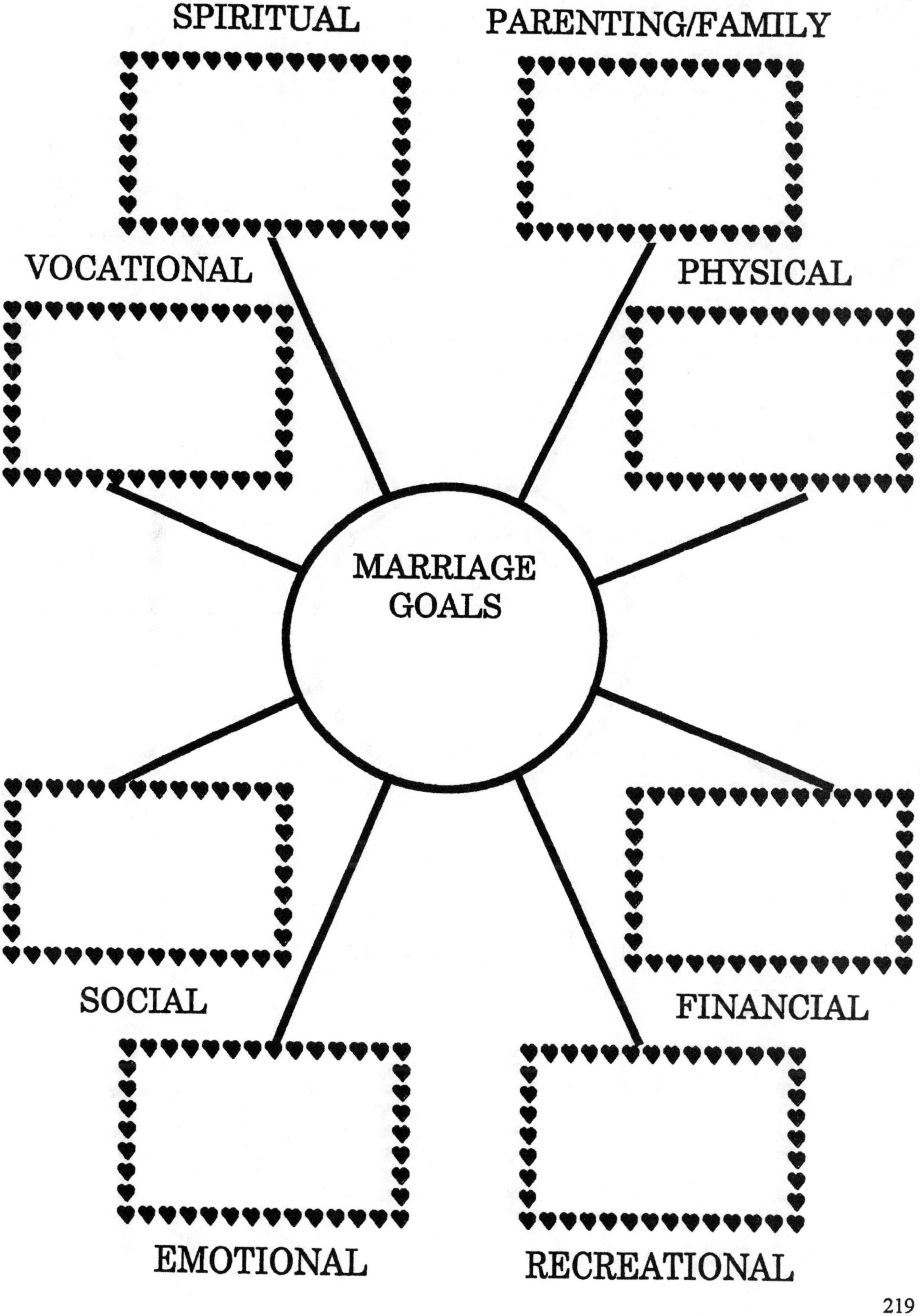

SPIRITUAL

PARENTING/FAMILY

VOCATIONAL

PHYSICAL

MARRIAGE GOALS

SOCIAL

FINANCIAL

EMOTIONAL

RECREATIONAL

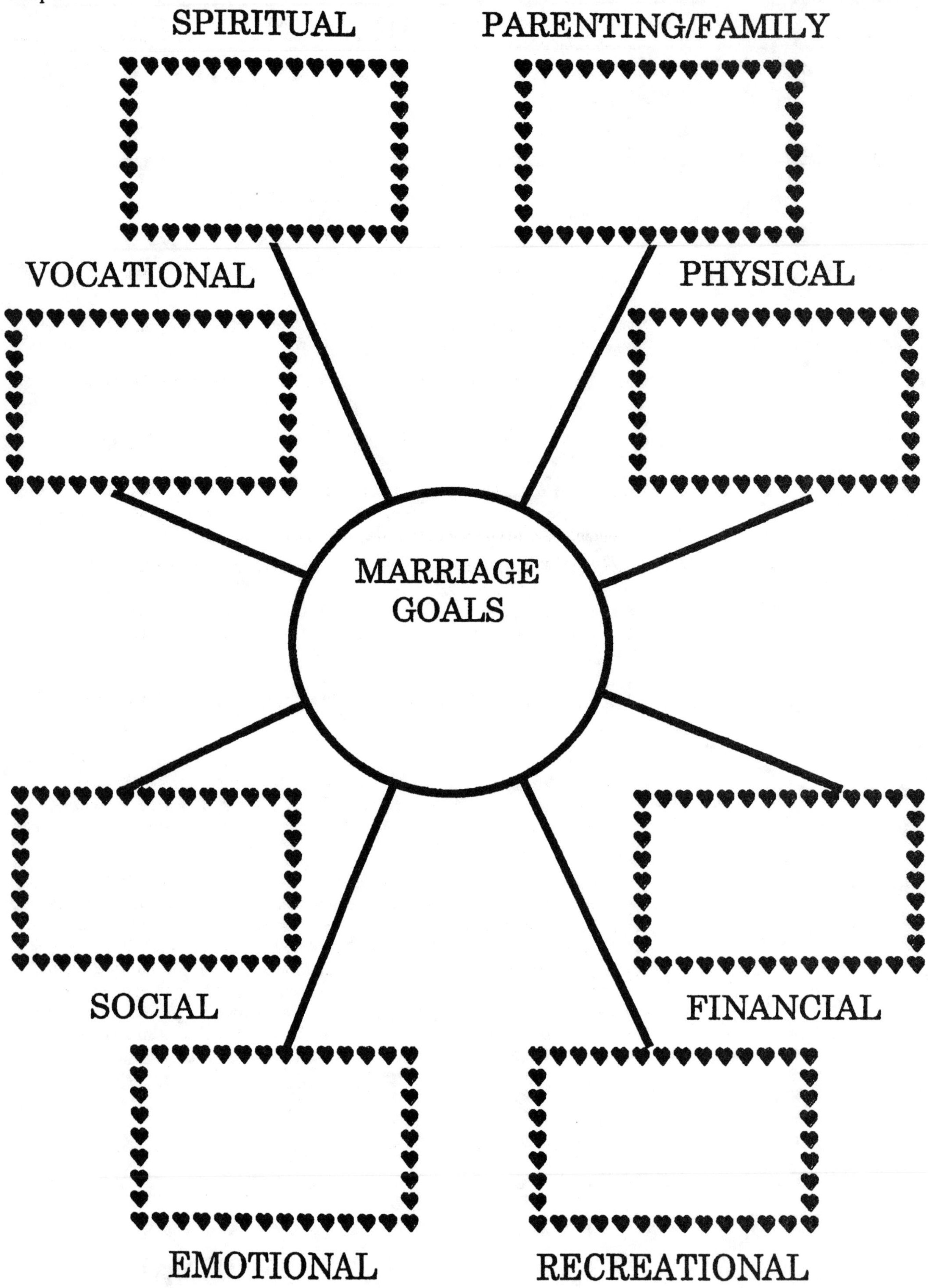

SPIRITUAL

PARENTING/FAMILY

VOCATIONAL

PHYSICAL

MARRIAGE GOALS

SOCIAL

FINANCIAL

EMOTIONAL

RECREATIONAL

Many waters cannot quench love, neither can the floods drown it....(Song of Sol. 8:7 KJV)

COMMITMENT
Chapter 11

Day 1

"I don't feel like getting the kids around for school this morning," Mary protested as she flopped back on the bed.

Her husband Tom glanced down at his watch, "Well, I'd do it for you, but if I don't leave right now, I'm going to be late for work."

Mary yawned and rolled over. "That's O.K. They don't need to go to school anyway. I'll just let them do what they want today."

Tom stopped as he was leaving the room. "Doesn't Tammy have a Geography quiz today? She studied mighty hard for it last night."

Mary opened one eye. "Be that as it may, I don't *feel* like getting the children off to school today, and I shouldn't have to do anything I don't *feel* like doing! People shouldn't have to do something if they don't *feel* like it, should they?"

Should they? Should a person follow their emotions wherever they lead? Do your emotions have to agree with your intellect for your will to operate? This is the question the opening dialogue dealt with. This is the bottom-line question, because how you answer it, affects the way you view every commitment and responsibility in your life. So let's examine it a little closer.

The Parts of a "Whole PERSONALITY": Intellect, Emotions and Will.

This is pretty standard information. You have an **intellect** — your mind which affects your behavior because of its thought processes. You also have **emotions** — your feelings which pull you in a particular direction. And thirdly, you have a **will** — your power to act or choose with purpose. These three parts make up your personality: how you think and respond to life.

Intellect

Emotions

Will

Any two of these can "gang up" on the other part. For instance, your feelings can pull you in the direction of eating an ice cream sundae. Your intellect can take emotion's side by thinking things like, "I really deserve that sundae. It won't hurt to eat just a little one." With your intellect and emotions working together, you'd better believe your will gives in, and you eat the ice cream sundae. But what if your intellect and will "gang up" on your emotions in this situation. Your thoughts would become statements like, "I can't eat that sundae, I promised myself I'd loose five pounds this month." You would then exercise your will and walk by the ice cream parlor.

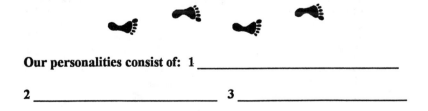

Our personalities consist of: 1 _____

2 _____ 3 _____

Our WILL Can Act Despite Our Emotions. Here are some examples in Psalms:

Psalm 42:5,6 — *Why are you downcast, O my soul? Why so disturbed within me? Put your hope in God, for I will yet praise him, my Savior and my God.* **My soul is downcast within me; therefore I will remember you** *from the land of the Jordan, the heights of Hermon* — *from Mount Mizar.* **Because** David was downcast, he chose to remember the Lord. His emotions would have kept him down; but his will, with help from his intellect, chose to look up to God.

Psalm 69:1-3 — *Save me, O God, for the waters have come up to my neck. I sink in the miry depths, where there is no foothold. I have come into the deep waters; the floods engulf me. I am worn out calling for help; my throat is parched. My eyes fail, looking for my God.* How is David feeling? To borrow our son-in-law's expression: "He's lower than a snake's belly in a wagon rut." You can't get much lower than that. But by verse 29, he exercises his will despite his feelings. *I am in pain and distress; may your salvation, O God, protect me.* **I will praise God's name** *in song and* **glorify him** *with thanksgiving* (69:29-30).

Psalm 22:1-2, 6 — *My God, my God, why have you forsaken me? Why are you so far from saving me, so far from the words of my groaning? O my God, I cry out by day, but you do not answer, by night, and am not silent....I am a worm and not a man, scorned by men and despised by the people.* Have you ever felt **so low**, you called yourself a **worm**? Maybe a worm's belly in a wagon rut is even **lower** than a snakes. But again, by verse 22, David makes a **decision** to trust God...**his will over-rides his emotions.** *I will declare your name to my brothers; in the congregation I will praise you. You who fear the Lord, praise him! All you descendants of Jacob, honor him! Revere him, all you descendants of Israel!* (22:22-23) David not only chooses to trust and praise God despite his emotions, he **encourages his friends** to do the same.

Which of these passages in Psalms do you think best illustrates the intellect and will operating despite emotions and why?

Wife: _____

Husband: _____

The NECESSITY to Decide.

Simply **knowing** you don't need **to feel** in order **to do** doesn't change your life, does it? You can know this **absolutely**, and still **react** to circumstances with your emotions instead of your intellect and will. You must **choose** to **respond** instead of **react** to circumstances and people.

There's a big difference between **responding** and **reacting**, and between **choosing** to do what honors God or allowing your behavior to follow the **line of least resistance**. The bottom line is: **you** must decide. Actually, to **not decide** is, in reality, a decision to deny responsibility. It *is* a decision to react instead of respond. It *is* a decision to follow the line of least resistance.

This is probably a familiar illustration, but we'll tell it anyway. Your personality — your will, intellect and emotions — is like a train with three cars. The engine is your

Psalm 42:5,6 — *Why are you downcast, O my soul? Why so disturbed within me? Put your hope in God, for I will yet praise him, my Savior and my God. My soul is downcast within me; therefore I will remember you from the land of the Jordan, the heights of Hermon — from Mount Mizar.*

Psalm 69:1-3 — *Save me, O God, for the waters have come up to my neck. I sink in the miry depths, where there is no foothold. I have come into the deep waters; the floods engulf me. I am worn out calling for help; my throat is parched. My eyes fail, looking for my God.*

Psalm 22:1-2, 6 — *My God, my God, why have you forsaken me? Why are you so far from saving me, so far from the words of my groaning? O my God, I cry out by day, but you do not answer, by night, and am not silent....I am a worm and not a man, scorned by men and despised by the people. I will declare your name to my brothers; in the congregation I will praise you. You who fear the Lord, praise him! All you descendants of Jacob, honor him! Revere him, all you descendants of Israel!*

Notes

Our emotions are the train's caboose.

will, the box car your intellect, and the caboose your emotions. When you live life "**on purpose**," the engine (your will) pulls the rest of the train. That's how a train is supposed to work. But when you live the life of **least resistance**, the caboose (your emotions) pulls the train. You don't want to be pulled around by your caboose the rest of your life, now do you?

Describe a time when you acted contrary to the way you felt (i.e. your intellect and will over-rode your emotions).

Wife: _____

Husband: _____

Write at least one personal application from today's study.

Wife: _____

Husband: _____

What does God want you to do to work out this application?

Wife: _____

Husband: _____

REFLECT TOGETHER: Read Psalm 42:1-11. Notice how many times David must remind his intellect and will to "gang up" on his emotions.

PRAY TOGETHER: Lord, you know how often we don't feel like doing what we should. Help us consistently decide to do what we "ought" and not let our emotions rule.

Day 2

Love is "a maximum of evaluation and a minimum of emotion."

Love Is a Decision

To love is a COMMAND. During our engagement, we heard a speaker say that love is "a maximum of evaluation and a minimum of emotion." We, like any other engaged couple, didn't believe that for a minute. We had a maximum of emotion and a minimum of evaluation. But after we were married for awhile, we realized the truth in that statement.

In the three following verses, **God commands us to love.** Now, He never gives us commands we are not capable of obeying. So "love" must be more than a feeling, for how could God command us to **"feel"**? Love **is** more than emotions, it is a **decision**...a decision to obey God's command.

> **Husbands are commanded to LOVE THEIR WIVES.** Ephesians 5:25 — *Husbands, **love your wives**, just as Christ loved the church and gave himself up for her.*

> **We are all commanded to LOVE OUR NEIGHBOR.** Galatians 5:14 — *The entire law is summed up in a single command: "Love your **neighbor** as yourself."*

> **We are commanded to LOVE OUR BROTHERS.** 1 John 4:21 — *And he has given us this command: Whoever loves God must also **love his brother**.*

These are just three of God's commands "to love." They are commands we can **choose to obey** whether we "feel" like it or not.

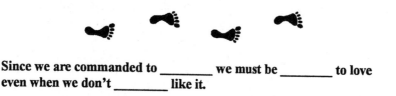

Since we are commanded to _____ we must be _____ to love even when we don't _____ like it.

To love is a LEARNING PROCESS — Titus 2:3-4 — *Likewise, teach the older women to be reverent in the way they live, not to be slanderers or addicted to much wine, but to teach what is good. Then **they can train the younger women to love** their husbands and children.*

Again, we see that love is much more than an emotion, because we can be taught to love. This is good news. It means we **can learn** to love our husbands, **learn** to love our wives, even in situations we don't feel we can.

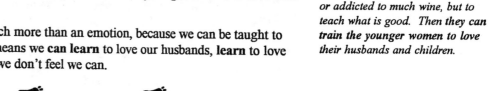

Since we can be _____ to love our mates (Tit. 2:3-4), love must be a _____ process.

We can love despite contrary FEELINGS or the absence of emotion. 1 Corinthians 13:7-8 — *It [love] always protects, always trusts, always hopes, always perseveres. Love never fails.*

If you are counting on the **feelings of love** to carry your marriage through, you are setting yourself up for disillusionment. The **feelings** of love go up and down, up and down, like a roller coaster. A roller coaster is fun to ride for three to five minutes...but you can't **live** on one. Love **is** emotional, but it's also **practical**. It's the stuff of life...every day...hour by hour...minute by minute.

We have had periods in our lives when we have both had to work. It was during such a time when we got home from work late one evening, quickly fed the family and ran off to a meeting. You know how church meetings can be; what was supposed to be a one-hour meeting, turned into two-and-a-half. It was after ten when we finally dragged through our front door. My (Harold) mind was on one thing, and one thing alone: to get horizontal as quickly as possible. But as I shuffled toward the bedroom, I heard Bette mumble, "I can't face that kitchen in the morning. I've got to do those dishes tonight." What? The dishes? Now?

As I looked longingly toward the bedroom and then back at Bette trudging toward the kitchen, I knew I had a choice. My feelings were pulling me to my pillow. I was

Ephesians 5:25 — *Husbands, love your wives, just as Christ loved the church and gave himself up for her.*

Galatians 5:14 — *The entire law is summed up in a single command: "Love your neighbor as yourself."*

1 John 4:21 — *And he has given us this command: Whoever loves God must also love his brother.*

Titus 2:3-4 — *Likewise, teach the older women to be reverent in the way they live, not to be slanderers or addicted to much wine, but to teach what is good. Then they can train the younger women to love their husbands and children.*

Corinthians 13:7-8 — *It [love] always protects, always trusts, always hopes, always perseveres. Love never fails.*

Notes

Loving actions speak louder
than words.

tired; I wanted to choose sleep. I had really **strong feelings** about my need for sleep. But what was the **loving choice**? I **knew** what it was. We hardly ever have to look far to find the loving choice, do we? It's usually staring us in the face whether we want to see it or not. And I knew that helping Bette in the kitchen was it. This led me to another choice. Was I going to go in the kitchen as a grump and grumble the whole time I helped, or was I going to go in there with a loving attitude? Do you ever do the right thing but with the wrong attitude so your mate will refuse your help, leaving you free to do what you wanted to in the first place? I don't always choose to love despite my feelings, but this time I did. With two doing the job, we finished in fifteen minutes and were asleep in twenty. But those fifteen minutes were profoundly important, because they communicated love to my wife. That simple decision to love **spoke louder than words**.

And I (Bette) have to tell you that Harold's decision to love me in such a practical way meant more than a bouquet of roses. I'm not discounting roses, mind you, but his act of love was far more valuable to me. He **chose** to do the loving thing despite feelings to the contrary. We all face such decisions every day.

Describe a similar choice you have made to love your mate when you didn't feel like it.

Wife: _____

Husband: _____

Write at least one personal application from today's study.

Wife: _____

Husband: _____

What does God want you to do to work out this application?

Wife: _____

Husband: _____

REFLECT TOGETHER: Read Titus 2:1-15. Notice how many people Titus is instructed to teach.

PRAY TOGETHER: Father, sometimes it feels like we will never learn to love, but we know you will complete this work in us. Teach us to love more consistently — by choice.

The need for COMMITMENT. Ecclesiastes 5:4,5 — *When you make a vow to God, do not delay in fulfilling it. He has no pleasure in fools; fulfill your vow. It is better not to vow than to make a vow and not fulfill it.* What does God call us if we make a vow and don't keep it? Fools! He calls us fools! God takes vows very seriously. When we promised to "love, honor and cherish" our mates, we made a **vow** of commitment to one another and to God.

You probably didn't understand at the time the magnitude of what you were vowing. You were vowing to **love** your mate — when you feel like it, when you don't feel like it, when he or she gains weight, when he looses his hair, when she looses her temper, when he takes more than he gives and when you have to give more than you take.

Now that you understand the significance of your vow of commitment, you must put your vow into practice. You exercise your vow when you **choose to love.** What would have happened in the scenario we just relayed if Harold had not made the loving choice? Would we have been welded closer? Would our bond have been tightened? Would our love have been deepened? No. But **all** of these happened because he chose to do the loving thing. Commitment is not nebulas. It is practical, every day acts of love that we must choose to do.

PLEASE NOTE: We know you may be in a second marriage. The first vows you took have been broken, perhaps not by your choice. We are not speaking of the past. The only thing we can do about the past is **forgive** and **be forgiven** for it. We trust you have dealt with God about that and have accepted His forgiveness and forgiven those who hurt you. If you have, you are now free to fulfill your vow with your present mate, and are held responsible by God to do so.

Commitment is a decision to CLEAVE. Genesis 2:22-24 — *Then the Lord God made a woman from the rib he had taken out of the man, and he brought her to the man. The man said, "This is now bone of my bones and flesh of my flesh; she shall be called 'woman,' for she was taken out of man." For this reason a man will leave his father and mother and **be united** to his wife, and they will become **one flesh.*** We like the way the King James Version translates the word "united:" *...a man will leave his father and mother and **cleave** unto his wife.* God's command for married couples is to "leave and cleave." We must **leave** all other ties that hold us, so that we can freely bond to our mate.

Our dependence now must be on one another, not parents, not sisters and brothers, not old loves. We must **cleave** to each other. Cleave simply means "to glue or cement together." We hear the word "bonding" a lot today. It means the same thing. Did you know it was Biblical to tell your mate, "Baby, I'm gonna stick like glue"? God's loving intent is to glue us together in a **permanent bond.**

Day 3

Ecclesiastes 5:4,5 — *When you make a vow to God, do not delay in fulfilling it. He has no pleasure in fools; fulfill your vow. It is better not to vow than to make a vow and not fulfill it.*

Genesis 2:22-24 — *Then the Lord God made a woman from the rib he had taken out of the man, and he brought her to the man. The man said, "This is now bone of my bones and flesh of my flesh; she shall be called 'woman,' for she was taken out of man." For this reason a man will leave his father and mother and **be united** to his wife, and they will become **one flesh.***

Notes

Matthew 19:6 — *So they [you and your mate] are no longer two, but one. Therefore what **God has joined together**, let man not separate.*

Malachi 2:15-16a — *Has not the Lord made them one? In flesh and spirit they are his. And why one? Because he was seeking godly offspring. So guard yourself in your spirit, and do not break faith with the wife of your youth. "I hate divorce," says the Lord God of Israel.*

Matthew 19:6 — *So they [you and your mate] are no longer two, but one. Therefore what **God has joined together**, let man not separate.*

Visualize this: Two pieces of paper glued together is a great illustration of "cleaving." If we held the paper so that you could see the face of one side and then the other, you would recognize they were indeed two distinct pieces of paper. But if we held them perpendicular to you so that you could see only their edge, they would look like one piece of paper. You and your mate are **two distinct persons**, and yet, when you married, God glued you together to make **one unit**. You are **two**, and yet, you are **one**. Because of this gluing, the pain is intense if you attempt to pull away from each other. If we tried to pull the two pieces of glued paper apart, they would rip and shred. The harder we tried to pull, the more we would rip them to pieces. Is it any wonder God declares He hates divorce? (Malachi 2:16) He loves you too much to see you **ripped apart**.

The media and Godless psychology try to convince us that if we aren't getting all we want from our marriage, we should get out. 'If the mate of your dreams has become a nightmare, well then, go look for someone else. Somewhere out there is the perfect partner for you.' What a **lie**! Most divorced people are lonely, impoverished and wish they were back in their marriages. What we hear from people going through divorce is this: "If I'd known there would be this much pain, I would have tried harder to make my marriage work."

To "cleave" means to _____ or _____ together.

What are some of the "tearing," and "shredding" effects of separation and divorce? (Together)

_____

_____

_____

When Harold was in Seminary, we had tremendous stress on our relationship. He carried a hefty load of classes, we had three small children, we each had jobs, he had papers to write and I (Bette) had them to type. We often had to exchange children in the school's parking lot in order to get to work on time. It was hectic! Little problems seemed gigantic and sometimes even unsolvable. One day during Harold's second year of classes, we had a big blow up. Neither one of us can remember what it was about, but, at the time, it was overwhelming. In the middle of the fight, I turned on my heal and marched away from Harold exclaiming, "I'm leaving and going home to Mother!"

That stopped me (Harold) cold. It hit me — this is serious; she really means it. I caught up with Bette on the stairs and physically sat her down beside me. "We've got to talk about this. Are you really leaving me?" We must have sat on those stairs an hour or more, talking about our vows...our promises before God and to one another. The more we talked, the more we settled on the conclusion that separation and divorce were not options open to us. We had made a commitment to cleave together, and no conflict could be big enough to make us break our vows. We hadn't even settled our argument at this time, but we resolved to work it out. And we resolved to find a solution to any and every conflict in the future, because we decided we were truly committed to each other and our marriage.

We made a profound decision together that day. We promised each other that no matter what, we were going to stick together. We have had many conflicts through the years since that day...some of them more serious than that one. But we've worked through them because we have known we have no other option. Verbalizing our commitment solidified it...made it **real** and **unbreakable** to us. We essentially had promised the same commitment in our wedding vows, but the restatement of them gave them substance and reality.

The necessity to make a commitment. It was important to our relationship that we make a **verbal restatement** of our commitment to one another. And we believe it is important for your relationship as well. We know you made vows at the altar just like we did. But now you know more of what they mean, so your recommitment will mean more than your original one.

We have restated our commitment to each other many times since then, because every day we understand more of what we're promising. In a sense, our promises are getting bigger as we comprehend the enormity of our commitment. It still means that come what may, we're going to stick together. Even though we now know how big those "come what mays" can be.

> Our promises are getting bigger as we comprehend the enormity of our commitment.

The residents of a small southern town climbed onto their roofs as the flood waters rose. Neighbors checked on each other to make sure all had escaped to higher ground. From a nearby roof, Harry called over to Mabel, "Hey, Mabel, where's George? Didn't he make it?" "Oh, George is down there," Mabel shouted back, waving her hand toward the water below. As Harry starred down at the water, he noticed a small hat swimming down one way in a straight line, then back up another way in a line, forming an ever-tightening square in front of George and Mabel's house. "Yeah," Mabel shook her head disgustedly, "George said that come hell or high water, he was going to mow the lawn today." That's how we need to look at commitment!

You will have the opportunity on day 7 of this study to restate your commitment to one another. We urge you to consider the vows we have provided for you in the light of what you know about commitment. You can make that time extremely meaningful, because you now know better what you are promising.

How would you rate your commitment level?

Wife: 1   2   3   4   5   6   7   8   9   10

Husband: 1   2   3   4   5   6   7   8   9   10

Write at least one personal application from today's study.

Wife: _____

Husband: _____

What does God want you to do to work out this application?

Wife: _____

Husband: _____

Notes

REFLECT TOGETHER: Read Genesis 2:20-25. Notice that God created marriage immediately after He created a man and woman.

PRAY TOGETHER: Help us keep our vows, Lord. We want our commitment to one another to stand the test of time, but we know we will need your help regularly along the way.

Day 4

Ministry Versus Manipulation:

Ministry is our commitment to **love in shoe leather**. When we minister to our mate, we are focusing on them and their needs. This is not an easy calling. It's much easier to focus on our own needs and try to manipulate our partner into meeting them. But every Christian spouse has been **called to the ministry**...ministry to our mate. The following are not easy concepts. But they are essential to our understanding the full measure of commitment.

Because only Christ can meet our DEEPEST NEEDS, we must turn to Him, not our SPOUSE, for the satisfaction of our personal needs for SECURITY (love) and SIGNIFICANCE (meaning/purpose). Romans 5:8 — *But God demonstrates his own love for us in this: While we were still sinners, Christ died for us.*

Romans 5:8 — But God demonstrates his own love for us in this: While we were still sinners, Christ died for us.

Physically, we all as human beings, need food and shelter. But there are two emotional needs which are just as necessary for us to live: the needs for **security** and for **significance**. We all have a deep need for security. We aren't talking about financial security here, but the **security of being loved** no matter what...unconditionally loved. This is the kind of love 1 Corinthians 13 speaks of. Unconditional love means we are loved, not because of what we do or don't do, but simply because we are. God sets 1 Corinthians' kind of love as the standard for the way we are to love, but, let's face it, only God can love this way all the time. That's why we must look to Him to meet this deep need of ours.

Our second greatest emotional need is for **significance**. We need to know we have meaning, that our lives have purpose. We all need to know we are valuable and make a difference in this world just by being alive. Jesus Christ alone can meet this great need. He made us with a purpose in mind. Psalm 138:8 says, *The Lord will fulfill his purpose for me....* He has a purpose for you and me being here. That makes us significant.

Psalm 138:8 — The Lord will fulfill his purpose for me....

When we marry, somewhere deep inside, we say, "O.K., you promised to 'love, honor and cherish' me. Now, do it. Show me you love me all the time. Never get angry with me, yell or disagree, or I will feel unloved. Oh, yes, one more thing. Always make we feel valuable. Show me how much you appreciate me, or I will feel unneeded." We set ourselves up for failure and disappointment when we expect our mate to meet all our needs for love and significance. They can't do it! But we will never be disappointed in Jesus' love and purpose for us. He loves us unconditionally. We may not always understand His love, but it's there, just the same. We may sometimes have trouble receiving His love, but He never withholds it. We must remind ourselves daily how much God loves and values us. We can't afford to listen to satan's doubts. God loves us and considers us infinitely valuable! We have absolute proof in the cross of Christ!

Do you agree that your mate cannot meet your deepest needs for love and meaning/purpose?

Wife: _____ Husband: _____

Who is the only one who can? _____

Because Christ satisfies our needs, we are **FREE** to minister to the needs of our mate, instead of **MANIPULATING** our mate to meet our needs. Galatians 5:13 — *You, my brothers, were called to be free. But do not use your freedom to indulge the sinful nature; rather, serve one another in love.*

Galatians 5:13 — *You, my brothers, were called to be free. But do not use your freedom to indulge the sinful nature; rather, serve one another in love.*

When we stop expecting our mate to meet our deep emotional needs for security and significance, and start expecting Jesus Christ to meet those needs, we will have great freedom. We're not asking you to believe what we *think*. We are asking you to believe and act upon absolute truth: Jesus Christ meets our every need! When we truly believe that, we are free from the bondage of trying to make our mate meet our needs. We can stop manipulating. ("If you loved me, you would....") We can stop pushing. ("Aren't you going to...?") We can stop making them feel guilty. ("Why don't you ever...?") We are free to love our mate unconditionally, whether they act like they love us or not. Our love is not held captive by the way our mate behaves. We are free to *serve in love*. Free to be ministers instead of manipulators.

Since Christ meets our needs and frees us to _____ we no longer need to _____ our mates to meet them or to focus our attention on our own needs.

Identify a few phrases (like "If you loved me, you would...."; "Aren't you going to...?"; "Why don't you ever...?") you have used to manipulate your mate in the past.

Wife: _____

Husband: _____

"If you loved me, you would...."

"Aren't you going to...?"

"Why don't you ever...?"

Write at least one personal application from today's study.

Wife: _____

Husband: _____

What does God want you to do to work out this application?

Wife: _____

Husband: _____

Notes

REFLECT TOGETHER: Read 1 Corinthians 13:1-8. How many characteristics of love does Paul list?

PRAY TOGETHER: Father, free us from using destructive manipulation. We know You are the only One who can really meet our needs — help us look to You and You alone to meet them.

Day 5

1 Timothy 6:18 — *Command them to do good, to be rich in good deeds, and to be generous and willing to share.*

How to Become a Minister to Our Mate: We have freedom in Christ to become ministers, so now we must learn how to be ministers.

Make a **COMMITMENT** to minister to your partner's needs with a **WILLING SPIRIT**. 1 Timothy 6:18 — *Command them to do good, to be rich in good deeds, and to be generous and willing to share.* Remember how Harold helped me (Bette) in the kitchen even though he was tired? He was ministering to my needs. But what would have happened if he had come into the kitchen grumbling and complaining? I probably would have told him to go on to bed, because I surely wouldn't have wanted his grudging help. He would have sabotaged his ministry to me. We can not minister to our mate begrudgingly, for that is not **ministering at all**. So the first thing we must do in learning how to minister to our mate is make a commitment to minister with a **willing spirit**.

Philippians 2:4 — *Each of you should look not only to your own interests, but also to the interests of others.*

Determine to become more AWARE of your partner's needs. Philippians 2:4 — *Each of you should look not only to your own interests, but also to the interests of others.* Study your partner. What does he need? Her needs are much like your own. He needs to be loved **unconditionally**. She needs to be loved when she makes **mistakes**, when he is **confused**, when she is **unlovely**. He needs to know you consider him of **great value**. She needs **listened** to, spoken **softly** to, **hugged**, **prayed** for, and treated **tenderly**.

Recognize that God Himself has EQUIPPED you to minister to your mate's needs in a unique way. Hebrews 13:20-21 — *May the God of peace...equip you with everything good for doing his will, and may he work in us what is pleasing to him, through Jesus Christ....* It's no accident you are married to your mate. Your mate was designed for you and you for him or her. No one in the whole world is so **uniquely equipped** to minister to your mate like you. Sure, you have baggage and hang ups, you fail and sin — but you are still specially equipped

Hebrews 13:20-21 — *May the God of peace...equip you with everything good for doing his will, and may he work in us what is pleasing to him, through Jesus Christ....*

to meet your mate's needs. This is part of your **significance**. This is part of God's purpose for your life. Sometimes you're going to feel like you can't do it. And you can't — not alone. But nobody said you had to do it alone. Jesus Christ knows how to meet every need, **He** will help you minister **right**.

Which of the 3 suggestions would be most helpful to you in becoming a better minister to your mate?

Wife: _____

Husband: _____

Discuss with your spouse your answers and how you are going to apply them.

Write at least one personal application from today's study.

Wife: _____

Husband: _____

What does God want you to do to work out this application?

Wife: _____

Husband: _____

REFLECT TOGETHER: Re-read Hebrews 13:20-22.

PRAY TOGETHER: May we be willing ministers to one another. Keep us learning more and more about how we can better minister to each other.

Day 6

Commitment is not some nebulous feeling. It is not a one-time decision somewhere in the past. It is not theoretical. It is real — every day. It is real in the decisions you make every day. It is real when you feel like it...and when you don't feel like it.

Here's a Personal Illustration: *Bette:* It was the night before my fortieth birthday. Harold and the kids were dishing out some heavy duty teasing about my big 4-0 when the telephone rang...so innocently. We didn't know that phone call would change our lives forever. I had a biopsy the week before on a growth beside my breastbone. The surgeon called that night to tell us I had two months to live. First, however, he wanted to surgically remove the grapefruit-size tumor, my breastbone, the ribs the tumor had grown through, my left breast and the sack from around my heart. Then somehow he was going to sew me back together so I could die in one piece. From my biopsy, the pathologists had diagnosed me with Malignant Thymoma...and no one lives with that.

Our family huddled together, crying and praying. Our children were only 13, 15 and

Notes

Friends prayed for us all night.

Psalm 138:3-8 — *When I called, you answered me....Though I walk in the midst of trouble, you preserve my life....The Lord will fulfill His purpose for me....*

In place of dread, God gave peace.

"If you can love me bald, I can love you bald."

17. We held them close and thought about how I might not live to watch them grow up. We were exhausted, our minds and bodies drained by a great dread. Harold and I clung to each other in the middle of the bed, not expecting to fall asleep. But we did. We immediately drifted into sweet, dreamless sleep.

We didn't know it then, but many friends had been called by our Pastor and a close friend and were praying for us all night. Finally, at four a.m., they felt peace and were able to sleep. They carried — literally carried — our burden all night so we could rest.

Harold: We awoke refreshed at four a.m., the time our Christian friends were able to sleep. We've since kidded them that they should have prayed 'til at least 6:00. After we awoke, we lay there in each other's arms and began to sing hymns and choruses, one after another, as they popped into our minds. And we read God's Word — mostly Psalms — claiming the promises of comfort and help and blessing.

When I called, you answered me....Though I walk in the midst of trouble, you preserve my life....The Lord will fulfill His purpose for me.... (Psalm 138:3-8). Great and true promises made by a loving God to millions of believers through the ages, but that morning they were for us alone. We had begun GTO Family Ministries just two years before. It was our niche — our calling. Was this to be the end of it? It couldn't be, not if helping couples **was** His purpose for us. We knew that somehow — somehow — we were going to make it through this. How? We didn't know. But the terrible dread that had overwhelmed us the night before was gone, and in its place God had given peace.

Bette: Peace. A difficult thing to keep in the days that followed — days filled with doctors, hospitals, tests, second opinions, third opinions. After the second opinion agreed with the first, I was sent for a consultation with the plastic surgeon who was to sew me back together after surgery. He recommended I see one more doctor, a surgical oncologist at University Hospital (University of California, San Diego). He called him then and there and arranged an almost impossible-to-get appointment for me the next day. That appointment resulted in more pathologists examining my biopsy block and diagnosing me with Hodgkin's Disease, not Malignant Thymoma. Hodgkin's Disease is cancer of the lymph system and is treated with chemotherapy and radiation, not surgery.

We were ecstatic when we heard the new diagnosis. Imagine being happy to discover you have Hodgkin's disease! But it is perspective. My chances, from a medical point of view, soared from 0% to 50%. I remember stopping at the grocery store on our way home. As we were getting out of the car, we spotted a good friend across the parking lot. I waved my arms excitedly and shouted, "Lynne, I've got Hodgkin's Disease! I've got Hodgkins Disease!" Like I said, it's perspective.

Harold: Then we started chemotherapy...every two weeks for nine long months. And with every month, every treatment, Bette grew weaker. After a few months, it became too difficult for her to crawl up and down stairs more than once or twice a day. Her nausea and pain seemed to worsen with each treatment.

Bette: My hair fell out by hand fulls. Soon, even my face looked bald. I felt so useless and ugly. I didn't feel human, much less feminine. But Harold would take my hand and say, "You're beautiful." I'd cry, "How can you even look at me? How can you still love me?" He'd smile and reply, "Hey, if you can love me bald, I can love you bald."

For almost a year, I could only take; I could not give. I couldn't iron his shirts, couldn't fix a decent meal, couldn't feel or look sexy — but Harold still showed me he loved me. He held a pan under my chin for me to throw up in, he let me cry on his shoulder, he made me talk about how I felt, and he reminded me regularly that I was still valuable. I knew beyond a shadow of a doubt that he was fully committed to me and to our marriage. And I knew he loved me — not in some ethereal way but in every day, nitty-gritty ways. We learned in the trenches what commitment and love and ministering really mean.

The most important thing on earth: our commitment to oneness. We didn't share our testimony with you to evoke your sympathy. What we want you to see is how important our commitment to truly love each other really is. We **can't afford** to put off nurturing our relationship with love. We hear couples say, "When I get that new job....When we buy that new house....When our kids get a little older...then we'll work on our relationship." It doesn't work that way.

We **can't afford** to put off nurturing our relationship with love.

We must nurture our relationship **now** — every day. We must decide to put love and ministry **into practice — every day.** The hard times will come. If you haven't already found that out, you will. And if you're not in the process of learning to put love into action, those hard times are going to pry you apart. Don't wait for circumstances to get better. Start learning to love and minister to each other **today.**

The Gaither's sing a song entitled "We Have This Moment."

We have this moment to hold in our hands

And to touch as it slips through our fingers like sand.

Yesterday's gone and tomorrow may never come,

But we have this moment today.

None of us have been promised more than today. Don't let today slip through your fingers. **Make it count** for your oneness, for your love and your commitment.

Don't let today slip through your fingers.

What can you do this week with your mate to treasure the moments you have?

Wife: _____

Husband: _____

Plan a special "getaway" together within 3 months. Agree to do it.

Write at least one personal application from today's study.

Wife: _____

Husband: _____

What does God want you to do to work out this application?

Wife: _____

Husband: _____

Notes

REFLECT TOGETHER: Read 1 John 4:7-16. How many times is the word "love" mentioned in this short passage of Scripture?

PRAY TOGETHER: Lord we know our moments are here and then so quickly gone. Help us live them to the fullest degree and treasure each one of them.

Day 7

WRAP-UP: Answer the following questions. Complete question #1 by yourself before discussing it and the others with your mate.

1.   **Ways I tend to**   **Ways I could**
    manipulate my partner: **minister instead:**

Wife: _____   _____

           _____   _____

           _____   _____

Husband: _____   _____

           _____   _____

           _____   _____

2. When you are alone together, sit down, facing each other, and declare basically the following to each other. "I love you. I am devoted to you. I'm committed to you and to our marriage. I will honor and cherish you and remain faithful to you until death separates us. And if it were ever necessary, I would lay down my life for you. (Spend some time to put the above in your own words.)

_____

_____

_____

_____

_____

_____

3. I recognize that only Christ can meet your deepest needs, but I want to minister to you more than I do. Give me some suggestions as to how I can be a better minister to you. I want to meet more of your needs.

Wife: _____

Husband: _____

REFLECT TOGETHER: Read James 2:14-26. Is James saying, "Just do it!"?

PRAY TOGETHER: Lord, just as a man said to Jesus "I believe, help my unbelief," we pray, "We're committed, help us to remain committed in love to one another throughout our lives until death do us part."

Mark 9:23,24 — Jesus said, "Everything is possible for him who believes." Immediately the boy's father exclaimed, "I do believe; help me overcome my unbelief."

GROUP DISCUSSION: If this study is being used in a group

setting, the following may be used as group discussion.

1. If you really treated love as a decision and not just an emotion, how would your behavior change? Give some practical examples.

2. Why is it easier to manipulate our partners rather than minister to them?

3. Case Study: Fred enters his home after a long day at work. His automatic, unplanned, and perhaps unconscious goal likely involves a desirable response from his wife Joan, perhaps a friendly greeting, a warm hug, or a prepared dinner. Suppose she welcomes him by asking, "Why are you so late? You said you'd be home by six and it's nearly seven."

Fred feels angry at Joan. He feels like retorting with, "Hey, thanks for the warm welcome! Sure is nice to come home!"

What should he do? Some of his options are (1) to express his anger, (2) to defend his late arrival, (3) simply to ignore Joan's comment and wash up for dinner, or (4) to soothe her with a warm embrace. Does he have other options? What are they? What would the loving thing to do be? What would you do if you were Fred? If you were Joan?

Have a frank discussion

SPIRITUAL INTIMACY
Chapter 12

Day 1

Spiritual Intimacy...It isn't something we hear much about. Haven't seen many books about it. Haven't heard many preachers preach about it. Yet it may very well be THE most important issue in your relationship as a Christian couple.

But most Christian couples have never thought much about Spiritual Intimacy. In fact, years ago, we heard Charlie and Martha Shedd report that according to their surveys, only 4% of all Christian couples even pray together on any kind of regular basis (not including grace before meals).

We have been taking a similar survey for the past several years as we have spoken in different Sunday School classes and churches. And we are glad to report that our survey is running a little higher — about 20-30% of couples praying together. But that's like saying to a dying man, "Good news, Mr. Milquetoast, your chances of living have gone from 4% to 30%!" Not a whole lot of encouragement, but it *is* a start.

If you are one of those couples who has never given Spiritual Intimacy much thought, this is your **wake up call**. Not a call for **perfection,** but for **progress.** And Spiritual Intimacy is the means to that progress. Would it surprise you to know that you and your spouse are **commanded** to be spiritually intimate, and that you have been given the **power** and **capacity** to be so? In fact, if you want to feel as close as you have always longed to feel as a married couple, then growing together in spiritual intimacy is an absolute necessity in your marriage.

We don't want to confuse you, though. Spiritual Intimacy is much more than simply reading the Bible and praying together. And it is not "De-de-de-de...De-de-de-de. You are traveling through time and space. There is a sign post up ahead. Next stop the Twilight Zone." But unfortunately, that's what spiritual intimacy means to many people — even Christians. Something nebulous spinning far away in space — hard to understand — hard to get hold of.

So, what *is* Spiritual Oneness? We can't give you a one line definition; it's more complicated than that. In fact, spiritual intimacy has at least seven elements that interweave in an intricate design to form a way of life. You see, it is a **process—not an event**...a journey—not the name of the destination.

SPIRITUAL INTIMACY: What is it?

1. Shared PURPOSE and GOALS in Life

Philippians 2:1,2 — If you have any encouragement from being united with Christ, if any comfort from his love, if any fellowship with the Spirit, if any tenderness and compassion, then make my joy complete by being like-minded, having the same love, being one in spirit and purpose.

Paul declares through the Holy Spirit, *If [since] you have any encouragement from being united with Christ, if [since] any comfort from his love, if [since] any fellowship with the Spirit, if [since] any tenderness and compassion, then make my joy complete by being like-minded, having the same love, being one in spirit and purpose* (Philippians 2:1,2). Think about it. If we as the body of Christ are commanded to be one in spirit and purpose, how much more are you as a Christian couple to be one in spirit and purpose? If you as a couple do not share a common goal in life, how will you ever reach it? If you are on different roads, headed in divergent directions, then is it any wonder you do not feel close?

Do you comprehend the difference it would make in your relationship if you both determined to choose the road you are going to walk together? The operative word is "choose." You as a couple must choose the road you will walk. Then you can say, "**This** is our purpose, **this** is our goal in life. We are headed in the same direction, on the same road together." The prophet Amos put it this way, *Can two walk together except they be agreed?* The obvious answer is, "Of course not!"

Amos 3:3 — *Can two walk together except they be agreed?* (KJV)

Perhaps you and your spouse have never discussed your purposes and goals. If not, you may not know if you are on the same road or not. Don't you think it's time to find out? How can you know if you are "like-minded" if you do not talk about what is on your mind? You should also consider that God says His purpose in our lives is to conform us into the image of His Son (Romans 8:29). So, if we are to be "like-minded" with each other and with God, our purpose should line up with His.

Romans 8:29 — *For those God foreknew he also predestined to be conformed to the likeness of his Son, that he might be the firstborn among many brothers.*

This is the first step in your spiritual intimacy journey: make sure you are taking the trip together. And, by the way, don't forget to pack your suitcases. Fill them with *encouragement* and *comfort* for one another, *fellowship* with the Spirit, *tenderness, compassion* and *love* just as Philippians 2 commanded. Keep them handy because you are going to need to pull them out and use them everyday.

Rate your experience of Sharing purpose and goals in your relationship on a scale of 1 to 10.

Wife: 1   2   3   4   5   6   7   8   9   10 (circle one)

Husband: 1   2   3   4   5   6   7   8   9   10 (circle one)

What are some steps you can take to make sure you as a couple are sharing the same purpose and goals in life?

Wife: _____

Husband: _____

Discuss your responses together.

Write at least one personal application from today's study.

Wife: _____

Husband: _____

What does God want you to do to work out this application?

Wife: _____

Husband: _____

Notes

PRAY TOGETHER: Read Philippians 2:1-11. Is there a connection between being humble and being "one in spirit and purpose"?

PRAY TOGETHER: Thank You, dear Lord, that You have a road for us to walk. We commit ourselves to walk it together with You.

Day 2

Now that you are sure you are traveling together on this spiritual intimacy journey, you are ready for the second ingredient.

2. Sharing the WORD and PRAYER

This is probably how most people define spiritual intimacy. It is *part* of spiritual intimacy. It is just not the whole of it. But as a fundamental element, it is the first priority after making sure you are on the same road together.

Colossians 3:16 — *Let the word of Christ dwell in you richly as you teach and admonish one another with all wisdom....*

Paul commands in Colossians, *Let the word of Christ dwell in you richly as you teach and admonish one another with all wisdom....* (Colossians 3:16). All this is saying is that we should read God's Word together and talk about it. This is beneficial in any of our relationships, but it is especially beneficial to the relationship between two believing spouses. You can become partners encouraging one another along the road, reminding each other of the reality of God's Word in your lives. Not preaching, mind you, or beating each other around the head and shoulders with Scripture verses. But allowing God's Word, richly living in you, to change you into the image of His Son, and then sharing that change with your partner.

Have you ever been around someone who hits you with a Bible verse for every need in your life? You trip over a rock and lie bleeding in the road. They smile sweetly and quote, "In everything give thanks for this is the will of God concerning you." Doesn't that make you feel better? Doesn't that make you a better person? Doesn't that make you want to ring their neck? If that kind of Biblical slap doesn't help you, what makes you think it will help your mate? You can share what God is doing in your life through His Word, but what your mate chooses to do is between him/her and God.

And prayer! Coming to God together as believers. Holding hands in the throne room. Sharing your fears and hopes and confessions in a three-way conversation.

Matthew 18:19-20 — *Again, I tell you that if two of you on earth agree about anything you ask for, it will be done for you by my Father in heaven. For where two or three come together in my name, there am I with them.*

In Matthew 18:19-20, we read, *Again, I tell you that if two of you on earth agree about anything you ask for, it will be done for you by my Father in heaven. For where two or three come together in my name, there am I with them.* We can't explain how this works, we just know it does. In some mysterious way, when the two of you pray together, you are promised power in prayer. In some special way, Jesus is there with you and your partner. What a promise! But what a waste if you two are **not** praying together!

If you and your life partner have never prayed together, you may feel a little awkward at first. Some of you may even have difficulty praying out loud in front of anyone. That's O.K., but you have to start somewhere. We suggest you begin by holding hands and praying silently. After you pray this way for a few months, it will become easier to pray short prayers aloud together. The benefit you both will receive is worth the little bit of discomfort.

Rate your experience of Sharing the Word and Prayer in your relationship on a scale of 1 to 10.

Wife: 1   2   3   4   5   6   7   8   9   10 (circle one)

Husband: 1   2   3   4   5   6   7   8   9   10 (circle one)

What specifically could you do to be more regular in spending time reading God's Word and praying together?

Wife: _____

Husband: _____

Discuss your responses together.

3. Shared GROWTH in Christ

You and your mate are walking down the road together. You're sharing with him/her all that good stuff from Philippians 2 you packed in your suitcase: comfort, love, tenderness, compassion, etc. You are reading the Scriptures and praying together as you walk. Jesus Christ has become someone easy to talk about. Now, as you walk along, you find yourself growing stronger spiritually, with more energy and stamina than before. This, dear friends, *should* be a natural progression.

But what should be natural to the "new creature in Christ" is often radically **un-natural** to our "old self." Our hearts want to obey God's life-giving principles of love and compassion, but they sometimes end up in the bottom of our suitcase. And what are those **old rags** on top? Bitterness and criticism. Every time you open your emotional suitcase, you must make a conscious choice to push aside the rags and rummage for the love and compassion. But each time you choose love and compassion makes it easier to find them in your suitcase the next time. For **God is at work** within us. He is the One who helps us discard the rags and choose the garments of righteousness as described in Philippians 2.

We have sometimes heard a wife or husband say something like, "My mate isn't growing in the Lord [like me]. I beg [nag and badger] him/her all the time to come to Bible study with me, but he/she just isn't interested." That spouse seems to be taking Hebrews 10:24, *And let us consider how we may spur one another on toward love and good deeds,* to actually mean, 'And let us consider how we may **badger** one another ....' or '...how we may **criticize** one another....' (There are those old **rags** again.)

The word in that verse is SPUR. A simple little word that means *to stimulate, to rouse to action.* Nagging is not spurring. Badgering is not spurring. Criticizing is not spurring. So how do we **spur** our traveling partner?

Sometimes, the best way to spur is to duck. That's right — **duck!** Our tendency is to try to grow *for* our mate rather than allowing them to grow at their own rate. We tell them what they should do, what they should think, even what they should feel. We have their growth pattern all planned and get very upset when they don't keep our schedule.

Our advice is *duck.* Although we think we are helping, sometimes our good intentions cause us to actually stand **between** our mate and God. So duck! You have to get out of the way so God can get a good shot at your mate.

Hebrews 10:24 — *And let us consider how we may spur one another on toward love and good deeds.*

Notes

Ephesians 5:19 — Speak to one another with psalms, hymns and spiritual songs. Sing and make music in your heart to the Lord.

This is not meant as condemnation upon you in any way. Your *intent* is not to hinder, but to help. But in reality, your action may be accomplishing the very opposite of what you really want. Ask yourself, "Is what I am doing working?" If not, then it is time to try something else: a closed mouth, soft answers, sweet smiles, and lots and lots of prayer. **That** is ducking. And when you duck, God, can work on your mate.

As you continue down the road together — *allowing* one another to grow — try applying Ephesians 5:19 to your daily journey. *Speak to one another with psalms, hymns and spiritual songs. Sing and make music in your heart to the Lord.*

We have some friends in San Jose, California who used to sing (they may still be singing) road signs to the tune of the "Alleluia Chorus." "Mer-ging traf-fic. Mer-ging traf-fic. Mer-ging tra-a-af-fic." They say it really helped shorten trips.

Yeah, well...maybe not road signs, but there are lots of edifying songs you can sing together, from familiar old hymns to the new praise songs. It's a good habit to get into.

Whenever the Gillogly's went on family vacations, we would sing together most of the way. We'd go through the alphabet singing songs whose titles matched each letter, with everyone taking a turn. Or we would spell H-O-R-S-E (or some other animal) with children's choruses. Even now that our family is grown and it's just the two of us, we sing together: in the car, during our devotions and when we paint or clean up the yard or take walks.

When we sing songs together like

> *You are my hiding place*
>
> *You always fill my heart*
>
> *With songs of deliverance*
>
> *Whenever I am afraid*
>
> *I will trust in you*

What do you think that does to our faith as we remind ourselves in song of God's faithfulness? That must be why God commanded us to do it!

Rate your experience of Sharing Growth in Christ in your relationship on a scale of 1 to 10.

Wife: 1 2 3 4 5 6 7 8 9 10 (circle one)

Husband: 1 2 3 4 5 6 7 8 9 10 (circle one)

What could you do to spur each other on the right way to growth in Christ?

Wife: _____

Husband: _____

Discuss your responses together.

> Write at least one personal application from today's study.
>
> Wife: _____
>
> Husband: _____
>
> What does God want you to do to work out this application?
>
> Wife: _____
>
> Husband: _____

REFLECT TOGETHER: Read Hebrews 10:19-25. Do you have to obey verse 23 before you can do verse 24?

PRAY TOGETHER: Oh, Jesus, we want to live in Your word and let it live in us. Show us ways to encourage one another to grow in You.

4. Shared MINISTRY

Day 3

Now you are ready for the fourth ingredient of spiritual oneness: shared ministry. Have you ever thought about how important the number "2" is to God? Think about it. Many times throughout Scripture, God sends **two** to accomplish His purposes: two angels to Abraham, two angels to Lot, two disciples to fetch the Palm Sunday colt, two angels at the empty tomb, and the 72 disciples sent out two-by-two, just to name a few.

Why does God minister so often by two's? Ecclesiastes 4:9-12 explains it. When there's a job to be done, two can usually handle it better, because they help each other through to the finish. There is a couple in Scripture that depicts this in a beautiful way. Their names are Aquila and Priscilla. Let's follow them through the Bible and learn from their example.

We start in Acts 18, skipping through the chapter, hitting only the highlights. *After this, Paul left Athens and went to Corinth. There he met a Jew named Aquila, a native of Pontes, who had recently come from Italy with his wife Priscilla, because Claudius had ordered all the Jews to leave Rome.* This is our introduction to this wonderful couple. They are new arrivals in Corinth, having moved there because of religious persecution. They are Jews who had probably grown up and gotten married in Rome. But Emperor Claudius did not like Jews, so they are now refugees in a strange city.

Paul went to see them, and because he was a tentmaker as they were, he stayed and worked with them....So Paul stayed for a year and a half teaching them the Word of God.... Aquila and Priscilla might have been refugees, but they were busy ones. They had already started their own business of tent making, and apparently had enough

Ecclesiastes 4:9-10a — *Two are better than one, because they have a good return for their work: If one falls down, his friend can help him up.*

Acts 18:1,2 — *After this, Paul left Athens and went to Corinth. There he met a Jew named Aquila, a native of Pontes, who had recently come from Italy with his wife Priscilla, because Claudius had ordered all the Jews to leave Rome.*

Acts 18:3,11 — *Paul went to see them, and because he was a tentmaker as they were, he stayed and worked with them....So Paul stayed for a year and a half teaching them the Word of God....*

Notes

Acts 18:18,19 — *Then he left the brothers and sailed for Syria accompanied by Priscilla and Aquila....They arrived at Ephesus where Paul left Priscilla and Aquila....*

1 Corinthians 16:19 — *meets in their* [Priscilla and Aquila's] *house.*

Acts 18:24,26 — *Meanwhile a Jew named Apollos...came to Ephesus ....He began to speak boldly in the synagogue. When Priscilla and Aquila heard him, they invited him to their home and explained to him the way of God more adequately.*

Romans 16:3, 4 — *Greet Priscilla and Aquila, my fellow workers in Christ Jesus. They risked their lives for me. Not only I but all the churches of the Gentiles are grateful to them.*

work to have Paul join them. From these verses, it seems he also stayed in their spare room for a year and a half. We don't know exactly at what point Priscilla and Aquila became Christians, but sometime during that extended visit, they came to know the Lord Jesus and grew under Paul's teaching along with the other Christians in Corinth.

Then he left the brothers and sailed for Syria accompanied by Priscilla and Aquila....They arrived at Ephesus where Paul left Priscilla and Aquila.... After a year and a half in Corinth, Paul declares that it is time to move on to Syria and start some new churches and encourage the believers there. What do Priscilla and Aquila do? They roll up their tents and proclaim, "You're going to need some help. We'll go with you." When the three of them arrived in Ephesus, Paul, after preaching in the synagogue, left our missionary couple in Ephesus to carry on. Can you imagine how they must have felt? They had been left alone in a foreign land, far from home, just the two of them. So they began their Ephesian ministry in the most logical place for Jews — the synagogue. They must have spoken convincingly there about the Messiah, because in verse 27, we are told that by the time Apollos got there, others had become Christians. And later in 1 Corinthians 16:19, Paul writes a letter to Corinth from Ephesus stating that the Ephesian church *meets in their [Priscilla and Aquila's] house.*

Meanwhile a Jew named Apollos...came to Ephesus ....He began to speak boldly in the synagogue. When Priscilla and Aquila heard him, they invited him to their home and explained to him the way of God more adequately. Can't you just see it? Priscilla and Aquila attend synagogue regularly, speaking a word for Jesus whenever given the opportunity. Then one Saturday, a stranger shows up and requests permission to speak. This guy really knows the Scriptures, and speaks *with great fervor and teaches about Jesus accurately, though he knew only the baptism of John.* The couple thinks, "This guy is good, but he doesn't have the whole picture." So they invite him to dinner and catch him up on the rest of the story. There would be so much they had to teach him, that they must have had him over to their home many times. Finally, the day came when Apollos was ready to go on alone. And Aquila and Priscilla and the rest of the believers in Ephesus gave him a big send off to Achaia.

Priscilla and Aquila were ready for God to use them anytime, anywhere. They worked together in ministry, bringing people to the Lord, opening their home whenever needed, giving of themselves to people who needed discipling, and letting go of their disciples when their work with them was done. This was indeed a couple God could count on. Can He count on you? Is your home open for Him to use? Is your time and energy available for the Master's use? Ministering together in your home is one of the most rewarding things you two will ever do. Do you believe that? Then it's time to throw another chicken leg in the pan, and invite someone home for dinner.

Ministering together may have an additional aspect as well. One of you may teach a Sunday School class or lead a boy's or girl's club or whatever. But you can still be ministering as a team by being involved in one another's service.

You can help each other prepare for class, serve in the nursery together, and, of course, you can pray together for one another's areas of ministry. Sometimes we have the attitude, "This is what I do. This is where I shine. Go away and do something else." If that's your attitude, you are cheating yourself out of your mate's spiritual, emotional and even physical support. We need to give support, and we also need to be willing to receive it.

There is one more reference we would like to share about Aquila and Priscilla: Romans 16:3 and 4. *Greet Priscilla and Aquila, my fellow workers in Christ Jesus. They risked their lives for me. Not only I but all the churches of the Gentiles are grateful to them.* We don't know how this couple risked their lives for Paul, maybe it was during the riot in Ephesus which exploded one time after Paul's preaching. Whatever it was, all the churches of the Gentiles owe them their gratitude to this very

243

day. You and I owe Priscilla and Aquila a debt of gratitude for helping save Paul's life. If they hadn't, we might not have half of the New Testament.

Do you think Aquila and Priscilla, while risking their lives for Paul, were thinking, "Wow, this is really significant. Why, we're changing the course of history! We're making a profound difference in the world!" That is all true, isn't it? But they didn't know it at the time. The point is, none of us know how significant what we do really is. Every time you open your home or give yourselves in ministry, you may be making a profound, significant difference in people's lives, and, indeed, the whole world. Someday, someone may be telling a group of people in a far distant land how they owe a debt of gratitude to **you**. It can happen if you let God use you as **His** couple. You can be sure of this, that as you walk along this spiritual intimacy journey, God wants to give you something **useful** to do **together**.

So what have Priscilla and Aquila shown us about shared ministry?

- **Their home was open and available for ministry to others** — both to individuals like Apollos and to groups like the church which met there.

- **They shared together in both ministries** — The passages don't say that Aquila took Apollos aside, nor that he alone led the church in their home — it mentions them **together** in **both** cases.

- **They were willing to move for the sake of ministry to others.** People were always more important than **things** to them.

- **And finally, they submitted their ministry to Paul's authority and guidance** as we should to our church leaders.

Their home was open.

They shared together in ministry.

They were willing to move.

They submitted to authority.

Rate your experience of Sharing Together in Ministry on a scale of 1 to 10.

Wife: 1   2   3   4   5   6   7   8   9   10 (circle one)

Husband: 1   2   3   4   5   6   7   8   9   10 (circle one)

What ministries can you share together?

Wife: _____

Husband: _____

Discuss your responses together.

Write at least one personal application from today's study.

Wife: _____

Husband: _____

What does God want you to do to work out this application?

Wife: _____

Husband: _____

Notes

REFLECT TOGETHER: Read Acts 18 for the complete picture of Aquila and Priscilla.

PRAY TOGETHER: Lord God, thank You that You have a ministry in mind especially for us. Use us as a couple to minister any way You want.

Day 4

5. Sharing at the CORE of Our Being

The fifth ingredient of Spiritual intimacy is complete transparency before God and each other. We talked a lot about transparency in the Communication chapters, but the point we want to stress here is that transparency before God **spills over** into transparency with our mates, and visa versa.

Spiritual Intimacy is a life long journey. Along the road, we must help each other over the rough spots, encourage one another when the way gets dark and shower one another with all those good virtues from Philippians chapter 2, always looking for that bright City which awaits us at the end of our journey. Most importantly, we must share transparently with one another and with that Third Person who travels with us, because *that* is what makes the road passable and the journey possible.

Remember the second element of Spiritual intimacy? The one about praying together? After traveling on this road for a while and learning to pray together, you will find it is easier to pray about *everything* with one another. As you begin to pray about your hopes and dreams and aspirations, as well as your failures and doubts and sin, you will become more and more open with the Lord and with each other. You will become less and less afraid to show the real you.

Paul states in Acts 24:16, *So I strive always to keep my conscience clear before God and man.* Can you see how this happens when you and your mate are consistently praying together? When you keep your conscience clear before God, it will also be clear before "man" — that is, your mate. Couple prayer is actually a three-way conversation which can become the most precious and intimate time of your lives.

Acts 24:16 — So I strive always to keep my conscience clear before God and man.

Another verse to consider concerning this intimate kind of sharing is James 5:16. *Therefore confess your sins to each other and pray for each other so that you may be healed....* Many couples are cheating themselves out of personal, emotional healing by refusing to be real and honest with their mates.

James 5:16 — Therefore confess your sins to each other and pray for each other so that you may be healed. The prayer of a righteous man is powerful and effective.

What if I am too proud to share my fears with my mate, but instead carry them around deep inside me? Will I be able to rid myself of those fears? No, they'll hang onto me and even **grow** as I keep them hidden. But if I honestly share them with my partner, and get them out where we both can see them, then they won't look so **big** any more. When we share our failures with each other, we **unmask** them and **defeat** their power over us. When we pray for one another in our areas of weakness, we enter into an attitude of **mutual help** rather than judgment. Our bond of friendship and trust is strengthened. Our relationship is healthier. The road is smoother.

Rate your experience of Sharing at the Core of your Being in your relationship on a scale of 1 to 10.

Wife: 1   2   3   4   5   6   7   8   9   10 (circle one)

Husband: 1   2   3   4   5   6   7   8   9   10 (circle one)

What could you do to share more at the core of your being with your mate?

Wife: _____

Husband: _____

Discuss your responses together.

6. Shared Hope of ETERNITY Together With Christ

1 Thessalonians 4:17-18—*After that, we who are still alive and are left will be caught up with them in the clouds to meet the Lord in the air. And so we will be with the Lord forever. Therefore encourage each other with these words.* That is exactly what we want to do: encourage you with this element of Spiritual intimacy.

Spiritual oneness transcends time. As a believing couple, we will *be with the Lord forever.* We are not saying we will be husband and wife in heaven. Just exactly what our relationship will be, we can not say. But the Bible clearly teaches that we will know our loved ones there. And what closer loved one do you have than your mate? We will be together *with the Lord forever.* This truth is a tremendous encouragement to us. When we are away from each other, we can trust one another into God's hands, because no matter what happens, we will be *with the Lord forever.* That eases our fears and gives us a strong sense of **security**.

We have each stood by the grave of a parent. Both times, our surviving parent was sustained through that terrible loss because both Bette's mother and Harold's father knew they would be with their partners again with the Lord forever. If we did not have this hope, how could we ever risk loving someone so deeply that we would be destroyed by never seeing them again? But we **will** see them again, and talk with them, and fellowship with them, and worship God together for all eternity.

We have also been given this hope so we will purify ourselves. *But we know that when he appears, we shall be like him, for we shall see him as he is. Everyone who has this hope in him purifies himself, just as he is pure* (1 John 3:2b-3). If eventually we are going to be pure in heaven, why bother purifying ourselves now? Verse 2 starts with, *Now we are children of God....* That's why we need, and are commanded, to be purifying ourselves **now** while we wait for Him to appear.

When we stand before Him as His children, He will be looking for a **family resemblance**. Will we meet Him with joy? Or will it be with shame, not because we **could not** put on the likeness of Christ, but because we **would not**.

God holds us responsible for whether or not we act like Him **inside** our front doors, as well as outside them. Whatever you do, don't sit by and let the day come when you

1 Thessalonians 4:17-18 — *After that, we who are still alive and are left will be caught up with them in the clouds to meet the Lord in the air. And so we will be with the Lord forever. Therefore encourage each other with these words.*

1 John 3:2b-3 — *Dear friends, now we are children of God, and what we will be has not yet been made known. But we know that when he appears, we shall be like him, for we shall see him as he is. Everyone who has this hope in him purifies himself, just as he is pure.*

Notes

Romans 8:29 — *For those God foreknew He also predestined to be conformed to the likeness of His Son, that He might be the firstborn among many brothers.*

meet your mate in heaven and must hang your head in regret and shame because you would not let the Lord conform you *to the likeness of His Son* in your home (Romans 8:29). If you are not acting like Jesus to your mate, then it is time to start allowing the Holy Spirit to change you. *Purify yourselves* because you are going to spend all of eternity together *with the Lord.*

Rate your experience of Sharing the Hope of Eternity together in your relationship on a scale of 1 to 10.

Wife:　　　 1　 2　 3　 4　 5　 6　 7　 8　 9　 10 (circle one)

Husband:　 1　 2　 3　 4　 5　 6　 7　 8　 9　 10 (circle one)

What could you do to make being "with the Lord forever" more real in your relationship?

Wife: _____

Husband: _____

Discuss your responses together.

Write at least one personal application from today's study.

Wife: _____

Husband: _____

What does God want you to do to work out this application?

Wife: _____

Husband: _____

REFLECT TOGETHER: Read 1 John 3:1-10. How important is it that we start purifying our lives right now?

PRAY TOGETHER: Oh, Lord, to think we will be together with You for all eternity is more than we can comprehend. But we thank you that it is true. In the meantime, help us purify ourselves so we will be ready for your coming.

7. Shared FAITH Even When It's Tough

Day 5

As you walk along the road in this spiritual intimacy journey, you are going to come across some ruts, chuck holes and boulders in your path. The enemy is going to make quite sure you encounter a lot of rough places. And why shouldn't he? Satan's agenda is to make you give up...to quit...not just the journey, but your entire marriage. And, oh, is he sneaky!

That is why God says, *Carry each other's burdens, and in this way you will fulfill the law of Christ* (Galatians 6:2). Picture yourselves walking along the road together. One of you is carrying a heavy bucket. The other picks up a sturdy stick and runs it through the bucket handle. You can each carry the bucket now by holding the ends of the stick. That is *how to carry each other's burdens*. When two hearts carry the same load, the burden is only half as heavy!

Galatians 6:2 — *Carry each other's burdens, and in this way you will fulfill the law of Christ.*

How beautifully this is depicted in Ecclesiastes 4:9-12. *Two are better than one, because they have a good return for their work: If one falls down, his friend can help him up. But pity the man who falls and has no one to help him up! Also, if two lie down together, they will keep warm. But how can one keep warm alone? Though one may be overpowered, two can defend themselves. A cord of three strands is not quickly [easily] broken.* Yes, there will be stones in the road, and you are going to stumble over some of them. But you are called to stick together, and help each other over or through the rough spots. You will be strong enough to hold each other up because you have been growing together on this spiritual journey. The *cord of three strands* — you, your mate, and your God — is **strong enough** to hold you up.

Ecclesiastes 4:9-12 — *Two are better than one, because they have a good return for their work: If one falls down, his friend can help him up. But pity the man who falls and has no one to help him up! Also, if two lie down together, they will keep warm. But how can one keep warm alone? Though one may be overpowered, two can defend themselves. A cord of three strands is not quickly [easily] broken.*

Have you discovered any stones in your road? Big, aren't they? At times they are overwhelming. If you haven't stumbled across any yet, believe us, you will.

We've stumbled over our share. We remember one that almost completely blocked the road about ten years ago. It was the boulder of *financial disaster*. A business we bought turned out to have two sets of books: the real ones and the ones we saw. Even though we purchased it through a reputable business broker, we "got took." We were about to levy suit against the seller for the $50,000 of debt she had placed upon us, when she declared bankruptcy and skipped the country. We were stuck with a huge debt service and no income from the business to meet it.

For four years, we worked and scraped to meet our debts, adding second and third mortgages to our home which we eventually lost. We faced foreclosure, but sold it just in time for barely enough to pay off the mortgages. Finally, we were forced to declare bankruptcy. What a horrifying and humiliating experience to find ourselves labeled "not credit worthy."

Can you imagine how overwhelming these stones and chuck holes seemed during those years? How easy it would have been to blame each other for our problems? Funny thing about obstacles though — they can either barricade you apart or shove the two of you closer together. It depends on which side of the obstacle you are each standing. We found that the trick was for both of us to stand on the **same side**. Then the barricade was between us and the rest of the world. And as long as that was true, we were safe.

Obstacles can either barricade you apart or shove the two of you closer together.

Always keep in mind this great truth: there are **three** of you walking together on this road, not just two. And when you get too weary to take another step, there's a Third Person, Jesus Christ Himself, Who is strong enough to hold both of you up until you

Notes

can face the next step together. *A cord of three strands [really] is not quickly or easily broken.*

Rate your experience of Sharing Faith in the Tough Times in your relationship on a scale of 1 to 10.

Wife: 1   2   3   4   5   6   7   8   9   10 (circle one)

Husband: 1   2   3   4   5   6   7   8   9   10 (circle one)

Which of the other elements of Spiritual Intimacy would help you prepare for future tough times? Circle them and talk about them together.

- Shared PURPOSE and GOALS in Life

- Sharing the WORD and PRAYER

- Shared GROWTH in Christ

- Shared MINISTRY

- Sharing at the CORE of Our Being

- Shared Hope of ETERNITY Together With Christ

The benefits of Spiritual Intimacy:

TRUST

TRUST: Think of all the benefits you will enjoy from Spiritual Intimacy. First of all, there will be growth of **trust** in your relationship. Trust is the foundation stone of your marriage. If it wobbles, the whole structure falters. But even if trust in your relationship has been damaged, you and your mate and the Lord can rebuild it through these steps of Spiritual intimacy.

Trust is developed in our relationship as we discover we can trust our mate to be honest with us, and as we come to feel that our love is safe with them. All the steps in your Spiritual Intimacy journey will **lead** to trust. You can't be honest with God without being honest with your mate when you are growing in the three-way relationship that Spiritual oneness creates.

BONDING

Genesis 2:24 — *For this reason a man will leave his father and mother and be united to his wife, and they will become one flesh.*

BONDING: Secondly, there will be significant **bonding** between you. We hear a lot about bonding nowadays. It is simply *the gluing of two objects together in a strong seal.* That about says it. As Genesis 2:24 declares, you two have been *glued together* by God Himself. Spiritual intimacy helps the glue to set.

Have you seen the commercial for a miracle glue that bonds anything it comes into contact with (including skin)? They glue a guy's hat to a beam and lift it high off the ground. And there he is, stuck in his hat to that beam, flailing in the air. That is *some* kind of glue! But the glue that holds you together is stronger, because it is **Holy Glue.**

ENDURANCE: The third benefit you will receive from Spiritual intimacy is **endurance.** Your relationship will be able to endure time and trials because you and your mate are part of a *cord of three strands.*

SIGNIFICANCE: And finally, you and your partner will come to know you are significant. **Significance** is knowing you have purpose in life, that you make a difference by being alive. Like Aquila and Priscilla, God has a job for you to do as a couple. You are important to His plan. We all need to feel significant, and Spiritual intimacy helps us realize that God has a **profound purpose in our marriage.**

Notes
ENDURANCE
Eccl. 4:12 — *A cord of three strands is not quickly [easily] broken.*
SIGNIFICANCE

List the benefits of Spiritual Intimacy, adding any others you can think of.

_____ _____ _____

_____ _____ _____

Of all the benefits listed, which do you value the most?

Wife: _____ Husband: _____

Talk about it together.

Write at least one personal application from today's study.
Wife: _____
Husband: _____
What does God want you to do to work out this application?
Wife: _____
Husband: _____

REFLECT TOGETHER: Re-read Ecclesiastes 4:9-12. How many ways are two better than one?

PRAY TOGETHER: Thank you, precious Lord, that You are the strong third strand of our cord. Whatever may come our way, we know our "cord of three strands" is strong enough to hold us safe.

Day 6

How do you get it? That's the Big Question, isn't it? How and where do we start? Remember, we said that Spiritual oneness is a way of life. There is no simple formula, 1- 2- 3 and you've got it. No, it is a **process** that will last the rest of your lives. But there is a tool to guide your first steps. You can use this tool over and over again as you determine to incorporate each phase of becoming spiritually one. It is called a "covenant."

> **Definition of COVENANT**— A covenant is a binding agreement between two parties, like a contract. Your marriage itself is a covenant. And you and your wife or husband can make a covenant together concerning almost anything in your marriage.

Covenant includes a

P

O

P

A

<u>P</u>LAN to accomplish your goal.

<u>O</u>BLIGATION to work the plan.

<u>P</u>ROMISE to keep the covenant.

<u>A</u>CCOUNTABILITY to hold to agreement.

P O P A!

PLAN

Suppose you and your mate agree that the first step you want to take on your Spiritual intimacy journey is to read the Bible and pray together at least two to three times a week. **The first move is to make a PLAN together to accomplish your goal.** Such a plan might be to read the book of John together, reading one chapter Monday, Tuesday and Thursday mornings by setting the clock for 6:30 and spending 15 to 20 minutes in reading and prayer. That would be a good start. Or perhaps you want to use a particular devotional book. Whatever you do, you need to plan the details of how you are going to succeed in your covenant.

OBLIGATION

Next, you must OBLIGATE yourself to work the plan. Notice, we said obligate yourself. You can not obligate your mate, your mate must obligate him(her)self. You can only obligate yourself, because you are the only person you have control over. In order to obligate yourself to your part of the plan, you each need to choose which part you will be responsible for. One of you may be responsible for making sure the alarm is set. Someone needs to be responsible for making the first move to get up when the alarm sounds. As you both look at your plan to accomplish the covenant, try to think of all the necessary duties involved in it, and choose who will be **responsible** for each.

PROMISE

Then, you must PROMISE to keep the covenant. Again, you must promise for yourself, and your mate must promise for himself/herself. You can not *make* your partner promise anything. You are responsible only for yourself and for your promise. Your promise might sound something like this, "I promise to keep this covenant with you. I promise that even when it is not convenient, I will get up early and read God's Word and pray with you on the days we designated. I know God takes my promise seriously, so I have every intention to keep my covenant with you."

ACCOUNTABILITY

Finally, you must make yourself ACCOUNTABLE to your mate to keep your covenant. Accountability and considering couple-devotions a priority go hand in hand. You must believe it is a priority in order to willingly make yourself accountable to your mate. Making yourself accountable might mean you give your mate permission to throw a wet washcloth on your face if you are more than 5 minutes late in getting up. Or you might give him or her permission to remind you that you obligated yourself to not be grumpy. Caution: in accountability, you can only dispense the consequences your partner has given permission for. It is important that each of you make yourself accountable in this way.

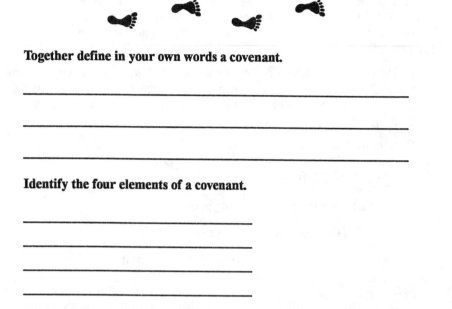

Together define in your own words a covenant.

_____

_____

_____

Identify the four elements of a covenant.

_____

_____

_____

_____

Why a Covenant? Luke 14:28-30 — *Suppose one of you wants to build a tower. Will he not first sit down and estimate the cost to see if he has enough money to complete it? For if he lays the foundation and is not able to finish it, everyone who sees it will ridicule him, saying, 'This fellow began to build and was not able to finish.'*

Do you have any unfinished towers in your life? We do. And we, like that guy who started the tower, have a choice to live life on purpose, or to live it on accident. Sure, making and keeping a covenant is hard work. But it takes work to finish towers. And covenants are great construction tools.

Example of covenants in Scripture: 1 Samuel 18:3-4 — *And Jonathan made a covenant with David because he loved him as himself. Jonathan took off the robe he was wearing and gave it to David, along with his tunic, and even his sword, his bow and his belt.*

Jonathan and David made a covenant to be friends regardless of the circumstances. They pledged their loyalty to one another even though Jonathan's father Saul tried repeatedly to kill David. Jonathan considered his covenant with David of greater importance than loyalty to his own father.

God expects us to keep our covenants— Numbers 30:2 — *When a man makes a vow to the LORD or takes an oath to obligate himself by a pledge, he must not break his word but must do everything he said.*

Ecclesiastes 5:4,5 — *When you make a vow to God, do not delay in fulfilling it. He has no pleasure in fools; fulfill your vow. It is better not to vow than to make a vow and not fulfill it.*

Covenants are very important to God, and He expects people to keep them. He even calls us "fools" if we don't. So, don't make a covenant unless you mean to keep it.

Luke 14:28-30 — *Suppose one of you wants to build a tower. Will he not first sit down and estimate the cost to see if he has enough money to complete it? For if he lays the foundation and is not able to finish it, everyone who sees it will ridicule him, saying, 'This fellow began to build and was not able to finish.'*

1 Samuel 18:3-4 — *And Jonathan made a covenant with David because he loved him as himself. Jonathan took off the robe he was wearing and gave it to David, along with his tunic, and even his sword, his bow and his belt.*

Numbers 30:2 — *When a man makes a vow to the LORD or takes an oath to obligate himself by a pledge, he must not break his word but must do everything he said.*

Ecclesiastes 5:4,5 — *When you make a vow to God, do not delay in fulfilling it. He has no pleasure in fools; fulfill your vow. It is better not to vow than to make a vow and not fulfill it.*

Notes

Without covenants, we may have many unfinished _____ in our lives.

_____ and _____ made a covenant together in 1 Samuel 18:3-4, which they faithfully kept until Jonathan's death. If you would like to read more about how David kept their covenant even after Jonathan's death, you will find the account in 2 Samuel 9.

God calls us _____ if we fail to keep our covenants (Ecclesiastes. 5:4-5).

We know this is going to take effort on your part. But you know by now that worth-while things **take effort**. If you're like the rest of us, you're already overwhelmed by demands on your time, emotions, mind and body. If you simply **add** Spiritual Intimacy **on top** of everything else in your life, it might slide off the pile, taking your determination to change with it.

If something 'has to give' in your busy life to allow room for you and your mate to start building Spiritual Intimacy together, we urge you to make that sacrifice and push something less critical aside. Then you will have room to make Spiritual Oneness the priority it should be. Choosing to grow together spiritually will enable you to bond closer as a couple than you ever dreamed possible. We sincerely pray you and your spouse will choose to walk this Spiritual intimacy journey with us. It is worth it!

Are you willing to make Spiritual Intimacy a priority in your relationship?

Wife: _____ Husband: _____

If so, are there some things you will have to restructure or get rid of?

Wife: _____

Husband: _____

Write at least one personal application from today's study.

Wife: _____

Husband: _____

What does God want you to do to work out this application?

Wife: _____

Husband: _____

REFLECT TOGETHER: Read Ecclesiastes 5:1-7 for more about making vows.

PRAY TOGETHER: Lord God, we know you take making a covenant very seriously, so we want to keep our covenants with each other. Help us submit ourselves in accountability to one another.

WRAP-UP: Together complete one of the following assignments.

Day 7

1. If you do not already have a covenant to read and pray together on a continuing basis, then structure a covenant to do so. Make sure you use all 4 elements: Plan, Obligation, Promise & Accountability.

2. If you already have a covenant to read and pray together regularly, then structure a covenant around Shared Ministry or one of the other elements of Spiritual Intimacy. Again make sure you use all 4 elements: Plan, Obligation, Promise & Accountability.

REFLECT TOGETHER: Re-read Matthew 18:19-20. What a promise!

PRAY TOGETHER: Oh, God, help us make spiritual intimacy a priority in our relationship. We don't want any more unfinished towers in our lives, so we commit ourselves to keeping our covenants with each other.

GROUP DISCUSSION: If you are using this study in a group setting, the following may be used as group discussion questions.

1. Why do you think there are so few Christian couples who read the Bible and pray together regularly?

2. Give some examples of couples sharing a ministry together.

3. Relate an occasion when you experienced Shared Faith in the Tough Times and tell how it has strengthened your relationship.

4. Give some examples of covenants and evaluate each to see if they are POPA covenants.

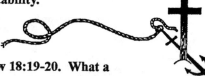

Have a frank discussion

A Postscript On Spiritual Intimacy

Experiencing _Life_ is prerequisite to experiencing Spiritual Intimacy.

One of the assumptions made in Chapter 12 and in many other places throughout this book, is that you as husband and wife share life in Christ together as Believers. If this is not true, you will not be able to fully experience Spiritual Intimacy. If this is not true, you may have found many of the other principles taught throughout the book to be unacceptable and impossible to be experienced. If only one or neither of you are Christians, much of this book can not be applied. However, the **principles are true**, and many, when applied, will improve the quality of your relationship _regardless_ of whether or not you have a real and growing relationship with the Lord.

Because the principles taught in this book are true and practical and their application definitely results in growth in intimacy, we pray many couples will **do this study** regardless of their faith or lack thereof. But we would be shamefully remiss if we did not explain the basic Gospel message before closing this publication. If it is helpful for just one person finding the way to Life, it is well worth the effort and space.

Though many assert that mankind is basically good and getting better, the Bible declares the opposite — men and women are basically sinful and naturally, by themselves, are <u>utterly incapable of ever being good enough to merit acceptance by God</u>. All of our righteousnesses heaped on top of one another are but "filthy rags" to God (Isaiah 64:6). This has been mankind's condition ever since the first man chose to willingly sin — choosing independence from God.

Since no man or woman can ever attain righteousness on their own, there had to be another way provided for us by God. Because God loves us so much, He provided The Way. He sent His only Son, Jesus Christ, into the world to live, suffer and die on the cross for the sins of the whole world. **Christ alone** could pay the debt and penalty of sin (Romans 6:23), because He was both God and man, sinless throughout His life here on earth. He paid the penalty for mankind's sin with His death — but He did more than that, for He rose from the grave and conquered death to sit at the right hand of the Father. <u>Had Christ not risen from the dead, any faith in Him would be meaningless</u> (I Corinthians 15:17).

Jesus Christ, the risen Savior of the world, calls and beckons all men and women to come to Him, believe on Him as their Lord and Savior and share the promise of eternal life with Him (Matthew 11:28-30). This is God's stated will — that all mankind would believe and be saved (2 Peter 3:9). But He forces no one — <u>you must respond to His gracious and free provision willingly</u>. He says "Whosoever will may come" (Revelation 22:17; Romans 10:13). God promised that once Christ was "lifted up" on the cross, He would "draw" all men to Himself (John 12:32). He draws and invites everyone to come, but **each person** must freely choose to **respond to that invitation**.

What happens when you respond to His invitation? You come to share in eternal life, as well as a relationship and fellowship with the God of the universe (Father, Son and Holy Spirit). As a Believer in Christ, you also share fellowship with all other Believers as the "body of Christ" here on earth. The Comforter, the Holy Spirit, which Christ promised the Father would send (John 14:16,26) **resides**, or lives, **in you** and **unites** you with all fellow Believers. We, as Believers or saints, share this "new life" here on earth, as well as possess a promised inheritance with all the saints of all time ultimately in heaven (John 14:2,3).

Isaiah 64:6 — _All of us have become like one who is unclean, and all our righteous acts are like filthy rags...._

Romans 6:23 — _For the wages of sin is death, but the gift of God is eternal life in Christ Jesus our Lord._

I Corinthians 15:17 — _And if Christ has not been raised, your faith is futile; you are still in your sins._

Matthew 11:28 — _Come to me, all you who are weary and burdened, and I will give you rest._

II Peter 3:9 — _...He is patient with you, not wanting anyone to perish, but everyone to come to repentance._

Revelation 22:17 — _...Whoever wishes, let him take the free gift of the water of life._

Romans 10:13 — _Everyone who calls on the name of the Lord will be saved._

John 12:32 — _But I, when I am lifted up from the earth, will draw all men to myself._

John 14:16 — _And I will ask the Father, and he will give you another Counselor to be with you forever._

John 14:3 — _And if I go and prepare a place for you, I will come back and take you to be with me...._

255

What must you do to respond to God's call to salvation? Freely and sincerely pray a simple Sinner's Prayer such as this one:

God, I realize I am a sinner in need of salvation, and without You I will face the full penalty of death and eternal separation from You. I choose, instead, to trust in your grace and mercy extended to me through the death, burial and resurrection of Christ Jesus. I trust also in Your promise of eternal life which You gave to those who believe on You. Lord, I believe and trust You as my Lord and Savior. Come into my life and seal it as Yours through all eternity. May I grow in wisdom and knowledge as I begin a love relationship with You as one of Your very own children. Thank You. In Jesus' name, Amen.

That's it? That's all? **NO! It's not!** This is just the **beginning** of a continuing and growing love relationship with God. He will never leave you or forsake you (Hebrews 13:5), though at times you may tend to leave Him (Isaiah 53:6). So what do you do when that happens? When you realize you have been "going your own way" away from God, you simply turn to Him and confess your sin as I John 1:9 says, *If we confess our sins, he is faithful and just and will forgive us our sins and purify us from all unrighteousness.* He **IS faithful** and just and **WILL forgive** our sin and cleanse us from all unrighteousness.

Is there more? Yes, there is. We must cultivate this love relationship with God by reading, studying and obeying the Scripture, praying and relating to other Believers in a local church (an assembly of Believers meeting near you). Why get involved in a church? Because He commands us to do so (Hebrews 10:25). He also says in Proverbs, people sharpen each other like iron (Proverbs 27:17). Believers sharpen one another and "spur one another on toward love and good deeds" (Hebrews 10:24). We **NEED** each other in order to grow in Christ. Don't forsake meeting together!

Two final aspects to the Christian life: **Worship** and **Ministry**. Corporate **worship** is when Believers come together to express our love for God and attribute worth and praise to Him. We *need* it and God *loves* it. **Ministry** is finding your place of service to others in the local church. It may be an upfront type of ministry, such as teaching, organizing, leading music etc.; or it may be a less visible one, such as helping set up or clean up, visiting the ill, assisting a teacher, etc.

So don't stop with the Sinner's Prayer! Keep on growing, fellowshipping, ministering and worshipping until He comes again as He has promised to do (John 14:3). **May He find us faithful when He comes!**

When you as a couple become Believers, you will be able to experience spiritual intimacy in ways you never thought possible. When you both open your hearts to what God wants to do in you, and really seek to obey Him and apply His principles in your relationship, your love will deepen and grow like you've never known before. God promises to bless us when we obey Him (James 1:25), and we can tell you by experience He keeps His promise! The following startling statistics prove it! As you know, the national divorce rate is 1 in every 2 marriages end in divorce. However, according to a recent Harvard study, for couples who regularly **read the Bible together**, **pray together** and **attend church together**, their divorce rate is **1 in 1,287 (that's less than .08%)**.

This book is full of God's Word and God's principles. Obey Him and **experience oneness** for yourselves!

Hebrews 13:5 — *...God has said, "Never will I leave you; never will I forsake you."*

Isaiah 53:6 — *We all, like sheep, have gone astray, each of us has turned to his own way; and the Lord has laid on him the iniquity of us all.*

I John 1:9 — *If we confess our sins, he is faithful and just and will forgive us our sins and purify us from all unrighteousness.*

Hebrews 10:25 — *Let us not give up meeting together...let us encourage one another -- and all the more as you see the day approaching.*

Proverbs 27:17 — *As iron sharpens iron, so one man sharpens another.*

Hebrews 10:24 — *And let us consider how we may spur one another on toward love and good deeds.*

John 14:3 — *And if I go and prepare a place for you, I will come back and take you to be with me....*

James 1:25 — *But the man who looks intently into the perfect law that gives freedom, and continues to do this, not forgetting what he has heard, but doing it – he will be blessed in what he does.*

INTIMACY RESOURCE LIST

MARRIAGE AND INTIMACY ENHANCEMENT

Achieving God's Design for Marriage, Harold & Bette Gillogly, Joy Publishing
The Marriage Builder, Lawrence J. Crabb, Jr., Zondervan
Strike the Original Match, Charles R. Swindoll, Multnomah Press
The Romance Factor, Alan Loy McGinnis, Harper & Row
Sex Begins in the Kitchen, Kevin Leman, Ventura, Regal Books
Slaying the Marriage Dragons: Protecting Your Marriage from the Enemies of Intimacy, Dr. Douglas
    E. Rosenau, Victor Books
The Two Sides of Love: What Strengthens Affection, Closeness and Commitment?, Gary Smalley &
    John Trent, Focus on the Family Press
Communication: Key to Your Marriage, H. Norman Wright, Regal Books
More Communication: Keys for Your Marriage, H. Norman Wright, Regal Books
Staying in Love: What Wives and Husbands Can Do to Keep Their Love Alive, William J. Diehm,
    Augsburg
Romancing Your Marriage, H. Norman Wright, Regal
Love Life for Every Married Couple, Ed & Gaye Wheat, Zondervan

SEXUAL ENRICHMENT

A Celebration of Sex, Dr. Douglas E. Rosenau, Thomas Nelson
Solomon on Sex, Joseph C. Dillow, Thomas Nelson
The Act of Marriage: The Beauty of Sexual Love, Tim & Beverly LeHaye, Zondervan
The Gift of Sex: A Christian Guide to Sexual Fulfillment, Clifford & Joyce Penner, Word
Intended for Pleasure, Ed & Gaye Wheat, Revell
The Intimate Marriage, Howard & Charlotte Clinebell, Harper & Row
Celebration of Sex, Dan & Sandra McGee, Family Touch

SEXUAL AFFAIRS

The Prodigal Spouse: How to Survive Infidelity, Les Carter, Thomas Nelson
Love Must Be Tough, James C. Dobson, Word
Rebonding: Preventing and Restoring Damaged Relationships, Donald M. Joy, Word

SPECIFIC SEXUAL ISSUES

*Restoring the Pleasure: Complete Step-by Step Programs to Help Couples Overcome the Most
    Common Sexual Barriers*, Clifford and Joyce Penner, Word
A Safe Place: Beyond Sexual Abuse, Jan Morrison, Harold Shaw
The Wounded Heart, Dan Allender, NAV Press

Making Peace with your Past, Tim Sledge, LifeWay Press

GTO FAMILY MINISTRIES'
RESOURCE ORDER FORM

1. *Experiencing Oneness* $14.95

2. *Achieving God's Design for Marriage* Leader's Guide $24.95

3. *Achieving God's Design for Marriage* Couple's Guide $10.00

4. 10 copies *Achieving God's Design for Marriage* Couple's Guides $100.00
   (1 additional **Couple's Guide** included)

5. 20 copies *Achieving God's Design for Marriage* Couple's Guides $200.00
   (1 **Leader's Guide** or 2 additional **Couple's Guides** included)

6. Complete set of Overhead transparencies $50.00

7. Complete set of *GTO Seeds for Growth* articles $15.00

8. Q-TIPS Quarterly Newsletter for Pastors & Leaders .... N/C

9. GTO FAMILY MINISTRIES Newsletter .... N/C

Call us at **1-800-546-5486**
or fill out the form below and mail it to:

GTO FAMILY MINISTRIES
P.O. Box 140785
Nashville, TN 37214

NAME: _____

STREET: _____

CITY: _____ STATE: _____ ZIP: _____

TELEPHONE # _____

ITEM # (s): _____ QTY (s): _____

Enclose check or money order for the appropriate amount to "GTO"
(Book-Rate Shipping and handling are included – call if you desire other shipping)
Tennessee residents please add Sales Tax – TN churches provide Tax Exempt certificate